Merry Chr...
to Mike
from Douglas Mawby.
2005

MW00329147

History of the
MOTORCYCLE

This is a Parragon Publishing book

First published in 2004

Parragon Publishing
Queen Street House
4 Queen Street
Bath BA1 1HE, UK

Copyright © Parragon 2004

ISBN: 1-40543-952-1

All rights reserved. No part of this publication may be reproduced, stored in a retrieval system, or transmitted in any
form or by any means, without the prior written permission of the copyright holder.

A copy of the CIP data for this book is available from the British Library upon request.

The rights of Roland Brown to be identified as the author of this work have been asserted in accordance
with Section 77 of the Copyright, Designs and Patents Act of 1988.

Created, designed, produced, and packaged by Stonecastle Graphics Ltd

Designed by Paul Turner and Sue Pressley
Edited by Philip de Ste. Croix

Printed and bound in China

The author and publishers have made every reasonable effort to contact all copyright holders. Any errors that may
have occurred are inadvertent and anyone who for any reason has not been contacted is invited to write to the publishers
so that a full acknowledgement may be made in subsequent editions of this work.

Photographic credits:

British Film Institute: pages 41(b), 56(t), 79(t), 79(bl, br), 104(t, cl, cr), 179(c)
Phil Masters: pages 42, 100(c), 112(b), 116(t, b), 118(bl), 119(t, b), 121(b), 138(tl, tr), 189(br)
Andrew Morland: pages 24, 31(t, b), 35(t), 39(t, bl), 40(t), 46(b), 48(br), 51(t), 55(bl), 118(t)
Mortons Motorcycle Media Archive: pages 16(t, b), 17(b), 18(t, b), 19(t), 23(br), 26(b), 28(t), 30(b), 39(br), 41(t), 44(t), 49(t), 56(bl), 59(br), 67(t, c), 76(t), 89(tr), 98(c)
Garry Stuart: pages 8, 13(c), 15(bl), 21(t), 22(t), 27(t, b), 36(b), 38(t, b), 69(t, bl, br), 91(c), 98(b), 122(b)
Topham Picturepoint: pages 11(cr, br), 12(b), 13(t, b)

Roland Brown library/www.motobike.net (fees to Riders for Health); photos by:
BMW: pages 32(t), 37, 50(br), 70(t), 100(t, b), 114(t), 129(tr, cl)
Jason Critchell: pages 168(b), 170(t), 183(t, b)
Double Red: pages 178(c), 185(t)
Ducati: pages 54(t), 80(b, thanks Ludovica), 93(br)
Gold & Goose: pages 161(br), 186(tr), 190(tr)
Harley-Davidson: pages 14(l, r), 19(b), 20(t, b), 26(t), 28(b), 40(b), 57(t)
Honda: pages 51(c, b), 62(t), 64(t), 76(bl), 81(b), 105(bl), 112(t), 115(b), 120(t), 126(b), 127(t, c), 128(b), 129(cr), 137(b), 142(l), 143(cr), 150(t), 177(t), 189(tl), 192(c)
Milagro: pages 186(bl), 187(t)
Oli Tennent: page 177(b)
Others: pages 21(c, b), 33(b), 44(bl), 47(t, c), 52(t), 122(t), 132(b), 148(t), 150(c, b), 173(tr), 176(t), 179(t), 186(tl), 188(r), 190(cl), 191(l, r)

Photos © Roland Brown library/www.motobike.net, by:
Kevin Ash: page 95(t)
Roland Brown: pages 6, 10(l, r), 11(tl), 12(t), 15(t, br), 17(t), 22(b), 23(t, bl), 32(b), 33(t), 34(t), 35(b), 36(t), 59(t, bl), 71(c), 72(b), 74(t), 75(t), 77(b), 82, 83(r), 90(b), 93, 94(t), 95(b), 96(b), 97(bl, br), 98(t), 99(c, b), 102(b), 103(t, b), 107(t, b), 110(b), 111(b), 114(b), 115(t), 117(t), 118(br), 123(tl, tr), 129(tl, b), 131(t), 132(t), 133, 134, 135(bl), 136(bl), 137(t), 139, 141(b), 145(c), 146(b), 147(t), 148(br), 149(b), 152(bl), 153(t, b), 154(t, b), 155(t), 156(t) 157(b), 158(t, b), 159(t, c, b), 160(b), 161(tr, bl), 162(t), 163(t, b), 164(c), 165(b), 169(b), 170(br), 171(t), 172(t), 173(tl, b), 174(t, b), 175(tr, b), 176(bl, br), 178(t, b), 180(tr), 181(t), 182(tr, b), 184(t, b) 185(c, b), 186(br), 187(b), 188(l), 189(t), 192(t, b)
Jack Burnicle: pages 92(b), 93(bl), 97(t), 99(t), 104(b), 106(t)
Jason Critchell: pages 94(b), 156(bl)
Phil Masters: pages 29(t), 30(t), 33(b), 46(t), 47(b), 49(b), 50(t, bl), 52(b), 53(c), 54(t), 55(t, br), 57(b), 58(b), 60, 62(b), 64(b), 66(t, b), 67(b), 68(t, b), 70(bl, br), 71(t), 72(b), 73(t), 75(b), 77(t), 78(t), 80(t), 83(l), 85(t, c), 87(t, b), 88(t, b), 89(tl, b), 92(t, r), 111(t), 113(t), 117(b), 120(b), 121(t), 127(b), 131(b), 141(t), 142(r), 143(b), 144(t, b), 148(bl), 155(b), 160(t), 161(tl), 164(b), 165(t, c), 168(t), 169(t), 170(bl), 171(b), 172(b), 175(tl), 179(b), 181(b), 190(b)
Gold & Goose: pages 48(t), 63(t, b), 74(b), 90(t, c), 124(c), 128(t), 130(t, b), 136(br), 140(bl, br), 143(cl), 144(c)
Mac McDiarmid: pages 91(b), 125(t, b), 138(b), 144(t), 149(t), 149(t, b)
Brian J Nelson: pages 4, 182(tl), 190(tl)
Dale Stenton: page 164(t)
Oli Tennent: pages 29(b), 44(br), 45(t, b), 46(c), 48(bl), 53(t, b), 56(br), 58(t, c), 65(t, b), 71(b), 72(c), 73(b), 74(c), 78(b), 80(c), 81(t), 85(b), 86(t, b), 91(t), 95(c), 96(t), 101(t, b), 102(t), 105(t, br), 106(b), 108, 110(t), 113(b), 123(b), 124(t), 124(b), 126(t), 136(t), 140(t), 143(t), 145(t, b), 152(t, br), 156(br), 157(t), 166, 180(tl, b)

Thanks to all those whose bikes are pictured!

History of the
MOTORCYCLE

FROM THE FIRST MOTORIZED BICYCLES TO THE POWERFUL

AND SOPHISTICATED SUPERBIKES OF TODAY

ROLAND BROWN

p

Above: Honda's fastest FireBlade yet – the impressive CBR1000RR – handled superbly thanks to its race-derived chassis.

Contents

Above: *Honda's CB750, regarded as the 'first superbike,' heralded a new era of sophistication on its launch in 1969.*

Introduction

'The motorcycle is a perfect metaphor for the 20th century. Invented at the beginning of the industrial age, its evolution tracks the main currents of modernity. The object and its history represent the themes of technology, engineering, innovation, design, mobility, speed, rebellion, desire, freedom, love, sex and death.'

It says much about motorcycling's current status that the words above were written by Thomas Krens of the Guggenheim Museum, curator of the hugely successful *Art of the Motorcycle* exhibition that opened in New York in 1998, and was later toured around the world. The humble motorbike, once feared and despised by so many, has become a respected art form and barometer of social trends.

The Guggenheim's collection of more than 100 bikes did a great job of illustrating how the motorcycle has evolved from a simple steam-powered bicycle into a sophisticated, streamlined piece of two-wheeled sculpture capable of traveling at three miles per minute. Or, in another embodiment, from a big, slow-revving V-twin built before World War I into a big, slow-revving V-twin that looks equally old but incorporates an electronic engine-management system and various other carefully disguised modern features.

This book features several of those bikes plus many more to tell the story of the motorcycle. The landmark machines are all here, from Daimler's Einspur (generally accepted as the first model) to the Brough Superior; from Honda's CB750 four to the Harley-Davidson V-Rod. So too are many of the less well known but often equally fascinating machines that have entertained, empowered, and sometimes infuriated riders along the way.

The history of the motorbike is the story of the people who have built and ridden them over the years, as well as the machines themselves. The way bikes are used has changed just as dramatically as their performance. Developed initially to provide a more practical alternative to the horse or bicycle, motorcycles became a great liberating force that expanded their riders' personal boundaries.

Then the rise of the cheap motor car stole that unique advantage and led to a decline in motorcycling's fortunes, firstly in the United States, and decades later elsewhere. Recently motorcycling has found new popularity in affluent societies as a leisure pursuit and lifestyle statement. Meanwhile riders in countries such as China, now the world's leading motorcycle producer, are discovering the benefits of practical mobility enjoyed elsewhere a century earlier.

Bikes and their uses might have changed a great deal over the years, but so many of the sensations surrounding them remain the same: freedom of the open road, comradeship of other riders, the thrill of performance unattainable by other road users. Oh yes, plus a sense of vulnerability and social alienation too, some might add. Motorcycles might occasionally be museum exhibits these days, but they'll always be out of the ordinary. To many riders that's part of the appeal, and will remain so as the history of the motorbike is rewritten in years to come.

Iron Horse
1860s to World War I

Previous page: American firm Pope's Model L, built in 1913, was one of the finest of pre-World War I V-twins.

Below right: Gottlieb Daimler's Einspur had its saddle situated above the engine, which led to problems on its history-making ride in 1885.

Below: The Michaux-Perreaux was essentially a bicycle with the addition of a steam engine, which drove the rear wheel via twin belts.

Michaux-Perreaux (1869)

Engine:	Steam, single cylinder
Capacity:	304cc (22 x 80mm)
Maximum power:	N/a
Transmission:	Twin belts
Frame:	Tubular steel
Suspension:	Leaf-sprung saddle
Brakes:	None
Weight:	191lb (87kg) dry
Top speed:	9mph (15km/h)

The very first motorcycle ride was an exciting experience, despite being a slow and fairly brief one. Paul Daimler, aged 17, took an eight-mile (13km) round trip near Stuttgart in Germany on Einspur ('Single-track'), the creation of his engineer father Gottlieb. Reports indicate that his journey was enlivened when the hot engine set fire to the saddle, presumably making this the first, but not the last, example of a young motorcyclist riding as though his trousers were on fire.

Einspur is generally credited with being the world's first motorbike, following that brief journey on November 10, 1885, but in some ways it barely deserves that honor. For one thing, Daimler's wooden creation had four wheels, because on account of its very high saddle the bike was fitted with a pair of stabilizers like those used on children's bicycles. Like many parents since, Gottlieb Daimler was no motorcycle enthusiast. He had built the machine simply as a rolling test bed for his engine, and promptly abandoned Einspur to concentrate on the automobile production for which his name is still famous.

Daimler Einspur (1885)	
Engine:	Air-cooled inlet-over-exhaust two-valve single
Capacity:	264cc (58 x 100mm)
Maximum power:	0.5hp @ 600rpm
Transmission:	Single speed; belt final drive
Frame:	Wood
Suspension:	None
Brakes:	None front; shoe on wheel rear
Weight:	198lb (90kg)
Top speed:	7mph (12km/h)

In fact Einspur was not the first powered two-wheeler, because bikes had been built more than a decade earlier, but driven by steam rather than an internal combustion motor. Steam engines had been popular since early in the century. Large and heavy, they powered trains and luxury liners, as well as the steam carriages that had been in use since the 1830s.

Bicycles, on the other hand, had been a relatively late arrival. A simple two-wheeler called the draisienne or 'hobby-horse' had been invented in 1817 by a German called Carl von Drais, but this involved the rider in the tiring and potentially painful process of paddling along with his feet. It was not until 1861 that Frenchman Pierre Michaux and his two sons fitted a crank and pedals to the front wheel, creating a much more satisfactory velocipede, which was a success despite earning the nickname 'boneshaker' in Britain.

Michaux became Europe's largest velo manufacturer, his factory near Bar-le-Duc in eastern France producing more than 400 machines per year. Then he spotted another opportunity, and collaborated with an engineer named Louis Perreaux, who developed a lightweight steam engine that could power the velo. Steam was produced by a cylindrical multi-tube boiler, fired by alcohol fuel through a series of burners. The engine had a steel piston and cylinder, and two flywheels, which drove the rear wheel via belts on either side. Water tanks were fitted behind the boiler, and there was a steam pressure gauge in the rider's view, in front of the steering head.

This steam-powered bicycle was patented in 1868 and completed the following year. After pulling away under the power of conventional pedals, the rider introduced the engine with a regulator. Perreaux claimed to have reached a speed of 9mph (15km/h) on it. But despite its ingenuity, the Michaux-Perreaux was not a commercial success. The small boiler meant that the steam was quickly used up, limiting its range. And with its hot burners, steam, and high pressure, the machine could not have been very safe.

Similar experiments were taking place at the same time on the other side of the Atlantic, where Sylvester Roper of Roxbury in Massachusetts built a steam-powered bicycle that also dated from 1869. Roper's machine used a chassis from the Hanlon brothers, who built boneshakers and demonstrated them at local fairs and circuses. It differed from its French contemporary by having a frame made from hickory wood rather than steel, and a lower-slung engine that had two cylinders instead of one, and which drove the rear wheel via rods and cranks, instead of belts.

Above left: Early Americans: the 1896 steam-powered Geneva (left) and gas-powered Thomas of 1900, on display at the Guggenheim.

Above: Although regarded as the first motorbike, the tall Einspur required twin stabilizers to keep it upright.

Above: The Hildebrand brothers of Germany began by building a steam-powered bicycle.

Hildebrand & Wolfmüller (1894)	
Engine:	Water-cooled four-stroke parallel twin
Capacity:	1489cc (90 x 117mm)
Maximum power:	2.5hp @ 240rpm
Transmission:	Drive to rear axle
Frame:	Tubular steel
Suspension:	None
Brakes:	Friction spoon front; bar rear
Weight:	192lb (87kg)
Top speed:	28mph (45km/h)

Right: The world's first production bike was the 1489cc Hildebrand & Wolfmüller, built in 1894.

Above: Tricycles powered by engines from French firm De Dion-Bouton won many races in the last decade of the 19th century.

Familiar failings

Roper claimed his machine could be 'driven up any hill and outspeed any horse,' but he too faced the problem of carrying sufficient water, and turned to four wheels for his future creations. Other engineers continued to experiment. In 1884 another American, Lucius D. Copeland from Arizona, produced a steam-driven bicycle based on the American Star, a reversed 'penny-farthing,' with small front wheel and larger rear.

Copeland demonstrated his bike at fairs across the USA in an attempt to raise funds. He is reported to have built 200 machines in the world's first motorcycle factory a few years later, but initially found financial backing only after adding an extra wheel to produce a tricycle. Another steam bicycle was the Geneva, built by the Geneva Bicycle and Steam Carriage Co. from Ohio. Similar to Copeland's device, it featured a solid copper boiler on one side of the front wheel, with the water tank and engine on the other, driving the front wheel by friction pulley. Performance was little better than that of a bicycle, range was poor, and very few were built.

In France, Michaux and Perreaux also produced a three-wheeler with belt drive to the single front wheel. But the arrival of the internal combustion engine would soon make the steam-powered machines obsolete. Many alternatives to steam had already been considered, including clockwork, compressed air, and hydrogen gas. A Frenchman, Etienne Lenoir, had driven six miles (10km) near Paris in 1862 in a four-wheeled vehicle powered by a hydrogen gas engine. In 1879, an Italian named Giuseppe Murnigotti patented a motorcycle powered by a twin-cylinder hydrogen gas engine, claiming a top speed of over 12mph (20km/h), but it was never built.

Instead it would be the four-stroke engine powered by gas (or benzine, as it was then known) that would dominate both motorcycle and automobile production, and trigger the huge expansion in personal transport. The familiar four-stroke principle had been invented by French scientist Alphonse Beau de Rochas in 1862, and patented in revised form 14 years later by two Germans, Dr. Nicolaus Otto and Eugen Langen.

Otto gave his name to the four-stroke cycle (of induction-compression-combustion-exhaust) on which modern four-strokes still operate. It was his assistants Gottlieb Daimler and Wilhelm

Maybach who developed the principle into a successful static engine, which ran on mains-supplied hydrogen gas. And it was Daimler who, having seen the engine's potential, left his job at the Deutz Engine Company and persuaded Maybach to join him in developing the engine for use in a vehicle. Instead of using gas fuel they decided on benzine, which at the time was used mainly for cleaning clothes.

The vehicle that Daimler and Maybach had in mind was a four-wheeled horseless carriage. The duo had no great interest in motorcycles. It was simply for convenience that, after spending the next two years developing an engine, they bolted it into a home-made wooden chassis that had two main wheels, plus two stabilizers that prevented it from leaning in bends. Even so, Einspur, generally accepted as the world's first motorcycle, was an impressive and influential piece of engineering.

Its powerplant was a 264cc single whose vertical cylinder had no fins and was cooled with the help of a powered fan. Its inlet valve was opened by piston suction, and sat above a cam-driven exhaust valve, in the layout that would be commonly used later and given the name inlet-over-exhaust (or ioe). Twin flywheels were enclosed in a cast aluminum crankcase. Ignition was by a hot tube, which projected into the cylinder and was heated by a bunsen-style burner. Carburation was a float device created by Maybach. The motor turned at 750rpm, very fast by previous standards, and produced roughly half a horsepower.

Daimler and Maybach bolted the engine into a wooden frame, based on that of a boneshaker bicycle, which they built in their garden shed workshop in Canstatt, near Stuttgart. Final drive was by belt, with a moveable pulley acting as a simple clutch. A handlebar twist control, as pioneered by Michaux-Perreaux, operated both this and the rear brake at the same time. Daimler later added a simple two-speed transmission, though its effect was limited because the bike had to be stopped to swap between ratios.

That was not a concern during Einspur's history-making first ride in 1885. Paul Daimler rode the eight miles (13km) from Canstatt to Unterturkheim and back, returning safely despite the minor fire caused by the saddle's location above the hot engine and burner. Despite the bike's promise, its creators were mainly interested in developing its engine for their horseless carriage.

Above: Early versions of the Motocyclette from the Paris-based Werner brothers placed the engine above the front wheel. The later 'new Werner' of 1901 would become the first with the engine located low, between the wheels.

Above: Indian built its first bike in 1901, pre-dating Harley-Davidson by two years. The 264cc single-cylinder engine replaced the seat tube, forming a stressed member of the frame. The humped rear fender held gas and oil.

Left: The British-made Holden, which entered production in 1899, was the world's first four-cylinder bike. Its 1047cc engine featured two pairs of horizontal cylinders, each containing a single piston with a crown at each end. Exposed conrods drove the rear wheel via a crank.

Harley-Davidson (1903)	
Engine:	Air-cooled inlet-over-exhaust two-valve single
Capacity:	412cc (76 x 89mm)
Maximum power:	3hp
Transmission:	Single speed; belt final drive
Frame:	Tubular steel
Suspension:	None
Brakes:	None front; pedal rear
Weight:	198lb (90kg)
Top speed:	30mph (48km/h)

Above: Harley-Davidson's founders were, from left to right, Arthur and Walter Davidson, William Harley, and William Davidson. They built their first bike in a small wooden shed in Milwaukee in 1903, and by 1910 were producing over 1000 machines per year.

Right: The first Harley-Davidson was powered by a 3hp inlet-over-exhaust engine, angled forward in a loop-style frame, with belt final drive. Performance was unspectacular, but the bike gained a reputation for strength. Just three Harleys were built in 1903 and 1904.

After Maybach had ridden it to test some modifications over the next few months, Einspur was abandoned before being destroyed by a fire in 1903. Existing machines are replicas.

At around this time British engineer Edward Butler was developing an alternative three-wheeled machine that he called the Velocycle, and which he had patented in 1884, a year before Einspur's arrival. Partly to avoid infringing Otto's patents, Butler used a two-stroke engine, with two horizontal cylinders, one each side of its single rear wheel. The determined Butler took several more years to raise the funds to build his first machine, which he renamed the Petrol-Cycle and tested in east London.

Unfortunately Butler became a victim of Britain's draconian speed limit, which restricted mechanized vehicles to just 4mph (6.5km/h) on open roads and half that speed in towns. He was dismayed to discover that the limit applied to his Petrol-Cycle, not just to steam-powered vehicles as he had imagined. Butler's backers concentrated on developing his engine for static and marine use, but he refused to give up and redesigned the machine with a four-stroke engine. It had a top speed of about 12mph (19km/h) and incorporated several innovative touches. But development was intermittent, and was eventually abandoned.

Another outstanding early machine was produced by Frenchman Félix Millet, who in 1889 unveiled a tricycle powered by a radial five-cylinder engine placed inside a wheel. A two-wheeled version soon followed, with its engine initially in the front wheel and then, after a redesign, in the rear wheel, the crankshaft supplying direct drive to the wheel. This probably became the first ever racing motorcycle when it was entered in the Paris-Bordeaux-Paris race in 1894. The event was abandoned shortly after its start, but the following year a Millet was leading the Paris-Orléans race when it crashed, ending up in a ditch.

The year of 1894 was a momentous one in motorcycle history, for in that January four German pioneers patented the Hildebrand & Wolfmüller, or H & W – the world's first production bike. Munich-based brothers Heinrich and Wilhelm Hildebrand had built a steam-powered bicycle several years earlier, and joined with compatriots Alois Wolfmüller and Hans Geisenhof to develop a large parallel twin four-stroke engine. This heavy device promptly broke the bicycle frame they fitted it into, so the quartet created a much stronger replacement, with the fuel tank between the four steel downtubes.

The H & W was an impressive machine, and the first to be called a motorcycle ('*motorrad*' in German). The 1489cc four-stroke parallel twin's cylinders lay horizontally, with its pistons driving the rear wheel via long connecting rods, in steam engine fashion. There was no flywheel, apart from the solid rear wheel itself; broad rubber bands were used to help the pistons on their return stroke. A timing device on the rear wheel regulated the opening of the exhaust valves; inlet valves were automatic (i.e. suction-operated).

Induction was by a surface carburetor, a set-up that effectively combines carburetor and fuel tank, as air passes over the surface of the fuel before entering the engine via a regulator. Ignition was by a simple hot platinum tube, as pioneered by Daimler. Power output was 2.5hp at 240rpm. There was a twistgrip throttle to control engine speed but no clutch, so each time the bike stopped it had to be bump-started.

Neat features included the liquid-cooled engine's water tank, which was built into the curved rear fender; and the use of a frame downtube to double as the oil tank. There was also an exhaust muffler in front of the motor. The H & W was innovative in its use of pneumatic tires, which had been patented by Scottish vet John Boyd Dunlop in 1885. But the braking system was less sophisticated, comprising a simple spoon that pressed on the front tire, plus a pedal-operated rear bar that scraped on the ground.

That sounds like a barely adequate way to slow a machine with a top speed approaching 30mph (48km/h), but such concerns did not put off eager would-be motorcyclists. With orders worth more than two million marks, the Hildebrand and Wolfmüller firm built a new factory for 1200 employees, in addition to a smaller plant where the bikes were assembled. After a successful demonstration in Paris, the *motorrad* was also licensed for production in France, where it was renamed the Petrolette. In May 1895 Alois Wolfmüller also took two machines to Italy, where he and an Italian rode them in the country's first motor race, a 62-mile (100km) return trip from Turin to Asti. They finished an impressive second and third, beaten only by a Daimler car.

After this promising start, problems were quick to follow. The two Petrolettes entered for the big Paris-Bordeaux-Paris race shortly afterward both broke down, and flaws in the design became clear, many relating to the crude hot tube ignition. Starting was often difficult, and the lack of flywheel effect also made for erratic progress. Customers in both Germany and France

FN Four (1906)	
Engine:	Air-cooled inlet-over-exhaust eight-valve in-line four
Capacity:	412cc (48 x 57mm)
Maximum power:	4hp
Transmission:	Single speed, shaft final drive
Frame:	Steel twin downtube
Suspension:	Telescopic front; rigid rear
Brakes:	None front; drum and contracting band rear
Weight:	165lb (75kg) dry
Top speed:	40mph (64km/h)

Below: Belgian firm FN's sophisticated Four.

Above: FN's four-cylinder engine had four mica windows in its crankcase to reveal oil flow.

Left: America's Pierce Arrow four, dated 1911.

Early Racers

Motorcycle competition began in Continental Europe in the last decade of the 19th century. While speed restrictions caused problems in countries including Britain – where the limit was raised from 4mph (6.5km/h) to 12mph (19km/h) in 1896, and to 20mph (32km/h) in 1903 – French riders had few such problems. Races between cities became popular and events such as the Paris-Bordeaux-Paris were important for publicity and machine development. Distances were often well over 100 miles (161km), with bikes competing against cars and tricycles, including the increasingly fast and successful De Dion-Bouton trikes.

By the turn of the century the racing trikes were big, twin-cylinder devices producing up to 8hp, with fat tires, drop handlebars, and fearsome performance. But a crash at the Paris-Roubaix race in 1900 injured several spectators. The popularity of the 'mototris' faded as two-wheelers took over, led by the

Werner factory. The inter-city events suffered another blow in 1903 when the Paris-Madrid race was abandoned at Bordeaux following a string of bad accidents.

Racing began slightly later in America, where in 1901 Pennsylvania-based George Holley rode his single-cylinder bike to victory in what is thought to be the first ever American motorcycle road race, from Boston to New York. 'That was quite a ride,' recalled Holley, later famous for carburetor manufacture. 'Cobblestones, mud, sand, chickens and people, but the engine kept purring and I arrived right on schedule. Of course, with the layer of mud and dust on my face even my own mother wouldn't have recognized me!'

Several countries entered the inaugural Coupe Internationale, held in France in 1904, which followed the Gordon Bennett series of car races, and allowed three bikes per nation. Unfortunately the event was abandoned after the course was sprinkled with nails, causing

many punctures. The race was also controversial the next year, when Austria won after a French rider had been disqualified for changing a wheel. In 1906 the Puch-mounted Austrians won again on their home course, despite rival teams' complaints about sidecars full of spares patrolling the circuit.

The following year saw the first Isle of Man Tourist Trophy race. Mainland Britain still had a 20mph (32km/h) speed limit, and the law did not allow roads to be closed for speed events. There were no such problems on the Isle of Man, where Charles Collier, one of the brothers who had founded Matchless, won the single-cylinder event on a 500cc JAP-powered machine, averaging 38.5mph (62km/h) over the 158-mile (254km) course. Rem Fowler won the multi-cylinder class on a Peugeot-engined Norton V-twin, at a slightly lower average speed.

Above: Riders line up at the start line for the Isle of Man TT in 1914, the year in which Cyril Pullin rode a Rudge single with novel multi-speed transmission to win the Senior race.

Top right: Harry (left) and Charlie Collier were co-founders of Matchless and noted TT racers. Charlie won the very first TT race in 1907.

began to demand refunds. By early 1897 the operations in both countries had collapsed, and Hildebrand & Wolfmüller had gone into liquidation.

At around this time, another important landmark in motorcycle development occurred when the De Dion-Bouton firm of Paris announced that it was planning to sell its single-cylinder engine to other manufacturers. De Dion-Bouton had been founded in 1882, when Count Albert de Dion had gone into business with Georges Bouton, after admiring a model steam engine that Bouton had built. After producing several steam carriages and a tricycle, the duo turned to the internal combustion engine, and built a 138cc single-cylinder unit that revved to over 1500rpm, twice as fast as Daimler's Einspur motor.

That first engine produced just half a horsepower, but with its capacity enlarged to 185cc and its output increased by 50 percent, the De Dion soon showed its potential. Tricycles powered by the little engine scored good results in several long-distance French races in 1896. And when De Dion-Bouton then began selling the motors to whoever wanted to bolt them into a modified bicycle frame, a new form of 'clip-on' motorbike was created, and the motorcycle industry exploded into life.

Over the next few years, dozens of firms, mainly from France, Germany, and Britain, created bikes by bolting De Dion engines into frames in a wide variety of locations. The bottom bracket was taken up by the bicycle pedals, which were retained as 'light pedal assistance,' or lpa as it was known, was still required on hills. But almost every other position was used for the engine, including above the front or rear wheel, to either side of the bike, and integral with the saddle tube – with widely differing effect on the balance and center of gravity of the vehicles.

Rival firms moved quickly to produce engine units of their own. French competitors included Clement and Aster, while the best known of the foreign alternatives was Fafnir of Germany. De Dion's own design was also built under license by companies including the Motor Manufacturing Company (MMC) from Coventry in England. Meanwhile many bicycle firms were taking the opportunity to expand into the booming market for powered two-wheelers. Leading British marques Excelsior, Matchless, and Raleigh began in this way, as did Peugeot and René-Gillet from France, Bianchi of Italy, and Motosacoche of Switzerland.

Eventually, in 1901, it was French firm Werner, founded by two Russian-born brothers living in Paris, that set the pattern that motorcycle design would follow for the next century and more. Michel and Eugéne Werner's first business was in cinema, and they built their first bike using a gas engine originally intended to power a film projector. This was so promising that they abandoned the film projection work to set up a factory for their 'Motocyclette.' They sold more

Above: Glenn Curtiss became the fastest man on earth in 1907 when he rode his 4.4-liter V8 machine at 136.36mph (219.4km/h) over a measured mile at Ormond Beach in Florida. The Chicago Daily News *reported that: 'No such speed was ever made by anything but a bullet.'*

Scott 2-Speed (1912)	
Engine:	Liquid-cooled two-stroke parallel twin
Capacity:	532cc (73 x 63.5mm)
Maximum power:	3hp
Transmission:	Two-speed, chain final drive
Frame:	Steel twin cradle
Suspension:	Telescopic front; none rear
Brakes:	Stirrup front; shoe-on-sprocket rear
Weight:	200lb (91kg)
Top speed:	50mph (80km/h)

Left: Alfred Scott's two-stroke twins had many advanced features, including the telescopic front forks seen on this 1910 machine.

Zenith Gradua V-twin (1914)	
Engine:	Air-cooled side-valve four-valve V-twin
Capacity:	550cc
Maximum power:	6hp
Transmission:	Gradua system; belt final drive
Frame:	Steel single downtube
Suspension:	Girder front; rigid rear
Brakes:	Stirrup front; contracting band rear
Weight:	Not known
Top speed:	50mph (80km/h)

Above right: Freddie Barnes of Zenith, which was based in Surrey, England, was responsible for the early breakthrough in motorcycle transmissions with the Gradua system, which allowed gearing to be varied without changing the tension of the drive belt. This Zenith V-twin's gearing is changed using the 'coffee-grinder' handle whose knob can be seen above the tank.

Below: Wolverhampton-based bicycle firm Sunbeam moved into motorcycle production in 1913 with this neat 349cc, 2.5hp single with enclosed 'oil bath' chain cases.

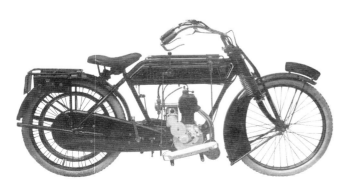

than 300 machines in 1898, even though the engine's location above the front wheel made for heavy steering and a oily rider.

By the turn of the century, MMC of Britain was building Werners under license, and annual production had reached over 1000 units. In 1901 the brothers redesigned the Motocyclette with its engine placed low, between the wheels, creating the 'new Werner.' Although other manufacturers had tried this layout before, the Werners' success, and the French firm's efforts to protect its patent, have resulted in the new Werner being regarded as the machine from which most modern motorcycles are descended.

New firms join in

Still more European companies joined the rush to become motorcycle manufacturers, some of them carefully modifying their designs to get round the Werners patent. New marques included Ariel, Coventry Eagle, Royal Enfield, Singer, and Riley from Britain; FN and Minerva from Belgium; Puch of Austria; Adler, Opel, and NSU from Germany; and Terrot of France. Although the output of the Werner and other singles rose toward 3hp by the end of the century, the fairly light bikes still generally used slip-prone final drive belts instead of the heavier chains.

By this time, the motorcycle's popularity in Britain had been increased by the lifting of the law that limited speed to walking pace, and required someone to walk in front of the vehicle waving a red flag. The Emancipation Run from London to Brighton on November 14, 1896 celebrated the limit being raised to 12mph (19km/h) and the abandonment of the need to wave the flag. (The commemorative London to Brighton run for old vehicles still takes place annually.)

Even before the Emancipation Act was passed, Major Henry Capel Lofft Holden had been developing an exotic machine that would become the world's first four-cylinder motorcycle, and arguably the first superbike. Holden's engine had a capacity of 1047cc and arranged its cylinders in two horizontal pairs. Each pair of cylinders was joined, forming a pipe-like shape, and contained a single piston with a crown at each end. Two large gudgeon pins (one to each pair of pistons) extended through the cylinder walls to long, exposed connecting rods, which turned the rear wheel via a crank arrangement.

Circuit Racing Arrives

The year 1907 was a momentous one because it saw not only the first Isle of Man TT race, but also the opening of the world's first artificially built race circuit: Brooklands. The 2.77-mile (4.46km) banked, egg-shaped track near Weybridge in Surrey, south of London, was designed by Henry Holden, of four-cylinder bike fame, and constructed of concrete. Hugh Locke King, the circuit's owner, intended it both for racing and as a high-speed test track for British manufacturers.

Brooklands was created mainly for car use, and bikes did not race there in 1907. But the first of many motorcycle races there took place the following year, when the two-lap sprint was won by Will Cook on a 984cc NLG, built by North London Garages, at an average speed of 63mph (101km/h).

Charles Collier of Matchless finished third in that race and was involved in another famous Brooklands battle in 1911, when he took on the American star Jake de Rosier of Indian in a match race. De Rosier came out of Collier's slipstream to win the first heat. The American lost the second heat with a burst tire, and won the decider when the Matchless' ignition failed. Collier gained some compensation shortly afterward when he raised the lap record to 91.37mph (147km/h).

Indian also made a big name for itself in 1911 at the Isle of Man TT, where the American marque's three-speed racers shocked the British industry by taking first, second, and third places in the Senior race, the first to be run over the famous Mountain course. Back home, de Rosier and Indian were leading lights in the sport of board-track racing, where motorcycles raced on steep wooden velodromes, sometimes battling at speeds of over 100mph (161km/h).

Board racing was exciting, popular, and backed by the leading factories including Excelsior, Flying Merkel, and Indian. The factory bikes were exotic and fast. Indian was the first to build a special eight-valve V-twin; Cyclone replied with an overhead-cam design.

Most had dropped handlebars, no silencing, and no brakes. Many had no throttle and ran flat-out, slowed only by a kill-switch. Riders wore little protective clothing and often crashed on the slippery, splintered tracks, the steepest of which, at St. Louis, Missouri, was banked at 62 degrees.

Stars such as de Rosier, Charles 'Fearless' Balke and Charles 'Crazy Horse' Verrill were well paid but often injured. The motorcycle world was shocked when de Rosier died in 1913, following injuries received in a crash almost a year earlier. Two riders and six spectators had been killed in 1912 when a bike went into the crowd at Newark, New Jersey. Public resistance to the 'murder dromes' grew, and a few years later the uniquely thrilling sport of board racing had been abandoned.

The Holden revved to 420rpm, produced about 3hp and reached a top speed of about 25mph (40km/h). The prototype was reportedly quiet and fairly reliable, but prone to overheating, so liquid cooling was added, delaying the start of production to 1899. Unfortunately for Holden, by this time light motor cars had become available at comparable cost. This was the first – but by no means the last – time that an exotic motorcycle would fail to sell because it was too expensive.

In the USA, progress had been slow until the turn of the century, with many people's skepticism summed up by the comment from Colonel Albert Pope, the leading bicycle manufacturer: 'You can't get people to sit over an explosion!' Despite this, Pope's Columbia motorcycle, built in Connecticut in 1900, was one of the country's earliest production bikes.

The following year saw the arrival of Indian, a marque that would have a more lasting impact. George Hendee was a bicycle manufacturer and former racer who built machines called the Silver King and Silver Queen. He teamed up with Oscar Hedstrom, a Swedish machinist and fellow bicycle race enthusiast who was working in New York. Hedstrom had fitted a modified De Dion engine to a tandem bicycle that was used for pacing cycle racers at Madison Square Garden.

Above left: Harley-Davidsons racing on a board track, where speeds reached over 100mph (161km/h) and many riders crashed on the steep, often splintered, wooden surface.

Top right: The banked turns and wide concrete straights of Brooklands allowed very high racing speeds, and also made the Surrey circuit very useful for performance testing.

Above: This Harley-Davidson catalog cover dates from 1913, by which time the Milwaukee firm's production had reached more than 5000 bikes per year. The cover picture's touring image is appropriate because at this time Harley declined to compete against rivals including Indian and Thor with a factory race team.

Below: This shot of one of the three original 1903 Harley singles shows the bike's sturdy construction and belt final drive.

At Hendee's request, Hedstrom designed a motorcycle that combined a diamond-frame bicycle chassis with a 264cc (16 cubic inch) single-cylinder engine that used his own cylinder barrel and crankcases. Hedstom angled the engine slightly backward as a stressed member of the frame, replacing the seat tube. The humped rear fender doubled as a twin-section tank containing gas and oil. A cylindrical case behind the front downtube held three rechargeable dry-cell batteries, which provided power for a spark ignition coil timed from the crankshaft.

Two examples of this first Indian are thought to have been built in 1901. The lightweight machine produced just under two horsepower, giving a top speed of about 30mph (48km/h). Pedals were provided for starting, and the bike used chain drive instead of the more common but slip-prone leather belt. Engine speed was regulated by a twistgrip on the right handlebar, which advanced or retarded the ignition timing. This mechanism reached the engine via a series of metal rods and joints, and sometimes broke when the handlebars were turned. But the generally well-built Indian became a success, and was followed in 1907 by the firm's first V-twin.

At around the time that Indian was beginning production, an important partnership was being formed when two Milwaukee-based friends, Bill Harley and Arthur Davidson, became interested in the internal combustion engine. The pair worked for the same engineering firm, Arthur as a pattern maker, Bill as a draftsman. Initially they planned to power a small boat to save effort on their fishing trips. But both were also cyclists, and with the help of a German acquaintance who was familiar with the De Dion engine, they fitted a single-cylinder motor into a bicycle frame in an attempt to create a powered two-wheeler.

The first engine was not a success. But the duo persevered and in 1902 they had completed a production engine, helped by family and friends including Ole Evinrude, who advised on carburetor design and would later become famous in the marine world. Arthur Davidson had two elder brothers, Walter and William, who worked for the railroad and were trained as a mechanic and toolmaker respectively. Both joined the new operation, encouraged by their Scottish-born father, who built the first factory, a small wooden shed with the words: 'HARLEY-DAVIDSON MOTOR CO.' on its door.

The firm's first machine was ready for testing in 1903, the year that the Wright brothers made the first powered flight. The bike featured an inlet-over-exhaust single-cylinder engine, inclined forward in a loop frame, and produced about 3hp, good for a top speed of 30mph (48km/h). Final drive was by belt, and even this first model epitomized future Harley-Davidsons by being sturdy and rather heavy. It was a success, and production numbers rose from three bikes in 1903 to over 150 in 1907, and more than 1000 by 1910.

While Harley-Davidson and many other firms were producing singles in increasing numbers, other configurations were making an impression too. The most glamorous was the four-cylinder machine introduced by Belgian firm FN in 1904. Like several other motorcycle operations including Britain's BSA, FN was originally an armaments manufacturer that had begun building first bicycles, then single-cylinder motorbikes. But the Four, designed by Paul Kelecom, was much more sophisticated.

The 362cc in-line four had a notable advantage of smoothness over singles, as its inner and outer pairs of pistons moved in opposite directions, canceling out primary vibration. Valvegear was familiar inlet over exhaust; the long one-piece crankshaft ran in a cast-iron crankcase, which contained four small mica windows that could be used to check oil flow. Final drive was by shaft, neatly enclosed in a frame tube.

Sophisticated and successful

The chassis was based on a twin-loop steel frame, with tubes running to each side of the engine. There was no rear suspension but the FN featured one of the first telescopic forks, in a system combined with a parallelogram linkage. The front wheel had no brake but the rear had two: a drum that was operated by the rider pedaling backward; and a hand-operated contracting band acting on the outside of the drum.

When it was unveiled in 1904 the exotic Four caused a sensation, and it proved wrong those who thought it too complex by becoming a commercial success too. The engine was rated at 3.5hp and gave a modest speed of about 35mph (56km/h), because transmission was single speed until a two-speed gearbox and clutch were introduced in 1908. Engine capacity grew to 412cc and then to 491cc in 1911, increasing top speed to over 40mph (64km/h). The Four was updated and its engine enlarged again to 748cc just before World War I, during which the occupied factory produced bikes for the Germany army.

The United States gained a sophisticated in-line, shaft-driven four of its own when Percy Pierce of Buffalo, New York, built a bike called the Arrow after returning from Europe with an FN. Pierce was clearly influenced by the Belgian machine, but the Arrow was no copy. Its 696cc motor had a side-valve instead of ioe layout, and the frame comprised large-diameter steel tubes which held fuel and oil. The Pierce Arrow had a top speed of 50mph (80km/h), and it was smooth as well as reliable enough to win several endurance events. But it was not profitable, and Pierce abandoned production in 1913.

An even more exotic American bike was the Curtiss V8, a stunning prototype which Glenn Curtiss built and rode to a claimed speed of 136.36mph (219.4km/h) on the hard sand of Ormond Beach in Florida in January 1907. The 4.4-liter (265ci) air-cooled V8, which produced 40hp at 1800rpm, had been designed to power an airship. The New Yorker rode it through a measured mile in 26.4 seconds to become 'the fastest man on earth,' as he was widely known. But a broken drive shaft damaged the V8's chassis, preventing a return run, and Curtiss's speed did not gain official recognition.

Engineers on both sides of the Atlantic created a wide variety of motorbikes in the early years of the 20th century, among the most innovative being Alfred Angas Scott. The Yorkshire-based engineer's specialty was the two-stroke parallel twin, the first of which he built in 1904. Four years later Scott, one of 12 brothers, began production of an enlarged 333cc version with water-cooled cylinder heads.

Scott's two-stroke had a unique exhaust note, a soft purr that rose to a high-pitched yowl that became a trademark. His bikes were notable for advanced features including the world's first kick-start, and a two-speed gearbox that was also Scott's design. The chassis was equally clever, featuring a frame of straight, triangulated steel tubes and the novelty of telescopic front forks. A cylindrical fuel tank, painted in the factory's favored purple color with two silver bands, added to the distinctive look.

Scott himself rode to numerous victories in hillclimbs following the fine-handling twin's debut in 1908, and successfully updated his machine in subsequent years. Rivals resorted to campaigning to get the two-stroke handicapped (by multiplying its capacity by 1.32). Scott exploited this in his advertising, and also improved performance by increasing the actual capacity to 486cc and then to 532cc in 1912, by which time top speed had reached 50mph (80km/h). Isle of Man TT victories in 1912 and 1913 boosted the Yorkshire firm's profile still further.

Above: *This Harley V-twin dates from 1913.*

Below: *Excelsior's Lee Humiston gave the Chicago firm publicity in 1912 with the first ever 100mph (161km/h) board track lap.*

Below: *Henderson's refined four was boosted in 1913, when Carl Stevens Clancy become the first motorcyclist to ride around the world.*

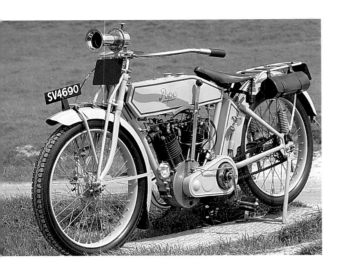

Top: The Pope Model L's leaf-spring front and plunger rear suspension gave the 1000cc V-twin a comfortable ride by 1913 standards.

Above: American firm Flying Merkel's V-twins were notable for their orange paintwork and clever chassis. This Model V dates from 1911 and features a sprung rear wheel whose movement maintains constant drive belt tension. Alongside the 6hp Model V, Merkel offered a Model VS with larger, 7hp V-twin engine. Flying Merkel production ended in 1915.

Transmission revolution

The 1908 Scott's two-speed gearbox was a notable improvement over single-speed alternatives. But the real breakthrough in motorcycle transmission came in the same year when Surrey-based Freddie Barnes, who had formed the Zenith firm three years earlier, invented the Gradua system. Until this point, riders had adjusted belt-driven bikes by changing the position of the crankshaft pulley that took the engine's drive to the rear wheel. The flaw of that system was that if belt tension was correct in high gear, it was too slack in low.

Barnes' Gradua system solved this problem using a long handle, nicknamed the 'coffee-grinder,' which ran vertically up the right side of the motor. The bottom of the shaft was connected to both the crankshaft pulley and the rear wheel. When the rider turned the coffee-grinder, both the pulley and the spindle moved together, so gearing could be altered while the drive belt remained correctly tensioned.

Such was the Gradua system's advantage over single-speed engines that in 1911 Barnes won more than 50 hillclimbs, after which the organizing Auto-Cycle Union banned the geared bike from many events. Zenith capitalized on this by producing a new badge, featuring the word 'Barred' and the image of a motorbike behind the bars of a jail. Zenith carried on using the logo and retained a reputation for performance long after the Gradua had been superseded by Rudge's Multi-gear system, which used a similar variable belt without needing to move the rear wheel.

Gears became increasingly important as power outputs increased. Singles remained the mainstay of most manufacturers. But enlarging capacity in search of extra performance also added to vibration, which taxed the transmission and frames that were already suffering from the combination of rough roads and crude or non-existent suspension.

The simplest solution was the V-twin, as an extra cylinder could be fitted without too much trouble into the typical diamond frame structure. In the United States, particularly, the long distances and rugged roads led to a demand for more power, and the rearward incline of many bikes' single cylinders invited the addition of a forward one. Indian produced one of the first V-twins in 1907, by mounting two cylinders at 42 degrees on a common crankcase. A year later, the twin's ioe valvegear was updated with mechanical inlet valve as an option, although many riders preferred the limited – but trusted – suction-operated automatic inlet valve.

Other manufacturers were making their mark, too. One of the biggest was Excelsior, whose race bikes often got the better of main rivals Indian and Harley-Davidson. The Excelsior Supply Company began building bikes in Chicago in 1907, with a simple 438cc, 3.25hp single, and three years later introduced an 820cc V-twin model with cylinders spaced at 45 degrees. In 1911, the year that Excelsior was taken over by bicycle maker Ignatz Schwinn, this was followed by a 1000cc model.

The big Excelsior V-twin was a fast and impressive machine that was gradually developed in the following years. Racing was valuable for development and publicity. Stars including Joe Wolters and Jake de Rosier scored numerous wins on the Chicago-made bikes, and the firm gained publicity in 1912, when Lee Humiston recorded the first official 100mph (161km/h) lap, at a board track in Los Angeles.

In contrast the Henderson company, later to be united with Excelsior, produced sophisticated in-line four-cylinder bikes that became known more for long-distance ability than for speed. Brothers William and Tom Henderson built their first machine in Detroit in 1912, placing the pillion in front of the rider. Their 965cc, 7hp four adopted a more conventional arrangement the following year, when Carl Stevens Clancy gave the firm a boost by becoming the first motorcyclist to ride around the world.

Most American firms preferred the V-twin layout, however, including Massachusetts-based Pope, which also produced some notably refined machines. The American Cycle Manufacturing Company, which had been founded by Albert Pope, started in 1911 with a single, and the following year built a 1000cc V-twin with pushrod-operated overhead valvegear instead of the common inlet-over-exhaust. The Pope was powerful, fast at over 60mph (97km/h) and comfortable too, thanks to an advanced plunger-type rear suspension system.

Another firm famed for performance was Merkel, or Flying Merkel, as the machines were known after the first of Joseph Merkel's generally bright orange 1000cc V-twins was launched in 1910. These too had a clever rear suspension, a cantilever system similar to that later used by Vincent, plus a sprung front fork that further improved handling and comfort. Racers including the famous Maldwyn Jones scored many successes for Merkel over the next few years, leading to advertisements boasting that: 'If it passes you, it's a Flying Merkel.'

The other main manufacturer of V-twins was Harley-Davidson, whose first attempt was the Model 5D of 1909. This 811cc (50ci) unit adopted the 45-degree angle that Harley would retain, but the 7hp bike was unreliable and promptly withdrawn. Chief engineer William Harley persevered, and the firm returned two years later with the much improved Model 7D (Harley regarded 1904 as year zero, so 1911 was the seventh model year), which was more reliable and sold well.

For 1912 the V-twin was made available with a larger 989cc (61ci) engine, developing 8hp, and could be ordered with the option of a clutch (in the rear wheel hub), and with chain instead of belt final drive. Further improvements included a more sophisticated lubrication system, a new frame that gave a lower seat, and a sprung seat post – the curiously named 'Ful Floteing' system – for added comfort. The Model 10F of 1914 incorporated more advances: footboards, enclosed valve springs, a kick-starter, clutch, and two-speed transmission. Harley was on its way. And, as that list of features confirmed, the motorcycle had come of age.

Harley-Davidson Model 10F (1914)	
Engine:	Air-cooled four-valve inlet-over-exhaust 45-degree V-twin
Capacity:	989cc (84 x 88.9mm)
Maximum power:	11hp
Transmission:	Two-speed, chain or belt final drive
Frame:	Steel single downtube
Suspension:	Girder forks; rigid rear
Brakes:	None front; expanding band rear
Weight:	310lb (141kg)
Top speed:	60mph (97km/h)

Below: Most Harleys in 1912 were singles.

Left: Harley's Model 10F V-twin from 1914 has footboards, two-speed box, and acetylene lamp.

Below: Bikes were much used in World War I. Here members of the British Army's 60th Signals Division prepare their bikes in 1912.

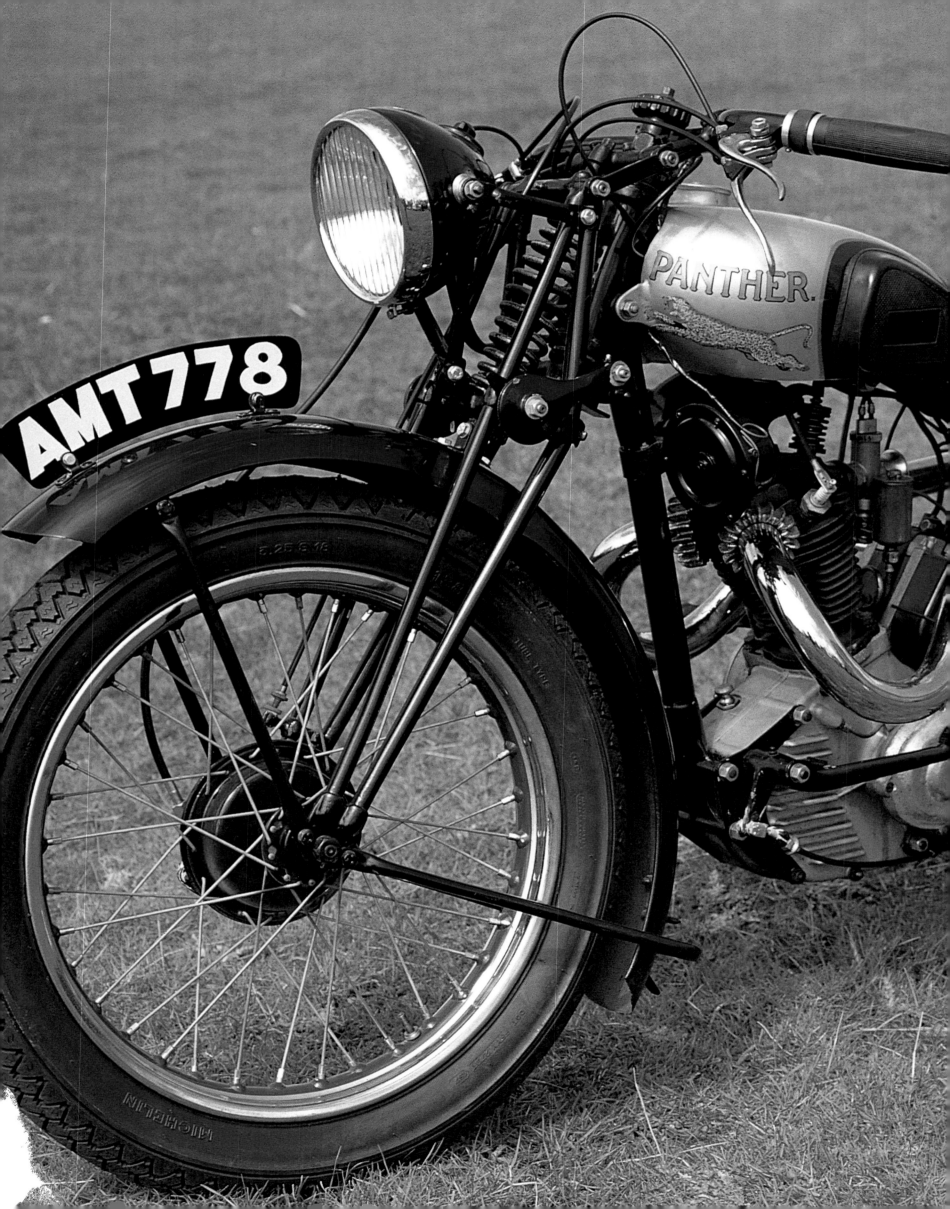

Boom and Bust
1914–1939

fter the dramatic advances during the early years of the 20th century, the changes that occurred in motorcycle design and technology after the start of World War I were more gradual. By 1914, the motorcycle's basic format of four-stroke gas engine and steel chassis was firmly established, albeit with a variety of cylinder arrangements, and most of the main mechanical features had been introduced. Steam power, tricycles, and other early devices had been abandoned; gearboxes, chain drive, and suspension had become commonplace.

By contrast, the motorcycle industry experienced a turbulent time on both sides of the Atlantic. In Britain there was initially a rapid expansion, triggered by the growing numbers of engineering firms that had begun specializing as manufacturers of various components. Companies including JAP and Villiers built engines; Sturmey-Archer became known for gearboxes. Other companies concentrated on producing frames, wheels, or suspension parts.

This led to large numbers of firms and individuals starting up as motorcycle manufacturers by assembling these components into bikes, and proudly displaying their own marque name on their bought-in fuel tanks. By 1914, the number of British motorcycle manufacturers had risen to more than 50, most of them based close to each other in the Midlands cities of Birmingham and Coventry, where the industry would continue to be centered for many years.

Sales were healthy, too, at least in Britain where the 1910 registration total of 36,000 had increased to 123,000 by 1914. Despite this, most of the smaller marques would soon go out of business. They could not compete with larger firms that had the resources to design and develop new machines, and to test them thoroughly on the road and in international competition. Firms such as Matchless, Sunbeam, and Triumph thrived; many others faded away with the advent of World War I.

The same period also saw a motorcycling boom in America, in sales and also in the number of manufacturers and the increasingly sophisticated machines they were producing. The country's size, often undeveloped roads and cheap gasoline combined to create a demand for extra horsepower, with the result that the large-capacity V-twin engine became popular. As in Europe, firms such as Thor, Spacke, and Joerns-Thiem built engines for sale, while other specialists produced parts such as gearboxes and wheels.

In 1913 there were no fewer than 36 motorcycle marques spread across the States. Indian co-founder Oscar Hedstrom retired that year, leaving his old firm as the world's largest, with a record annual total of 32,000 bikes built at 'the Wigwam,' its large factory at Springfield in

Previous page: Panther's 1934 250cc Model 70 used the firm's sloping single cylinder layout.

Above: The sturdy nature of Harley-Davidson's bikes made them well suited to military work in World War I. Many V-twins were fitted with a sidecar carrying a machine-gun.

Right: In 1916, sisters Adeline and Augusta Van Buren rode Indian Powerplus V-twins the 5500 miles (8850km) from New York to San Francisco – via Pikes Peak, Colorado – to prove women could help the war effort as dispatch riders.

Indian Powerplus (1916)	
Engine:	Air-cooled side-valve four-valve 42-degree V-twin
Capacity:	988cc (79.4 x 100.8mm)
Maximum power:	18hp
Transmission:	Three-speed, chain final drive
Frame:	Steel single downtube
Suspension:	Leaf-spring front & (optional) rear
Brakes:	None front; drum rear
Weight:	410lb (186kg)
Top speed:	65mph (105km/h)

Massachusetts. Harley-Davidson was the leading challenger to Indian, the Milwaukee firm being known for robustness in contrast to its rival's reputation for speed. Other marques offering twins included Excelsior, the next biggest, plus Dayton, Emblem, Jefferson, Pirate, Iver-Johnson, Monarch, and Reading-Standard.

Few people realized it at the time, but this would be a high point not only for Indian but for the whole American motorcycle industry. For it was also in 1913 that Henry Ford set up the world's first automobile production line at his factory in Highland Park, Michigan, further increasing the efficiency with which he could produce the Model T car, which was already a big hit following its introduction five years earlier. From now on US motorcycle firms would increasingly struggle to compete with Ford, whose car could be sold so cheaply that only the most enthusiastic rider could resist it.

The US bike firms' problems were not caused by lack of invention. While the efforts of European companies were inevitably concentrated elsewhere during World War I, the Americans took over as world leaders in two-wheeled engineering, introducing a long list of significant features including the twist-grip throttle, starter motor, electric lighting, foot-operated clutch, and drum brake on the rear wheel.

Indian's most famous model of this period was the Powerplus, which was launched in 1916 as a more powerful version of the firm's existing 42-degree V-twin. Designed by Charles Gustafson, Sr., it featured a side-valve layout instead of the ioe (inlet-over-exhaust) arrangement that Indian had used since its first twin in 1907. The 998cc engine produced 18hp, considerably more than the old Big Twin model, and had an impressive top speed of over 60mph (97km/h).

Chassis design was to Indian's familiar high standard, with optional leaf-spring rear suspension – an advanced feature at the time – plus a similar arrangement for the front wheel. Cable controls replaced the original model's complicated system of rods and linkages in 1918, by which time the Powerplus had become firmly established, helped by the exploits of the hard-riding Erwin 'Cannonball' Baker, who set a series of long-distance records.

Some of the smaller American firms adopted a variety of different engine and chassis features. Iver-Johnson and Reading-Standard used side-by-side (or 'flathead') valve layout, while Feilbach

Above left: Indian's Powerplus featured side-valve operation for its 998cc V-twin engine.

Below: Cyclone's innovative overhead-cam V-twins were powerful but unreliable.

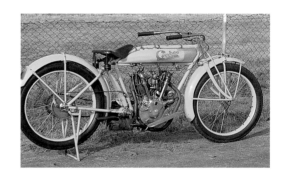

Cyclone (1916)	
Engine:	Air-cooled sohc four-valve 45-degree V-twin
Capacity:	996cc
Maximum power:	25hp @ 5000rpm
Transmission:	Chain final drive
Frame:	Steel single downtube
Suspension:	Leaf spring front & rear
Brakes:	None front, drum rear
Weight:	280lb (127kg)
Top speed:	85mph (137km/h)

Right: *The amazing Wolseley Gyrocar, built in Birmingham in 1913, could remain stationary due to its huge, electrically driven gyroscope. Commissioned by Russian Count Peter Schilovski for military use, it ran successfully in tests. Only one was built before World War I broke out in 1914, and the Count disappeared. After the war the car lay abandoned and Wolseley's directors decided to bury it intact, in case the Count returned. In 1938 it was exhumed to be displayed in the company's museum, but was scrapped in 1948.*

Above: Two early women riders enjoying the luxury of a Harley and wicker sidecar.

and Peerless adopted shaft final drive, instead of chain. Manufacturers including Pope, Flying Merkel, and Jefferson followed Indian in using sprung frames, instead of the old-style rigid rear ends. Various different front suspension designs were also used.

Arguably the most innovative marque, if not the most successful, was Cyclone, whose powerful V-twins made a big impact during their short time in production. Cyclone's 996cc V-twin, designed by Andrew Strand and built in St. Paul, Minnesota by the Joerns Motor Manufacturing Company, was the world's first production roadster with overhead camshafts, which were driven by bevel shaft. The exotic 45-degree motor also contained lightweight conrods and a roller-bearing crankshaft.

Cyclone claimed a top speed of 100mph (161km/h) for its exotic machines, which were generally finished in bright yellow. That claim was ambitious but Cyclones were good for a genuine 85mph (137km/h) and their reputation was boosted by a string of race wins. Factory rider Don Johns was fast and spectacular, particularly because his bike's engine was 'ported' – vented to the open air through ports which opened when the pistons neared bottom-dead-center.

This was thought to increase performance, and certainly made the flame- and smoke-belching Cyclone look fearsome, especially in night races. But the powerful V-twins suffered from reliability problems, and were too expensive to sell in sufficient numbers. By the end of the 1916 racing season Cyclone had abandoned production. With the United States fast becoming a nation of car owners, most of the other smaller motorcycle firms would soon follow.

Military machines

Over in Europe, motorcycle firms had become preoccupied with World War I. In Britain, production of civilian bikes (and cars) was prohibited by the Ministry of Munitions from November 1916. Many civilian machines had already been commandeered for military use. Britain's War Office ordered large numbers of bikes, as the motorcycle had become a vital part of the military effort, replacing the horse as a means of communicating when telephones could not be used.

The most popular and commonly used bikes on the Allied side were the 3.5hp Triumph 500cc Model H, and the 2.75hp Douglas flat-twin. Douglas was a Bristol firm that had built trucks and cars before beginning motorcycle production, concentrating on flat twins with cylinders in-line with the bike. The little 2.75hp twin had capacity of 348cc and a top speed of not much more than 40mph (64km/h). But it lived up to its 'Lightweight' designation by weighing only 170lb (77kg), which aided maneuverability in difficult conditions.

Ironically Triumph, one of many marques with origins in the bicycle trade, had been founded back in 1902 by two Germans, Siegfried Bettmann and Mauritz Schulte. The firm's military machine, the Model H, was a 3.5hp, side-valve single that began the war as a single-speeder, before being uprated with a three-speed Sturmey-Archer gearbox. The reliable single earned the nickname 'Trusty Triumph,' which would benefit the Coventry firm for many years afterward. After the war the H would be modified by noted tuner Harry (later Sir Harry) Ricardo using a four-valve head and central spark plug to produce the outstanding Model R or Triumph Ricardo, with top speed increased to 75mph (121km/h).

American bikes were also used by the Allies, notably Harley and Indian V-twins, plus the Henderson four. All were sometimes fitted with sidecars, which could be used to mount machine guns. The Germans also made use of bikes, notably from NSU, Brennabor, and Wanderer, plus Austrian-built Puch singles and twins. The Wanderer, a 600cc V-twin producing 4hp, was particularly popular.

Production of civilian bikes took some time to restart after the war ended in November 1918, partly due to shortages of coal and raw materials including iron, steel, and rubber. Eventually the British industry recovered, with yet more small firms springing up to assemble machines using bought-in components. Motorcycle development gained from a leap in technology triggered by the war. This was particularly notable in metallurgy, as tougher steels plus strong and light alloys improved the performance and durability of engines.

Harder steels added strength to valve springs and camshafts, while the new alloys meant engine designers could specify pistons made from aluminum instead of heavier iron or steel, allowing increased engine revs and higher power outputs. Four-stroke engine design advanced alongside the improved materials. Side-valve layouts were commonly replaced by pushrod-operated overhead valves by the early 1920s, and shortly afterward by overhead camshafts, normally operated by shaft and bevel gears.

Among the pioneers in this respect was Norton, an old firm that had risen to early prominence (boosted by Rem Fowler's TT win in the inaugural year of 1907) with side-valve singles and twins, notably the sporty 490cc Model 16H and the 633cc Big Four, a softly tuned, 4hp machine that was popular for use with a sidecar, the main form of family transport at the time. Founder James Norton was a former TT competitor who had become unwell with a heart condition that

Above: The 2.75hp model built by Bristol-based Douglas in 1923 had a 348cc side-valve flat-twin engine with cylinders in line with the bike. Similar Douglas models were much used by Allied dispatch riders during World War I, when their light weight of about 170lb (77kg) aided maneuverability on rough ground.

Left: This 633cc Norton Big Four was built in 1937 but the name dated back 30 years to the Birmingham firm's original model of that name, which was powered by James Lansdowne Norton's first ever engine, and produced just 4hp. The dependable side-valve single remained in production until 1954.

Above: During the 1930s the Isle of Man TT was dominated by the 'unapproachable' Nortons. Scottish star Jim Guthrie won a total of six TTs.

required lengthy convalescence. His firm had suffered and gone into liquidation in 1913, but had been revived shortly afterward as Norton Motors Limited.

The new firm was jointly run by Norton and Bob Shelley, brother-in-law of Dan 'Wizard' O'Donovan, a Brooklands-based racer and tuner. O'Donovan revamped the Model 16H to produce the Brooklands Special or BS, arguably the world's first production racer. The tuned 490cc single, still with side-valve layout, was sold with a certificate confirming that it had exceeded 75mph (121km/h) at Brooklands, or 70mph (113km/h) in slightly softer Brooklands Road Special (BRS) trim.

In 1922 Norton converted the single-cylinder engine to overhead-valve operation, with pushrods and rockers, to create the Model 18. The new bike performed well, as it proved by winning the Senior TT two years later. Sadly the white-haired 'Pa' Norton died in the following year, aged 56, after his heart condition had worsened.

The firm fought back, and took the 490cc single to its next stage in 1927, with the launch of the CS1, short for Cam Shaft Mk 1. The new engine, designed by Walter Moore, used a shaft and bevel arrangement to drive its overhead camshaft. Its 29hp output gave a top speed of 90mph (145km/h). The CS1 was raced successfully by Stanley Woods and others, and the following year was sold as a super-sports roadster. (Designer Moore later left for Germany's NSU, where he created a very similar motor that inspired the phrase 'Norton Spares Used.')

By this time Norton had begun a lasting rivalry with BSA, whose full name of the Birmingham Small Arms Company revealed a background in gun manufacture. After turning to bicycle production in the 1880s, BSA had begun building motorcycles with engines from firms including Minerva of Belgium. The first all-BSA bike, a successful 499cc side-valve single, appeared in 1910, and was followed by a series of V-twins in the 1920s, notably the Model E, whose 770cc, 50-degree engine produced 6hp. The Model E was popular with family sidecar owners, and could be bought with a matching 'chair' in BSA's green and white paintwork.

In the mid-1920s BSA embraced mass-production methods to build large numbers of the Model B or 'Round Tank,' a cheap and simple 250cc side-valve single that was popular with learners and delivery riders. Another successful single was the 'Sloper,' designed by Harold Briggs and named after its angled-forward cylinder. Introduced in 1926 as the S27, with a notably quiet 493cc overhead-valve engine, the Sloper was later built with 350 and 600cc capacities, and remained popular into the 1930s. A similar layout had been adopted back in 1904 by Yorkshire firm Phelon & Moore, whose bikes were sold under the Panther name. The firm's first bike was a 500cc single whose sloping cylinder also acted as the frame tube. Panther would continue to build Slopers, with remarkably few changes, into the 1960s.

Sunbeam's classy singles

Another marque that thrived in the 1920s was Sunbeam, the Wolverhampton firm whose founder John Marston had built his first bike in 1912 at the age of 76. Sunbeam's motorcycles, like the bicycles that preceded them, became known for high-quality construction. The first, a 350cc single, incorporated a fully-enclosed drive chain that earned it the nickname 'Little Oil Bath.' The single also featured a multi-plate clutch, two-speed gearbox, and a cleverly designed quickly detachable rear wheel that facilitated puncture repair.

John Marston died in 1918, followed shortly afterward by his son Roland, and the family was forced to sell the business to pay death duties. But Sunbeam thrived under its new owners, Noble Industries (later to become chemical giant ICI). Riders including George Dance and Tommy de la Hay earned a string of victories in competitions including hillclimbs and the Isle of Man TT, beginning when de la Hay won the 1920 Senior race after Dance had set the fastest lap.

In 1922 Sunbeam won again through Alec Bennett, who was also riding a 500cc side-valve single known as the 'Longstroke' due to its 77 x 105mm engine dimensions. Team-mate Dance was almost unbeatable in hillclimbs and sprints for the next few years. Sunbeam's competition success would continue throughout the decade, notably with Senior TT victories by Charlie Dodson in 1928 and '29, although the firm would later pay the price for concentrating on racing to the detriment of roadster development.

An enterprising British firm that hit problems quicker than most was ABC, the All British (Engine) Company, whose sophisticated 398cc transverse flat-twin caused a sensation when it was unveiled in 1919. Talented young engineer Granville Bradshaw's bike featured overhead valves and a four-speed gearbox with car-style H-gate lever. The chassis was also cleverly designed, with tubular steel frame tubes splayed out to protect the engine's cylinders in a crash, plus suspension and drum brakes at both front and rear.

The ABC was built at Sopwith's former aircraft factory in Surrey, and also licensed for production by Gnôme et Rhône, also a former aero engine firm, in France. More than 40,000 orders were received, following positive press tests that reported lively acceleration and a 60mph

Opposite above: Norton's Model 18, introduced in 1922, featured the firm's first engine with pushrod-operated overhead valves instead of side valves. By the time this bike was built in 1937, the Model 18 had been restyled, and replaced as Norton's sportiest single by the overhead-cam CS1 and International.

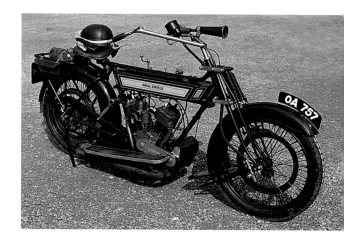

Above: Royal Enfield was best known for V-twins when this bike was built in 1919. Its swept-back handlebars and girder front suspension were typical period features. Front and rear wheels were slowed by brakes working on dummy rims inside the main rims.

Above: BSA's Model E, introduced in 1919, was a 770cc V-twin that became successful due to its reliability and competitive price. Features include girder forks, no rear suspension, enclosed drive chain, dummy rim brakes, and tank-mounted plunger for manual oil supply.

BMW R32 (1923)

Engine:	Air-cooled side-valve four-valve flat-twin
Capacity:	494cc (68 x 68mm)
Maximum power:	8.5hp @ 3200rpm
Transmission:	Shaft final drive
Frame:	Steel twin tube
Suspension:	Leaf spring front; rigid rear
Brakes:	Drum front; rim rear
Weight:	269lb (122kg)
Top speed:	55mph (89km/h)

Right: BMW's first ever bike was the 494cc R32, built in 1923 and featuring the same layout of horizontally opposed twin-cylinder engine and shaft final drive that the German firm would be using more than 80 years later.

Below: The exotic Megola, built in Germany from 1922, was powered by a 640cc radial five-cylinder engine located in its front wheel. Both this Sport model and the softer Touring option came with twin rear-wheel brakes plus fuel gauge and rev-counter as standard equipment.

(97km/h) top speed, plus good handling and a smooth and comfortable ride. But teething problems caused a delay in production and the price rose from £60 to £160, causing most orders to be canceled. A reputation for unreliable starting did not help, and Sopwith soon went into liquidation. Although French production continued for a while, fewer than 3000 bikes were built before the ABC story ended in 1923.

ABC's demise contrasted sharply with the lasting impact of another flat-twin of the same era: BMW's R32. After the end of the war, Germany's motorcycle industry had suffered along with the rest of that defeated country, with the economy in chaos, unemployment high, and raw materials scarce. Nevertheless a number of German firms succeeded in building simple, lightweight bikes, based on engines such as the 174cc two-stroke single built by Bekamo of Berlin, or the 100cc two-stroke from DKW.

The Bayerische Motorenwerke, which had built BMW aircraft engines during the war, was one of many German firms that turned to motorcycle manufacture in the early 1920s. The first BMW bike was a simple motorized bicycle called the Flink, which was powered by a proprietary Kurier 148cc two-stroke engine, and was not a success. In 1921, BMW engineer Martin Stolle designed a 494cc flat-twin side-valve engine, designated the M2B15, which the Munich firm sold to other manufacturers including Victoria, Heller, and Bison.

In 1923 engineer Max Fritz created the R32 by turning the flat-twin engine at 90 degrees, bolting on a three-speed gearbox and setting it in a triangulated, twin-tube steel chassis, with shaft final drive. Front suspension was by leaf spring working on a trailing-link fork; the rear end was unsprung. The motor produced 8.5hp, good for a top speed of about 55mph (89km/h), and the R32 was neatly finished and well built, with electric lighting and enclosed valvegear. It was launched at the Paris show and, although fairly expensive, it sold well and set the pattern for BMW roadsters that continues to this day.

Variety from Germany

Germany's other well-known manufacturer of flat-twins was Victoria, a former bicycle firm that built motorbikes using bought-in BMW motors, before hiring former BMW designer Stolle to create new powerplants of similar design and capacity. In 1928 Victoria added a range of single-cylinder models powered by British-built Sturmey-Archer engines ranging from 198 to 499cc. NSU, another German marque, preferred V-twins. The firm's 7hp 350cc twin scored top ten places in the TT in 1913. After the war NSU had some success with bigger V-twins, such as the 1000cc 18PS Sport, which was good for 75mph (121km/h).

Two-stroke bikes were also popular with German manufacturers, especially Zündapp and DKW. Founded by Danish-born J.S. Rasmussen, DKW began with small clip-on engines, and quickly progressed to small-capacity two-stroke bikes. By the end of the decade it was the world's largest manufacturer. As well as huge numbers of small bikes, DKW built larger machines such as the ZSW500, a 494cc water-cooled two-stroke parallel twin that was popular for solo and sidecar use.

Germany also produced the curious Megola, featuring a radial five-cylinder engine in its front wheel. Designer Fritz Cockerell's first prototypes housed the powerplant in the rear wheel, but he switched to the front to create the production Megola, which was first built in 1922. Each of the five air-cooled cylinders had a capacity of 128cc, giving 640cc in total. There was no gearbox or clutch; instead, while the motor and wheel turned forward, the crankshaft spun at six times the speed in the opposite direction, balancing the driving forces.

The engine produced 10hp and revved to 3600rpm, turning the front wheel at 600rpm and giving the Megola a top speed of 60mph (97km/h). The chassis was almost as innovative as the engine, and featured a sheet-steel frame that gave an armchair riding position. The touring version of the Megola emphasized its two-wheeled car theme with integral footboards and legshields, plus a bucket-type car seat. There was no room for a front brake but the rear wheel had two, independently operated by hand and foot.

Alongside the laid-back touring Megola there was a Sport model, which had a conventional saddle and rigid rear end, though it shared the leaf-spring front suspension design. The Sport also had a more powerful, 14hp engine, and was timed at 90mph (145km/h) at Berlin's Avus circuit. Despite the Megola's curious layout it was reasonably successful. Approximately 2000 were sold before production ended in 1926.

Another unlikely machine of very different style was the long, Czech-built Böhmerland, probably the only bike ever designed specifically to carry three people – two on a low dual-seat, plus a third above the rear wheel. Albin Liebisch's machine, known as the Cechie in its home country, was powered by a conventional 598cc air-cooled, pushrod-operated single engine producing 16hp. This was normally fitted with a three-speed gearbox with hand change, but some models featured two gearboxes – the second one operated by either passenger!

The Böhmerland's length was increased by a large tool-box behind the rear wheel, which like the front wheel was a cast aluminum disc, lightened by cutaway sections. Three models were produced, the ultra-long 'Langtouren' (long tourer) and the relatively normal but still lengthy Jubilee, from which was derived a sportier Racer. Other features included twin fuel tanks either side of the rear wheel, and unusually bright two-tone color schemes. Handling was very heavy but the bike was capable of 60mph (97km/h) and was reasonably reliable. It remained in production for 15 years from 1924, although only about 1000 were built during that time.

Neracar (1921)	
Engine:	Air-cooled two-stroke single
Capacity:	221cc (63.7 x 70mm)
Maximum power:	2.5hp
Transmission:	Chain final drive
Frame:	Pressed steel
Suspension:	Hub-center front; rigid rear
Brakes:	None front; twin drums rear
Weight:	200lb (90kg)
Top speed:	35mph (56km/h)

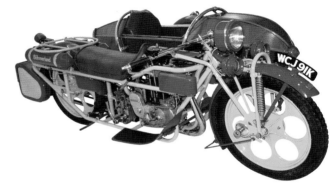

Above: This Böhmerland had a rack over its rear wheel, but a seat could be fitted instead to carry two passengers without need for the sidecar.

Below: Carl Neracher's feet-forward Neracar was built in both two-stroke, as here, and four-stroke engined versions during the 1920s.

Above: Moto Guzzi's 498cc Condor single, introduced in 1938, was the Italian marque's first customer road racer. It was good for 100mph (161km/h) and very successful.

Below: Guzzi's Omobono Tenni won the Lightweight TT in 1937, setting a lap record on the way to the first all-Italian TT victory.

An equally curious contemporary was the Neracar, whose name was doubly appropriate because not only was it invented by an American named Carl Neracher, it was also 'near a car' in its design and level of weather protection. With a feet-forward riding position, motorcycling's first example of hub-center steering, and its engine partly enclosed by pressed steel panels, the Neracar was a revolutionary machine. It entered production at Syracuse in New York in 1921, and in Britain the next year, built by luxury car firm Sheffield-Simplex at the former Sopwith factory in Surrey, previously home to ABC.

Early American-built bikes were powered by a 211cc aircooled two-stroke engine, later enlarged to 285cc for more performance, with drive taken directly from the engine's external flywheel via a friction arrangement. Later, British-built Neracars used more powerful Blackburne four-stroke engines with conventional gearboxes. Either way, the Neracar was efficient, comfortable, remarkably stable, and reasonably inexpensive, if not particularly fast.

In 1926, Sheffield-Simplex introduced an upmarket De-Luxe model with rear suspension, an air-cushion bucket seat, adjustable windshield and an instrument panel. But although the firm advertised numerous aristocrats among its customers, most motorcyclists preferred their bikes sporty and more conventional, and the luxurious machine was too civilized and unusual to sell in great numbers. By the end of that year, production of the Neracar had ended in both Britain and the United States.

Italy had not been among the leading countries during motorcycling's earliest years, but that nation's bike industry began to grow, especially when lightweight machines were freed from road tax in 1922. Numerous small bikes followed, along with larger machines from a manufacturer that would soon become famous: Moto Guzzi. The firm had come into being at the end of World War I when two Italian Air Service pilots, Giovanni Ravelli and Giorgio Parodi, had devised a bike along with engineer and mechanic Carlo Guzzi.

Ravelli was killed in a flying accident but in 1921 the other two, backed by Parodi's wealthy father, set up a factory in Mandello del Lario, on the bank of Lake Como in northern Italy. Their first production machine, called the Normale, was a 498cc single with a horizontal cylinder, large external flywheel (soon nicknamed the 'bacon slicer'), unit-construction three-speed gearbox, and magneto ignition. The bike was slim, low, and fast, and Guzzi's reputation for performance grew when a prototype racing single won its second ever event, the Targa Florio in Sicily.

The soundness of Guzzi's horizontal single design was confirmed by sales success and many race victories in subsequent decades. Remarkably the firm, still based at Mandello, would produce the 500cc Falcone single into the 1970s, complete with bacon-slicer and identical cylinder dimensions of 88 x 82mm. Guzzi also introduced chassis innovations, notably with the 1928-model GT, which featured the world's first fully sprung frame. A special swingarm worked a pair of springs located under the engine in a box-like housing. Damping was provided by friction units either side of the rear wheel.

Other Italian marques rose to prominence in the 1920s, notably Benelli, which was founded by six Benelli brothers from Pesaro on the Adriatic coast, and produced its first bike in 1921. Tonino, the youngest brother, helped establish the firm with his racing exploits. A rival racing firm was Garelli, whose founder Adalberto Garelli had previously worked for Bianchi. Under his own name Garelli produced a 'split-single' two-stroke, featuring two parallel cylinders, and two pistons on one crankpin. The powerful two-stroke won many races, providing plenty of publicity for Garelli's roadsters.

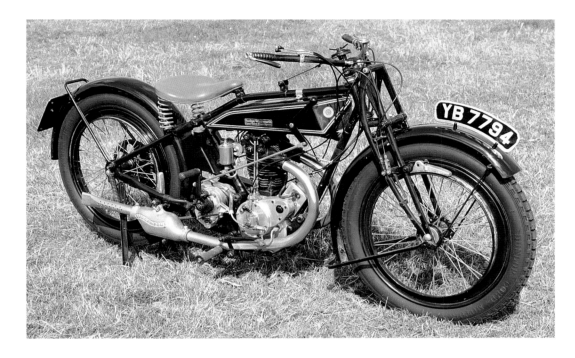

Left: *Rudge was a leading exponent of four-valve technology in 1926, when this 500cc single was built. Graham Walker's victory in the 1928 Ulster Grand Prix led to the sportiest Rudge model being renamed the Ulster.*

Below: *The American Excelsior marque introduced its Super X in 1925, featuring unit-construction engine and gearbox. Its capacity of 750cc was unusual at the time, but became popular following the Super X's success.*

Velocette's singular success

Britain's Velocette had also found success with a two-stroke, the 206cc single that the Birmingham firm, founded by John Goodman (a German-born engineer formerly called Johannes Gütgemann), had released in 1913. That model, enlarged to 250cc, remained popular after the war. But it was for four-strokes that Velocette became known, notably with the 350cc overhead-cam single, designed by John's son Percy, that was released in 1925. Alec Bennett won the next year's Junior TT by fully ten minutes. Bennett won again in 1938, and Freddie Hicks' victory the following year made it three out of four for Velocette.

Bennett's factory bike was a tuned version of the K model, and Velocette brought much of its performance to the street with the KSS, which was good for 80mph (129km/h). Even faster was the KTT, a hugely successful 'over-the-counter' racebike, which was launched in 1930. In 1932 the firm offered the KSS with a significant optional feature: a modern style positive-stop, foot-operated gearchange, as devised by development engineer Harold Willis and already fitted to the factory racebikes.

Another marque that achieved racing success through innovative engineering was Rudge, which had pioneered adjustable gearing with its belt-drive Multi system before the war, and had won the Senior TT in 1914. Rudge turned to chain drive and a three-speed gearbox in the 1920s, and became a leading exponent of four-valve cylinder heads, producing the 500cc single on which Graham Walker (the firm's sales manager, and father of British TV commentator Murray) won the Ulster Grand Prix in 1928. Rudge called its sportiest roadster the Ulster in recognition, and retained the name for many years.

The Ulster was fast, with a top speed of over 90mph (145km/h), and featured an innovative braking system whereby the foot-pedal worked both front and rear drums, with the hand-lever also operating the front brake. Rudge's success continued into the 1930s, notably with a Senior and Junior TT double in 1931, but racing was very expensive and the motorcycle trade was suffering in the poor financial climate. The firm turned to selling engines under the name Python, but in 1933 the receiver was called in and the racing department closed.

Henderson KJ (1929)

Engine:	Air-cooled eight-valve inlet-over-exhaust in-line four
Capacity:	1301cc
Maximum power:	40hp
Transmission:	Three-speed, chain final drive
Frame:	Steel twin cradle
Suspension:	Girder front; none rear
Brakes:	Drum front & rear
Weight:	495lb (225kg)
Top speed:	100mph (161km/h)

Above right: The Henderson KJ, known as the Streamline, was a fast and sophisticated 1301cc in-line four, named after its streamlined fuel tank, which held an illuminated instrument panel. Introduced in 1929, it was short-lived because Excelsior-Henderson abandoned production two years later.

The poor financial climate was caused by the Depression that had hit America following the Wall Street Crash of December 1929. The impact was devastating in a US motorcycle market that was already drowning in a tidal wave of cheap cars. Already, the large number of bike firms that had sprung up in the boom years had been cut to a mere half-dozen, which relied heavily on exports and sales to US police forces. Even export demand was significantly down, in 1930 dropping to barely 10,000 from 38,000 ten years earlier.

The highest-profile casualty was Excelsior-Henderson whose boss, the 70-year-old Ignatz Schwinn, shocked the industry when in 1931 he suddenly abandoned motorcycle production and retired. Excelsior had become the third of the 'Big Three' American marques following the firm's acquisition by bicycle maker Schwinn in 1911. Six years later Schwinn had formed Excelsior-Henderson after buying Henderson, manufacturers of fast and glamorous in-line fours. The new company's Chicago factory had been famous as the largest in the world, complete with its own roof-top test track.

Excelsior continued to specialize in V-twins, notably the Super X of 1925, which boasted the novelties of 750cc capacity and unit construction (combined engine and gearbox). Aided by its

Right: Indian produced its Four from 1927 after buying rights to the four-cylinder Ace. The model was revised with a stronger crankshaft for the 1265cc engine, plus a new frame, leaf-spring front suspension, and paintwork in Indian's traditional dark red.

The Record Breakers

The title of the world's fastest motorcyclist was hotly disputed in the years between the wars. A small group of riders pushed the limits of courage, ingenuity, and mechanical strength to new heights as they raised the official two-wheeled record from its 1920 figure of 103.18mph (166km/h), held by America's Leslie 'Red' Parker on a Harley-Davidson, to over 170mph (274km/h).

Two early adversaries were Claude Temple of Britain and America's Bert Le Vack, who each rode thundering, hotted-up V-twins. Each set a record at around 108mph (174km/h) at Brooklands, before the scene moved to the long Arpajon straight, near Paris. Le Vack raised the record to 119.74mph (192.7km/h) only to be beaten soon afterward by Temple, and then by Captain Oliver Baldwin on a Zenith-JAP. Back came Le Vack, who raised the record to 129.05mph (207.68km/h) on his JAP-engined Brough Superior in 1929.

Two weeks later Ernst Henne made his first successful attempt, recording 134.6mph (216.6km/h) on a partially enclosed BMW flat-twin whose 750cc supercharged flat-twin produced 75hp. Henne wore white overalls, a streamlined helmet – and, for some attempts, a conical tail strapped to his backside! Joe Wright twice took the record, the second time breaking the 150mph (241km/h) barrier on a Zenith-JAP near Cork in Ireland in 1930. Then Henne began a series of four record-breaking runs, finally setting a speed of 169.14mph (272.2mph) on a closed section of autobahn near Frankfurt.

Britain's next challenger was Eric Fernihough, who in 1937 rode a supercharged, 1000cc JAP-engined Brough Superior to 169.7mph (273.1km/h) in Hungary. Italian Piero Taruffi went fractionally faster on a Gilera, missing the record because he did not increase the old figure by the required amount. Any controversy was forgotten when Henne, his 500cc 'blown' (supercharged) BMW now fully enclosed following extensive wind-tunnel testing, raised the record to 173.67mph (279.49km/h). Back in Hungary, Fernihough replied with a 180mph (290km/h) one-way run on his Brough, but tragically crashed on the return run and was killed. Henne's record stood until 1951.

relatively lightweight chassis, featuring twin-cradle frame and leading-link forks, the Super X was too good for many larger-engined rivals in both oval racing and hillclimbing. Harley and Indian joined in with 750cc (45 cubic inch) models of their own, leading to the rise of Class C racing.

Henderson's four-cylinder machines had always been fast and sophisticated, and became even more so with the introduction of the Model KJ, known as the Streamline. Its 1301cc air-cooled ioe in-line four produced 40hp, giving a top speed of 100mph (161km/h), and the handsome Streamline's upmarket specification included leading-link front forks plus an illuminated speedometer set into the gas tank.

Such a high-end motorbike was always likely to struggle in the Depression. Indeed, founders Tom and William Henderson had long ago justified a price rise by admitting that: 'it would be impossible to continue production on the present high standard without an actual loss on every machine.' Schwinn was not prepared to do that, and Excelsior's similar lack of profitability left him with little alternative but to quit motorcycle manufacture.

Above: Ernst Henne's flat-twin record breaker has no fairing but features carefully shaped bodywork plus a tank pad for its near-prone rider. Henne also cheated the wind with a streamlined helmet, white overalls, and, sometimes, a conical tailpiece of his own.

Harley-Davidson Model 61EL (1936)	
Engine:	Air-cooled ohv four-valve pushrod 45-degree V-twin
Capacity:	989cc (84 x 88.9mm)
Maximum power:	40hp @ 4800rpm
Transmission:	Four-speed, chain final drive
Frame:	Steel twin downtube
Suspension:	Springer forks; rigid rear
Brakes:	Drum front & rear
Weight:	515lb (234kg)
Top speed:	100mph (161km/h)

Above right: The Model 61E, known as the Knucklehead, was arguably Harley-Davidson's most important bike ever. The fast and stylish 989cc V-twin was launched in 1936, as the Depression was lifting, and gave the firm a decisive edge over old rival Indian.

Below: Los Angeles-based Al Crocker's overhead-valve V-twins were fast and light, but too expensive to sell in sufficient numbers.

Opposite below left: The British Excelsior firm's best-known model was the Manxman, a 250cc (and later 350 and 500cc) single with overhead camshaft driven by shaft and bevel gears.

Another luxurious four that had failed was the Ace, which had been designed by William Henderson after leaving the company he had founded. In 1922 the designer had been killed in a crash while testing a bike, and although the Ace was later updated, the firm went into liquidation and in 1927 was bought by Indian. The Springfield firm initially changed little, because the Four was a fine bike, with a smooth 1265cc motor, top speed of 80mph (129km/h), and good handling. Over the next few years the Four was rebranded as an Indian, produced with a traditional dark red paint option, and modified with a new twin-downtube frame and leaf-spring front suspension.

Indian's most important bikes during this period remained its V-twins, the large-capacity Chief and middleweight Scout, both of which were designed by Charles B. Franklin around 42-degree side-valve engines. The first Chief, launched in 1922, was derived from the Powerplus and featured a 998cc engine. It handled well and was good for 85mph (137km/h). But some riders wanted more cubes so a year later the motor was enlarged to 1213cc (74 cubic inches) to create the 'Big Chief.'

The mid-'30s Chief, complete with head-dress logo on the gas tank, was a good-looking bike, and could be ordered in a wide variety of colors because in 1930 Indian had been bought by Du Pont, the manufacturing giant that had connections in the paint industry. Indian listed 24 standard one- and two-color schemes, plus the extra-cost option of any other color from the Du Pont paint range.

The Scout, initially with a 596cc (37ci) engine that was bored-out to 745cc (45ci) in 1927, also earned a reputation for reliability. Among the best models was the 101 Scout of 1928, which featured improved handling from a new, lower frame. The 1934-model Sport Scout was another success, combining fine handling and a 750cc engine that responded well to tuning. It was stripped and used for hillclimbs, TT and endurance races, and Class C dirt-track racing.

But Indian had been badly hit by the Depression, and in 1933 had come close to bankruptcy after building a lowest ever total of just 1667 bikes. Inevitably Harley, too, struggled through the early 1930s. But crucially the Milwaukee firm pressed ahead with development of the bike that was arguably its most important ever: the Model 61E. Nicknamed the Knucklehead after the shape of its rocker boxes, the 61E was the first Harley whose V-twin engine used pushrod-operated overhead valves, instead of side valves. The motor also had a recirculating oil system instead of the crude total-loss system previously used.

Harley beats the Depression

The 989cc (61 cubic inches; hence the name) V-twin produced 37hp in basic Model 61E specification. The 61EL, with higher compression ratio, made 40hp and was good for a genuine 100mph (161km/h). A new twin-cradle frame, uprated spring front suspension, four-speed gearbox, and Harley's first standard-fitment speedometer added to the appeal. The Model 61E was stylish and fast, and despite a few early problems (notably oil leaks and a frame that was barely strong enough) it quickly became popular. With the Depression easing by 1936, the Knucklehead's first year, Harley sold more than 1700 units and gained a lasting edge over old rivals Indian.

Harley's success with the Knucklehead contrasted with the fortunes of Al Crocker's more exotic V-twin, which debuted in the same year. Los Angeles-based Crocker was a leading figure in American motorcycling; a dealer, engineer, and former rider with a passion for fast, light bikes. After building Indian-powered twins he had designed his own 500cc single for speedway racing, in collaboration with an engineer named Paul Bigsby, and then a roadgoing 998cc V-twin with cylinders at 45 degrees.

Crocker's classy V-twin produced 50hp from an overhead-valve motor with exposed valve springs. Its robust three-speed gearbox was cast integral with the frame, and used steel plates so that it could be aligned with the engine. Aluminum was used for parts including the gas tank, engine cases, and footboards, reducing weight to 480lb (218kg). With a top speed of 110mph (177km/h) the Crocker was faster than Harley's 61E, as well as lighter. But it was also considerably more expensive, and fewer than 100 examples of this outstanding machine were built before Crocker abandoned production.

On the other side of the Atlantic, a similarly high-profile engineer and entrepreneur was having more success with an equally upmarket V-twin. George Brough boasted that his Brough Superior was 'made up to an ideal and not down to a price.' Nottingham-based Brough was the son of a motorcycle manufacturer and had a talent for publicity. Hence the Superior name, which led his father to comment: 'I suppose that makes mine the Inferior?' The initial Brough Superior,

Brough Superior SS100 (1925)	
Engine:	Air-cooled ohv four-valve pushrod 50-degree V-twin
Capacity:	988cc (85.5 x 86mm)
Maximum power:	45hp @ 5000rpm
Transmission:	Four-speed, chain final drive
Frame:	Steel single downtube
Suspension:	Girder forks; twin springs rear
Brakes:	Drum front & rear
Weight:	396lb (180kg)
Top speed:	100mph (161km/h)

Top: This 1932-model Brough Superior SS100 was owned by Lawrence of Arabia.

Above: George Brough, seated, was a great character as well as a fine rider and engineer.

Triumph Speed Twin (1938)

Engine:	Air-cooled ohv four-valve pushrod parallel twin
Capacity:	498cc (63 x 80mm)
Maximum power:	29hp @ 6000rpm
Transmission:	Four-speed, chain final drive
Frame:	Steel twin downtube
Suspension:	Girder front; rigid rear
Brakes:	Drum front & rear
Weight:	365lb (166kg)
Top speed:	93mph (150km/h)

Right: Triumph's Speed Twin changed motorcycling for ever following its launch in 1938. When production of civilian bikes restarted in the mid-1940s, following World War II, Triumph's main rivals would introduce parallel twins of their own.

Below: Business was generally slow for the American marques during the 1930s, but Harley could at least rely on orders from services including many police forces.

introduced in 1925, was a side-valve V-twin called the SS80, after its top speed of 80mph (129km/h). The subsequent overhead-valve SS100 came with a signed guarantee that it had been timed at over 100mph (161km/h) for a quarter of a mile.

Brough assembled bikes from bought-in parts including engines, and would accept only the best. Firms including engine manufacturer JAP produced 'only for Brough' parts. The initial SS100 used a 988cc JAP motor that gave 40hp; later bikes were powered by a similar-capacity unit from AMC (Matchless). Brough promised 'hands-off stability at 95mph' (153km/h), and called his bikes 'the Rolls-Royce of Motorcycles' following a comment of this nature in a magazine test. The luxury car maker was unimpressed until a director called at Brough's Haydn Road base to find workers wearing white gloves to avoid marking the show bikes they were building, after which all objections were dropped.

George Brough himself was a fine rider, and along with fellow Superior riders including Freddie Dixon and Bert Le Vack won many hillclimbs, sprints, and races. The most famous owner was T.E. Lawrence (Lawrence of Arabia), who owned a string of Superiors, and died after crashing one in 1935, following a collision with a cyclist. Brough built numerous special models, including the long-distance Alpine Grand Sports and the SS100 Pendine, which featured low bars and tuned motor, and had a top speed of 110mph (177km/h). Fewer than 400 Broughs had been built when production stopped for good with the advent of World War II.

Another of the leading personalities of the 1930s was Edward Turner, a young engineer who was hired by Ariel boss Jack Sangster to design the ambitious Square Four – reportedly after Turner had drawn up the innovative engine layout on the back of a cigarette packet, then attempted to sell it to various manufacturers. Turner's design was essentially a pair of parallel twins with crankshafts geared together, sharing cylinder head, block, and crankcase. The original 497cc unit was so compact that it could be fitted into the frame from Ariel's 500cc single.

Ariel's first Square Four, launched in 1931, used chain-driven overhead cams and a four-speed

Burman gearbox. The bike looked deceptive because its exhaust manifolds were integral with the cylinder head, so only two exhaust pipes emerged from the engine. In 1932 the motor was enlarged to 597cc, giving added performance that was especially appreciated by sidecar users. In this form the Square Four made 24hp at 6000rpm, and was smooth to its top speed of 85mph (137km/h), but suffered from problems including overheating of the rear cylinders. In 1936 Ariel introduced new 597cc 4F and 997cc 4G models, designed by Val Page, with pushrod valve operation, extra cylinder finning and a tunnel between the cylinders for cooling air.

By this time Turner had left to take over at Triumph, which had been bought by Ariel boss Jack Sangster. He announced his arrival with the Tiger 70, 80, and 90 models, cleverly restyled and renamed versions of the Coventry firm's range of 250, 350, and 500cc singles. Turner then launched the model that would be his greatest achievement, and arguably the most influential British machine of all time: the Speed Twin. The 498cc parallel twin engine, with pushrod valve operation and 360-degree crankshaft (pistons rising and falling together), produced 29hp. It was smoother and gave better performance than the majority of singles that then dominated motorcycle production.

The Speed Twin used essentially the same frame and forks as the Tiger 90 single, and was slightly lighter. It handled well, and had efficient drum brakes. *The Motor Cycle* magazine speed-tested the 'utterly delightful' Speed Twin at an impressive two-way average of 93.7mph (150.8km/h), with a one-way best of 107mph (172km/h), and enthused about its ample power and almost uncanny lack of noise. Boosted further by a competitive price barely higher than that of the Tiger 90, the Speed Twin was an immediate success, and inspired the other British manufacturers to design parallel twins of their own. Triumph launched a sportier version, the Tiger 100, in 1939. It had barely entered production when the outbreak of World War II halted further development, but motorcycling would never be the same again.

Above: *Ariel took its 1000cc Square Four to Brooklands in 1936 to prove that its advertising boast of 'ten mph to a hundred in top' was true, with a timed demonstration. Pictured are designer Edward Turner (left), rider Freddie Clarke, and service manager Ernie Smith.*

Below left: *The unlikely looking two-wheeled star of George Formby's* No Limit *movie was his character George Shuttleworth's heavily patterned racer, the 'Shuttleworth Snap.'*

Bikes on Screen

Motorbikes have been appearing on film for almost as long as movies have existed, although rarely in a starring role. One early attraction for movie makers was the bike's potential for spectacular action, especially crashes. In

Love, Speed and Thrills (1915), Mack Sennett's sidecar chase sends numerous characters flying. The climax of Buster Keaton's *Sherlock, Jr* (1924) sees the hero, Keaton, leap onto the handlebars of his assistant's bike, only for the rider to be thrown off by a bump. Buster, perched on the bars, speeds through traffic junctions, over a collapsing bridge and under a tractor before hitting a pile of wood, flying unharmed through a window and saving the day.

The best-known early film featuring motorbikes is *No Limit* (1935), a romantic comedy starring George Formby and Florence Desmond. Formby plays George Shuttleworth, a chimney sweep who builds his own bike, the

'Shuttleworth Snap,' and enters the TT. During practice the Snap's brakes fail, with the result that he breaks the lap record and becomes an instant star. As the race approaches, jealous rivals try to prevent him from taking part.

Director Monty Banks shot the film on location in the Isle of Man. As well as four Formby songs, it contains an improbably realistic action scene, when Shuttleworth runs out of fuel near the finish and has to push his bike home. Formby collapsed after the 15th take on a hot day, and a doctor was called. But *No Limit* was made for the general public, not motorcycle enthusiasts. Some Formby fans regard it as his best film, but there is little race action or authentic atmosphere.

Mobility and Freedom
1940s and 1950s

Above: As the British motorcycle industry enjoyed its boom years, the annual London show at Earls Court – seen here in 1955 – featured stands from many rival firms.

Previous page: The era's fastest and most glamorous streetbike was Vincent's Black Shadow, with its tuned 998cc V-twin engine.

Above: This 1951 advert boasts that the Triumph Twin has a 'reputation second to none.'

Right: Indian's 500cc Model 741 Military Scout proved its worth during World War II.

The main motorcycling trend of the 1940s and '50s was the rise of the parallel twin. Single-cylinder engines remained popular with many riders, but the pattern for two-wheeled design had been formed before World War II with the launch of Triumph's Speed Twin. Its pushrod-operated, overhead-valve, twin-cylinder engine layout would dominate the next few decades, as other British firms joined in, introducing bigger, more powerful engines and improved chassis.

Once the twins had arrived, most manufacturers adopted an approach of refinement rather than revolution. Gradually, specifications improved. Shorter-stroke engines with barrels made from aluminum instead of iron gave more revs and power. Telescopic front forks and twin-shock rear suspension replaced girder forks and crude plunger or rigid rear ends. Paintwork became more colorful, electrics more sophisticated, and features such as speedometers, dual-seats, and pillion footrests were increasingly included.

The motorbike's image and function varied widely in different parts of the world. In post-war Europe the bike became increasingly popular as a means of transport, though in some countries the boom was short-lived. Motorcycling in Britain, in particular, enjoyed a 'golden age' in the 1950s, as the growing economy and desire for mobility led to a rapid rise in sales. But the situation was very different in the United States, where the motor car's grip tightened and the bike industry was depressed.

Most motorcycle manufacturers were kept busy in the early 1940s, as the war raged and factories concentrated on military production. Huge numbers of camouflage-painted machines emerged from the leading British factories, the majority of them simple 350 or 500cc side-valve singles such as BSA's M20 and Norton's 16H and Big Four. Both BSA and Norton later claimed to have built one in four of all bikes supplied to the Allied forces.

Triumph, whose factory at Meriden, near Coventry, was badly damaged by German bombing, produced not only motorcycles but stationary engines for pumps and generators. Other firms concentrated on lightweight bikes for use by airborne troops, notably Royal Enfield with its folding Flying Flea. Excelsior's Welbike was a compact 98cc two-stroke that fitted into a protective container for dropping by parachute.

Post-war expansion

The two surviving US manufacturers produced military models in their normal V-twin format. Indian's 500cc Model 741 Military Scout served with distinction, as did Harley-Davidson's 750cc WLA 45, which was supplied to Russian and Chinese forces as well as Americans, British, and Canadians. After the war ended, many ex-military 45s were converted to civilian use, and helped establish Harley in foreign markets.

Germany also produced many military bikes, the most influential of which was DKW's RT125, a 122cc two-stroke single with top speed of just under 50mph (80km/h). As well as being built in vast numbers in its own right, the RT125 was widely copied after the war. BSA's Bantam, Harley-Davidson's Hummer, the Soviet Moska, and Yamaha's first bike, the 1955-model YA1 'Red Dragon,' would all be based on designer Hermann Weber's efficient and reliable machine.

Germany's best known military bike was BMW's R75 flat-twin, which led indirectly to one of Britain's most ambitious models of the post-war years: Sunbeam's S7. During the war Sunbeam had been bought by BSA, which had acquired some captured R75s from the British government. Sunbeam wanted to develop a flagship roadster along BMW lines, but considered a flat twin inappropriate, so designer Erling Poppe created a 487cc overhead-cam tandem twin powerplant, incorporating R75 features including shaft final drive.

The mist-green-colored S7, launched in 1947, was a luxurious machine with balloon tires and large skirted fenders. Unfortunately the expensive, 25bhp Sunbeam was slow by 500cc standards, with a top speed of only about 75mph (121km/h), and didn't handle very well, due mainly to its weight and fat tires. Its motor also used a lot of fuel and was unreliable, partly due to a tendency to overheat.

Sales were poor, and two years later Sunbeam introduced a sportier version of the tandem twin, the S8. This retained the original 487cc engine capacity and shaft final drive but was more conventional, with new telescopic forks, narrower tires, and paintwork in Sunbeam's traditional black. Its engine gained performance with higher compression ratio and a new exhaust system, and was more reliable due to increased oil capacity and other improvements.

The S8's reduced weight and uprated chassis meant it handled better than the S7, too. The sportier model was much more popular than the original, which continued in updated S7 De Luxe form. But it would not be enough to save Sunbeam, which was eventually closed down by BSA in 1957 – after which the famous Sunbeam name was used only for scooters.

Another firm producing unusual twins was Scott, the Yorkshire marque that had built some of the most innovative machines of motorcycling's early years. In 1926, three years after founder Alfred Scott's death, Scott had introduced the Flying Squirrel, a 596 or 498cc two-stroke liquid-cooled parallel twin with more conventional layout that the firm's cylindrical-tanked early models. Production had continued through the 1930s and resumed after the war with few changes.

The Flying Squirrel offered a smooth 70mph (113km/h) cruising speed plus stability and a distinctive character, if not outstanding reliability. The struggling Yorkshire firm eventually went bankrupt in 1950. Scott was bought by an enthusiast named Matt Holder, who moved production to Birmingham, where small numbers would continue to be built right up until 1978.

Another firm building twins with limited success was Douglas, which had originally produced in-line flat twins and after the war used a BMW-style transverse cylinder arrangement, with a 350cc model called the T35. The last Douglas twin was the 1955-model 350cc Dragonfly, which featured a distinctive headlamp nacelle that merged with the fuel tank. The Dragonfly handled

Above: Many ex-military Harley WLA45 V-twins were converted to civilian use after the war.

Below: Sunbeam's S7 tandem twin featured distinctive paintwork and balloon tires.

Sunbeam S7 (1947)

Engine:	Air-cooled sohc four-valve tandem twin
Capacity:	487cc (70 x 63.5mm)
Maximum power:	25bhp @ 5800rpm
Transmission:	Four-speed, shaft final drive
Frame:	Steel single downtube
Suspension:	Telescopic front; plunger rear
Brakes:	Drum front & rear
Weight:	435lb (197kg)
Top speed:	75mph (121km/h)

Above: Scott built two-stroke parallel twins for many years, and by 1947 had enlarged the Flying Squirrel's liquid-cooled engine to 596cc. The twin was smooth and torquey, but the Yorkshire firm lacked money for development.

Above: Sunbeam's S8 was notably slimmer and sportier than its S7 predecessor. Although more successful, it could not save the firm.

Right: The Douglas Dragonfly, introduced in 1955, was stylish and handled well, but its 350cc flat twin engine's performance was mediocre and production ended two years later.

well, thanks to its Earles fork chassis, and cruised smoothly at 60mph (97km/h). But it was too expensive to sell in sufficient numbers, and Douglas ceased all production in 1957.

While Sunbeam, Scott, and Douglas struggled, the parallel (or 'vertical') twin cylinder layout, as pioneered by Triumph's Speed Twin before the war, was becoming more important. Triumph had already followed Edward Turner's original master-stroke with a hotted-up model called the Tiger 100 – its name highlighting the top speed of 100mph (161km/h). This became the marque's flagship when production at the Meriden factory restarted in 1946.

Along with higher compression ratio that helped increase its 500cc engine's peak output to a claimed 30bhp, the Tiger 100 featured silver paintwork and other new styling touches. The model enhanced Triumph's reputation for performance, and remained in the line-up throughout the 1950s, being updated with telescopic front forks in place of the original girders, and twin-shock rear suspension, instead of the early sprung-hub design.

BSA was quick to respond to Triumph's twin, and launched its own 500cc A7 twin in 1946. Designed by Val Page and Herbert Perkins, the A7 engine differed from its Triumph rival by having a single camshaft at the rear of the crankcases, instead of two at the side. The BSA unit was slightly less powerful and stylish than the Triumph, but impressively quiet, oil-tight and robust. It gained a little extra performance in 1949 with the launch of the A7 Star, complete with twin carburetors, increased compression ratio and 31bhp output.

Norton's first parallel twin was the Dominator Model 7, launched in 1949. Its designer, Bert Hopwood, had left Norton by the time the 29bhp Model 7 reached production. But his engine design, with a single camshaft in front of the cylinders, would be used for over two decades. Although the plunger-framed Model 7 handled reasonably well, it was overshadowed a few years later by the Dominator 88, with improved handling and reduced weight thanks to its Featherbed frame, borrowed from the Manx racing single.

The Manx had proved that single-cylinder machines were still competitive on the racetrack, most vividly when Geoff Duke won both the 500cc and 350cc world championships in 1951. The Manx was a post-war development of Norton's overhead-camshaft single, and was initially fitted with a single-tube 'Garden Gate' frame, and plunger rear suspension. The single's many race wins, often against more powerful multis, did much to maintain Norton's reputation for performance and quality.

Norton's Featherbed advantage

The most significant Manx development came in 1950 when Norton's race team boss Joe Craig adopted an innovative frame designed by Irish racer/engineer Rex McCandless. Its distinctive twin-loop cradle design gave much improved handling under racing conditions, as well as proving stronger and easier to manufacture. Duke's works team-mate Harold Daniell unwittingly christened the frame with his comment that the new bike felt like riding a feather bed.

The uprated Manx made a superb debut when it took the first three places in both Senior and Junior TT races in 1950. In later years the Manx was produced for sale both as the 500cc 30M and the 350cc 40M, with the larger model in particular being hugely successful. The lean and simple Manx, with its heavily finned engine, big silver tank, and Featherbed frame, became established as the archetypal pure-bred single-cylinder racer.

Equally famous was its BSA rival the Gold Star, a roadster-based single that also notched up hundreds of victories in Isle of Man Clubman's events, short circuit races, and unofficial burn-ups on the road. The 'Goldie,' especially the later 500cc DBD34 model, had an equally distinctive look based on its low, clip-on handlebars, and chrome-panelled gas tank with a badge displaying a gold star in a red circle.

The Gold Star dated back to pre-war days, when racer Wal Handley had earned a Brooklands Gold Star award for lapping the banked Surrey circuit at over 100mph (161km/h) on BSA's 500cc M23 Empire Star. In the following year BSA produced a replica marketed under the name M24 Gold Star. The name signified that each machine had been built using polished internals and other special parts, which increased output to 28bhp, or 33bhp when tuned to run on alcohol.

After the war, BSA produced a competition single called the B32, which was initially for trials but made a useful racer. It was followed in 1948 by the 350cc ZB32 Gold Star, and a year later by the 500cc ZB34. Both were fast and came with a choice of camshaft, gears, compression ratio, fuel tanks, exhaust system, and wheels. As with all Gold Stars, buyers received a certified dyno chart from their machine.

The Gold Star's arrival meant that the clubman racer had a bike that was keenly priced and ideally suited to both road and track. Gold Stars dominated the Clubman's TT in the early 1950s. Most famous of the line was the 1956-model DBD34, which incorporated race-proven modifications including steeper steering geometry, twin-shock rear suspension, and a big Amal

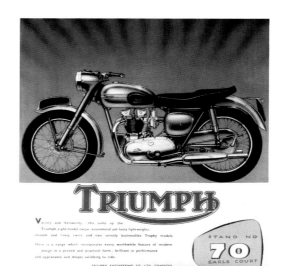

Top: Triumph's 'best motorcycle in the world' boast rang true in 1955, when the 650cc Tiger 110 featured telescopic forks and twin shocks.

Above: BSA relied on a more laid-back image in its 1955 advertising, which highlighted the range from 125cc Bantam to 650cc Golden Flash.

Left: This 500cc Norton Model 7 parallel twin, built in 1952, would be superseded a year later by the Featherbed-framed Dominator 88.

Above: Norton's Featherbed-framed Manx racing single, introduced to the works teams in 1950, was hugely successful and remained competitive for many years.

Below: BSA's DBD34 Gold Star was the ultimate single-cylinder sports bike of the late 1950s, with clip-on bars, revvy engine, close-ratio gearbox, and top-class chassis components.

Below right: The most popular 350cc racer in the 1950s and '60s was the AJS 7R, known as the 'Boy Racer.' The ohc single won thousands of races around the world, at all levels.

GP carburetor that raised its 500cc engine's peak output to 42bhp. The DBD34 Gold Star was a true racer on the road: demanding, temperamental, and extremely rapid.

Another firm producing rapid singles for road and track was Velocette, the Birmingham marque whose black-liveried racers had made a big impact before the war. In fact Velocette's most ambitious project of that era was a twin, the 500cc supercharged 'Roarer' debuted by Stanley Woods in the 1939 TT. When racing resumed after the war supercharging was banned, which put paid to the Roarer, but Velocette continued to record outstanding results with singles, notably the 350cc KTT production racer.

The ultimate KTT was the Mk VIII, which had been introduced in 1938 and remained competitive for many years. The 34bhp single was almost identical to Woods' TT-winning factory machine of that year, and was fast enough to take three more Junior TT wins after the war, ridden by Bob Foster and Freddie Frith. When the world championships began in 1949, Frith and Foster took the first two 350cc titles on works dohc or 'double-knocker' versions of the Mk VIII.

The overhead-camshaft singles earned Velocette's racing glory, but the bikes that made the money were the simpler, cheaper pushrod singles, notably the 250cc MOV and its derivatives the 350cc MAC and 500cc MSS. The MAC, in particular, was a long-running success, being produced from 1934 to 1960. Along the way it gained telescopic forks instead of girders, an aluminum cylinder head and barrel, and in 1953 a new, more sophisticated twin-shock frame to replace its original rigid (unsuspended) rear end.

Velocette was successful with its sporty singles, but failed spectacularly with its LE, or 'Little Engine,' co-owner Eugene Goodman's ambitious attempt to provide a civilized commuter bike. The LE was powered by a 149cc liquid-cooled side-valve flat twin with modest 6bhp maximum output. It featured a pressed-steel frame, leg-shields, and shaft final drive. Top speed was just 50mph (80km/h), and acceleration was hindered by the high weight of 260lb (118kg).

The LE had some merits, being quiet, smooth, comfortable, and practical. It also handled well. But its angular styling won few admirers, and the complex Velo was much more expensive than BSA's Bantam commuter bike. The LE sold very slowly, even after a capacity increase to 192cc had improved performance and tempted many police forces to buy it. Velocette's huge investment was lost, and plans to halt production of the 350 MAC were abandoned.

One single that outlasted even the MAC was Royal Enfield's Bullet. The Bullet name had first been used in the early 1930s, following Enfield's introduction of a line of 500, 350, and 250cc models. In 1949 the firm launched a new 350cc Bullet, featuring a more compact engine with an alloy head. The bike was quick, reliable, and handled well, and was joined three years later by a 500cc version. The Bullet was made in Britain until 1963, after which production continued in India, where the model had been built under license for some time.

Another long-lived single was Ariel's Red Hunter, which also had its origins in the early 1930s, with the sporty NH350 and VH500 models. During the war the smaller Hunter was developed into a successful military bike, the W/NG. Red Hunter production later resumed and continued throughout the 1950s, helped by typical chassis updates, with the model by now being known more for practicality than performance.

Germany's manufacturers had widely differing fortunes after the war. DKW was split, with its original factory at Zschopau, in the Russian-controlled eastern part of Germany, becoming IFA and then MZ. Much of MZ's output was simple two-stroke singles, notably the ES250, introduced in 1956. Most had curious styling, but were reliable as well as cheap to buy and run.

DKW resumed production with a civilian version of its much-copied wartime RT125 single, which was updated over the years. By 1957 the RT250VS, also produced in 200 and 175cc capacities, featured Earles forks and twin-shock rear suspension. In that year DKW merged with Victoria and Express to form the Zweirad Union, which later also included Hercules. DKW's influence faded, and the name became little used.

Horex, a German marque that had been building bikes since 1923, resumed production after the war and was later best known for its stylish Imperator single. This was introduced in 1954 with a 398cc ohc engine producing 24bhp, and a sophisticated chassis incorporating twin-cradle frame and twin rear shocks. But the German market was in decline, and Horex production ended in 1957. Various enthusiasts tried to revive the Horex name, without lasting success.

BMW had been successful during the 1930s with side-valve flat twins including the 750cc R12 and R71, and had already produced more modern overhead-valve twins, notably the 600cc R6. When production belatedly resumed after the war it was with the R24, a 250cc single that sold well. By 1950 the flat twins were being built again, starting with the R51/2, a 500cc overhead-valve machine that was essentially the pre-war R51 with a few detail changes.

BMW quickly updated the design, producing a new 500cc engine for the R51/3, plus a 600cc model, the R67. Ironically, given that BMW had pioneered oil-damped telescopic forks before the war, the German marque's main 1955 change was the introduction of Earles forks, designed by Englishman Ernie Earles some years earlier. The 500cc R50 and 600cc R69 also featured twin-shock rear suspension, and remained in production until the end of the decade.

Rival German marque Zündapp had built a luxurious 800cc in-line four, the K800, in the 1930s, and was also a leading producer of flat twins. The KS601 'Green Elephant' became Germany's fastest roadster when launched in 1950, with a top speed approaching 90mph (145km/h). Its 597cc ohv engine was fitted in a new tubular steel frame with telescopic forks, plunger rear suspension, and interchangeable wheels.

NSU concentrated on four-stroke singles, having begun after the war with the 98cc Fox, a 6bhp lightweight with a top speed of about 50mph (80km/h). In the early 1950s the 200cc Lux

BSA DBD34 Gold Star Clubman's (1956)	
Engine:	Air-cooled ohv two-valve pushrod single
Capacity:	499cc (85 x 88mm)
Maximum power:	42hp @ 7000rpm
Transmission:	Four-speed, chain final drive
Frame:	Steel twin downtube
Suspension:	Telescopic front; twin shocks rear
Brakes:	Drum front & rear
Weight:	384lb (174kg)
Top speed:	110mph (177km/h)

Below: The production version of Velocette's KTT Mk VIII, seen here on display at London's Earls Court Show in 1949, was a 348cc customer racebike based on world champion Freddie Frith's factory single of the same designation.

Bottom: Velocette's LE commuter bike won few friends with its angular looks, and was too heavy for its 149cc side-valve flat twin engine.

and 250cc Max offered increased performance, and NSU impressed on the racetrack with the powerful twin-cylinder Rennmax on which Werner Haas won the 250cc world championship in 1953 and '54. The final development of the Max was the Supermax, launched in 1956, by which time NSU was turning away from bikes in favor of car production.

The German firm did, however, continue high-volume production of its hugely successful 49cc two-stroke moped, the Quickly, of which more than a million were built before production ended in 1962. Few Europeans realized it at the time, but a more significant development of small-capacity bikes was going on in Japan, where a former car racer and piston ring manufacturer named Soichiro Honda had set up the Honda Technical Research Institute in a small wooden shed in Hamamatsu.

Honda began by attaching small two-stroke army-surplus engines to bicycles, and soon moved on to design a two-stroke engine of his own, completing the Honda Model A in 1947. The bike was simple and slow, but cheap and successful. Honda moved fast, enlarging the engine to 90cc, producing a three-wheeled vehicle, and in 1949 creating the first all-Honda machine, the 98cc two-stroke Model D, which was given the name Dream.

By 1950, the renamed Honda Motor Co was a thriving business employing 20 people, and Soichiro Honda had been joined by Takeo Fujisawa, the salesman who would help mastermind the firm's growth. The following year saw the 146cc Model E, Honda's first four-stroke. It produced 5bhp and was soon being built at a rate of 130 bikes per day – a Japanese record. The company grew even faster when Fujisawa arranged to sell the two-stroke Model E through bicycle dealers across Japan.

The first Honda that approached European quality was the Model J or Benly ('*convenience*'), a 90cc four-stroke single whose design owed much to NSU. It was launched in 1953 and sold well, but in the following year Honda almost went bust due to a combination of Japan's faltering economy, some ageing models, high wage demands, and over-ambitious production. Honda survived, and benefited when the market downturn caused the demise of big rival Tohatsu and many of the other Japanese manufacturers that had emerged after the war.

Honda's most important success came in 1958 with the C100, known as the Super Cub. Powered by a fully-enclosed, 50cc four-stroke engine producing 4.5bhp, it was reliable, economical and practical thanks to its legshields, large wheels, big fenders, well-padded seat, and

Above: Ariel's 1956-model Red Hunter 350 gave dependable, unspectacular performance.

Below: BMW's 500cc R50, introduced in 1955, handled well, thanks partly to its Earles forks.

Below right: The R51/2 of 1950 was essentially an updated 500cc pre-war flat twin. Like many bikes, it was often fitted with a sidecar.

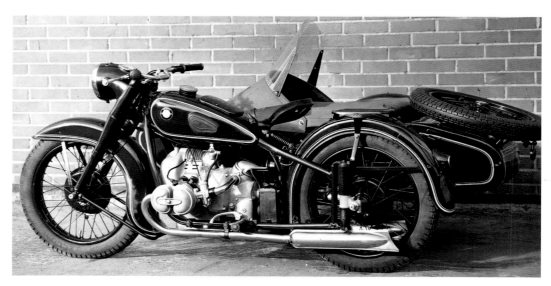

Left: Victoria's Bergmeister, launched in 1953, was the German marque's first post-war four-stroke. Its 347cc transverse V-twin engine produced 21bhp, giving a top speed of 80mph (129km/h), and featured shaft final drive.

Above: Honda's first four-stroke was the 146cc Model E, a three-valve single released in 1951.

good electrics. Backed by a clever advertising campaign based on the phrase 'You meet the nicest people on a Honda,' the Super Cub became hugely successful in the United States, and established Honda in many other world markets.

By this time Europe was already familiar with the attractions of the scooter, which had been pioneered in Italy after the war by Vespa and Lambretta. Introduced by aircraft manufacturer Piaggio in 1946, the original Vespa ('*wasp*' in Italian) was created by an aircraft designer named Corradino d'Ascanio, and featured leg-shields for maximum weather protection. The enclosed two-stroke engine pivoted on the pressed-steel frame to provide rear suspension. The original 98cc capacity was increased to 150cc by 1954, but the chassis layout would remain almost unchanged half a century later.

The Vespa's main rival was the Lambretta, produced by Innocenti of Milan. The Lambretta looked very similar but mounted its shaft-drive two-stroke engine lower, in front of the rear wheel, which improved weight distribution. The Lambretta was updated in the 1950s but was never as popular as the Vespa. Many other firms also built scooters, notably Zündapp of Germany, whose Bella, introduced in 1953, handled well due partly to its large wheels.

Other Italian firms adopted a different approach to commuter machines. A Bologna-based electronics components firm called Ducati had begun two-wheeled production after the war with the Cucciolo ('*puppy*'), a 49cc four-stroke engine clipped onto a bicycle frame. The light and simple bike was a success, and Ducati expanded to build sportier machines after appointing a new chief designer, Fabio Taglioni, who adopted the desmodromic system, which uses cams rather than springs to close the valves.

Taglioni made his mark in 1955 with the 100cc Gran Sport, nicknamed the Marianna, whose single-cylinder engine used a shaft and bevel gears to drive its overhead camshaft, a Ducati trademark for the next two decades. The Marianna was successful in races such as the Giro d'Italia, and led to larger singles including the 175 Sport of 1957. The following year, a 125cc desmo Ducati won several grands prix and finished second in the world championship.

One of the best known Italian bikes in the years after the war was Moto Guzzi's Dondolino, or '*rocking-chair*,' so nicknamed after its sometimes unstable high-speed handling. The 500cc

Below: Boosted by its 'You meet the nicest people…' advertisement, devised by Honda's US agency Grays, the C100 Super Cub sold in vast numbers in the States and helped change many people's attitude toward motorcyclists.

You meet the nicest people on a Honda. And the remarkable thing is the low cost of it all. Prices start about $215* Insurance is painless. Upkeep negligible. Honda's four-stroke engine demands 200 miles from a gallon of gas. And gets it. Plenty of drive. That's how you stay at the top of the class. World's biggest seller. HONDA

Dondolino racer, with its single horizontal cylinder in Guzzi style, was developed from the Condor of the mid-1930s, and itself led to the even more famous roadgoing Falcone ('*falcon*'). Introduced in 1950, the sporty Falcone cost half as much as the Dondolino and featured enclosed instead of exposed valves, and crankcases in aluminum instead of magnesium.

The Falcone made a fine roadster and also a successful racer, especially when boosted by Dondolino engine parts. In 1954 the original 23bhp model became the Falcone Sport and was joined by a Turismo version with higher bars and a detuned 19bhp engine. The Falcone remained in production through the 1950s with few changes. But Guzzi made its name with rapid racers, many of them shaped in a state-of-the-art wind tunnel at the firm's Mandello del Lario factory.

Guzzi's most successful racers were its horizontal singles, which won three 250cc world titles between 1949 and '52, and five straight 350cc championships from 1953. Potentially the greatest was the 500cc V8, introduced in 1956. Engineer Giulio Carcano's liquid-cooled, quad-cam, 90-degree V8 produced 72bhp, revved to 12,000rpm and was clocked at 178mph (286km/h) at the Belgian Grand Prix in 1957. But Guzzi, like most other Italian firms, quit racing that year before the mighty V8 had shown its full potential.

One of the Falcone's main rivals was Gilera's Saturno, a 500cc four-stroke single with more conventional vertical cylinder. The Milan-based marque introduced the Saturno as a racebike in 1940 and began full-scale production after the war. The Saturno, too, was built in Sport and Turismo models, the former benefiting from an aluminum cylinder head, higher compression, and hotter cam that increased peak output to 22bhp.

While Gilera's fabulous fours were beating all in grands prix in the early 1950s, the Saturno also won races and remained a popular roadster. Early models had girder forks and Gilera's own rear suspension system, featuring horizontal springs in boxes above the swingarm. Later versions were updated with telescopic forks and twin shocks. But by 1959 demand for the Saturno had dropped, partly because it cost as much as a Fiat 500 car, and production ended.

One Italian firm that defied convention was Rumi, founded after the war by Bergamo-based friends Donnino Rumi and Pietro Vassena. In 1950 they launched two models, a Sport and a Turismo, powered by 125cc two-stroke parallel twin engines with cylinders angled horizontally forward. The leaner Sport, especially, was stylish and quick, with a top speed of just over 60mph

Above: Italian scooters were fashionable during the '50s, and were boosted by their association with celebrities such as movie star John Wayne, seen here with a Vespa.

Moto Guzzi Falcone Turismo (1958)

Engine type:	Air-cooled ohv pushrod two-valve single
Capacity:	498cc (88 x 82mm)
Maximum power:	19bhp @ 4300rpm
Transmission:	Four-speed, chain final drive
Frame:	Steel twin downtube
Suspension:	Telescopic front; horizontal springs and friction dampers rear
Brakes:	Drum front & rear
Weight:	368lb (167kg) dry
Top speed:	75mph (121km/h)

Right: Moto Guzzi's 500cc Falcone single changed little during 18 years of production. This Turismo model dates from 1964.

Left: Gilera's 499cc Saturno Sport made 22bhp and provided plenty of performance in 1950. Two years later the firm from Arcore, near Milan, had updated the single with telescopic forks and twin rear shocks, in place of this bike's girders and horizontal rear springs.

(97km/h). Rumi expanded the range with high-performance Junior and Bicarburatore ('*twin-carburetor*') versions of the 125, and also built a small number of four-stroke V-twins before production ended in the 1960s.

Another entrepreneur who set out to satisfy Italy's post-war demand for personal transport was Count Domenico Agusta, the eldest of four brothers whose late father Giovanni had been an aviation pioneer. Domenico founded the Meccanica Verghera (MV) bike firm in the village of Verghera, outside Milan, and in 1945 launched his first bike, a 98cc two-stroke single that was known as the Vespa until complaints by scooter manufacturer Piaggio led to the MV being renamed the 98 2T.

The bike was a success and MV production expanded quickly, with improved models including the 125 TEL and its 1950-model successor the Lungo ('*riverside*'). This was a fine bike with 8.5bhp two-stroke engine, duplex cradle frame, and swingarm rear suspension. In standard form it was good for 65mph (105km/h), and when tuned made an 80mph (129km/h) racer that took several class wins in the Milano-Taranto and Giro d'Italia.

Agusta's glory years

MV also built outstanding small-capacity four-stroke singles, starting with the 175cc, overhead-camshaft CSTL that was released in 1953. By this time the firm had also begun its grand prix racing success, with Englishman Cecil Sandford's 125cc world championship win the previous year. Italian star Carlo Ubbiali went on to win five more 125c titles between 1955 and '60, plus three more in the 250cc class. In 1956, John Surtees won the first of his four 500cc titles for MV, beginning the Italian marque's long domination of the track.

Italy's Gilera and MV Agusta produced the fastest racebikes of the 1950s, but the era's fastest and arguably its greatest roadsters came from Vincent of Britain. The small firm from Stevenage in Hertfordshire, led by Philip Vincent and his Australian chief engineer Phil Irving, built small numbers of powerful, expensive V-twins that established an unmatched reputation for performance and high-quality engineering.

Philip Vincent had set up his bike business in 1927, and to gain credibility had bought the name HRD Motors from Howard Davies, a former TT winner whose bike-building firm had failed. Vincent-HRD's first bikes used engines from JAP, Rudge, and Villiers. But after problems

Above: Ducati began motorcycle production in 1946 with the Cucciolo, essentially a bicycle powered by a 49cc four-stroke engine that produced just 1hp.

Below: Rumi's 1954-model 125 Sport was light, agile and powered by an 8.5bhp air-cooled two-stroke parallel twin engine.

Vincent Black Shadow Series C (1949)

Engine:	Air-cooled ohv four-valve 50-degree pushrod V-twin
Capacity:	998cc (84 x 90mm)
Maximum power:	55bhp @ 5700rpm
Transmission:	Four-speed, chain final drive
Frame:	Steel spine
Suspension:	Girder front; twin shocks rear
Brakes:	Twin drums front & rear
Weight:	458lb (208kg)
Top speed:	125mph (201km/h)

Above: These riders are lining up at the start of the MotoGiro, one of the great long-distance Italian road races of the 1950s. The event has recently been revived as a test of endurance for both classic and modern bikes.

Right: Vincent's standard 1950-model V-twin, the Rapide Series C, developed 45bhp from its 998cc engine, and had the looks and handling to match its 110mph (177km/h) performance.

with JAP motors at the TT in 1934, Vincent and Irving designed their own 500cc high-cam single-cylinder engine. The 90mph (145km/h) Comet, released in 1935, was followed a year later by the firm's first V-twin, created by combining two cylinders at a 47-degree angle. The 998cc 45bhp Rapide thundered to 110mph (177km/h) but suffered from transmission problems.

After the war Vincent created the Series B Rapide, using a new 998cc unit-construction V-twin with cylinders at 50 degrees. The motor formed a stressed member of a compact and innovative chassis that incorporated diagonal twin rear shocks, and twin drum brakes on each wheel. The fast and sophisticated Rapide was joined in 1948 by the even more exclusive Black Shadow, whose tuned, black-finished, 55bhp engine gave a top speed of over 125mph (201km/h), recorded on a big Smith's speedometer calibrated to 150mph (241km/h).

American speed ace Roland 'Rollie' Free famously rode Vincent's race-spec Black Lightning to a record 150.313mph (241.89km/h) on the Bonneville Salt flats in Utah in 1948, wearing just swimming trunks and shoes to reduce wind resistance. Other Vincent heroics included George Brown's numerous sprint victories and records on bikes named Gunga Din, Nero, and the supercharged Super Nero. Vincent updated the range in 1949 with the Series C models, featuring improved rear suspension and Girdraulic front forks instead of the original girders.

But the exotic V-twins were too expensive to sell in sufficient numbers, and by the early 1950s Vincent was in financial trouble. Production continued under receivership, and the firm diversified by assembling lightweight NSU bikes under license. New Series D V-twins, the Black Knight and tuned Black Prince, featured all-enclosing fiberglass bodywork. But motorcyclists were not ready for such futuristic style in 1955. Sales were poor, and by the end of that year Vincent had abandoned production.

One of Vincent's rivals at the top end of the market had been Ariel's Square Four, which after the war had been built in 1000cc form only, the earlier 600cc version having been dropped. In 1949 the Ariel was revamped to create the Square Four 4G MkI, featuring a new all-aluminum engine. This was much lighter than the old iron unit, bringing weight down to a respectable 433lb (196kg) with plunger rear suspension, or even less with the rigid frame, which some riders preferred due to the plunger units' under-damped, rather vague feel.

Four-cylinder smoothness

As before, only two exhaust downpipes were visible, although the MkI emphasized its four-cylinder status with the words 'Square Four' on its timing cover. The Square Four produced 34bhp and was not dramatically fast, with a top speed of about 100mph (161km/h). Where the 'Squariel' scored was with its smoothness and its generous midrange torque, which gave effortless cruising ability and strong acceleration for overtaking.

In 1953 Ariel introduced the revamped 4G MkII. This was a stylish bike with a larger, rounded gas tank and a further updated engine featuring four separate exhaust downpipes. Even in this final form the MkII's engine was prone to overheat in traffic, and handling was mediocre. Ariel deemed further redevelopment too costly and abandoned production in 1958.

The Ariel was not the only four-cylinder model during this time. The Danish-built Nimbus also had a long life, being produced with few changes from 1935 until 1959. The bike was an unlikely combination of sophisticated 746cc sohc in-line four-cylinder engine in a simple frame made from metal strips. A maximum output of 22bhp gave the Nimbus a top speed of about 75mph (121km/h). But few were sold outside Denmark. The other leading Scandinavian marque was Sweden's Husqvarna, which had produced motorcycles in small numbers since 1903. During the 1940s Husqvarna built mostly lightweight two-stroke roadsters, before focusing on the off-road competition bikes for which it became well known.

Like Nimbus, American firm Indian had continued to build in-line fours by developing the machine that it had inherited when buying Ace in 1927. In the early 1940s the Indian Four's 1265cc smooth-revving side-valve motor produced 40bhp, giving a top speed of 90mph (145km/h). But the Four was expensive, and remained prone to overheating of its rear cylinder. It was eventually dropped in 1943.

Indian's most dramatic updates to the Chief and Scout V-twins came in 1940, when the Springfield firm introduced the distinctive skirted fender styling for which the models are best known. In the same year the Chief gained new cylinder heads and barrels with larger cooling fins, plus a new frame incorporating plunger rear suspension in place of the old hard-tail. A mid-'40s Chief was heavy, at over 550lb (250kg), and not particularly fast, but very stylish and comfortable.

Ariel Square Four 4G MkI (1952)	
Engine:	Air-cooled ohv eight-valve pushrod square-four
Capacity:	997cc (65 x 75mm)
Maximum power:	34hp @ 5400rpm
Transmission:	Four-speed, chain final drive
Frame:	Steel twin downtube
Suspension:	Telescopic front; plunger rear
Brakes:	Drum front & rear
Weight:	433lb (196kg)
Top speed:	100mph (161km/h)

Above: Ariel's 1952-model Square Four MkI.

Above: The MkII 'Squariel' had four pipes.

Left: The Danish-built Nimbus combined a four-cylinder engine with crude steel plate frame.

Movie Mayhem

The movie that influenced motorcycling more than any other was *The Wild One*, released in 1954 and starring a young Marlon Brando. The riot at the biker gathering at Hollister in California on the July 4th weekend in 1947 had already resonated throughout the US motorcycle world. Sensationalized coverage in publications including the influential *Life* magazine, which pictured a drunken biker with a beer in each hand, horrified many people across America.

The American Motorcycle Association was also alarmed, and issued a press release stating that 'only one percent of motorcyclists are hoodlums and troublemakers,' who would be 'outlawed' from its membership. This backfired by bringing together many of the biker gangs, who delighted in adopting the terms outlaw and one-percenter as their own.

Director Laslo Benedek's *The Wild One*, in which Brando's character Johnny clashes with the aggressive Chico, played by Lee Marvin, was loosely based on the events at Hollister. The movie brought the biker culture to a much wider audience, and had a lasting effect on the US public's attitude toward motorcyclists. Although tame by modern standards, *The Wild One* was violent and controversial enough to be banned for a period in some countries, including Britain.

The Wild One was the first big movie in which bikes were clearly identifiable, as previously machines had appeared with badges obscured. Brando's Johnny rode a 1950-model Triumph Thunderbird; Marvin's Chico a Harley-Davidson. Ironically, although Triumph agent Bill Johnson had attempted to halt production of the movie by writing to the

Motion Picture Association of America, the British marque's US sales were boosted by the exposure.

Above right: Brando and Mary Murphy are on a disguised Matchless here, but The Wild One's *two-wheeled star was Triumph's Thunderbird.*

Below: This 'Indian Brave' at the 1952 Earls Court Show is a British-built 248cc single.

In 1950 Indian enlarged the Chief's engine to 1311cc (80ci), fitted telescopic forks instead of girders, and specified a conventional right-hand throttle for the first time. The firm also attempted to compete with the British by building vertical twins, such as the 436cc Super Scout 249 and its successor the 250 Warrior, whose capacity was in fact 500cc. But these failed to save Indian. The famous 'Wigwam' factory built its last bike in 1953, after which Royal Enfield singles and twins were restyled and sold as Indians, without much success.

Right: This 1941-model Indian Four has been updated with a gearchange by foot instead of hand, plus telescopic forks from a later Chief.

Stateside struggle

The Springfield firm's failure to keep pace with rival Harley was one reason for its demise, but in contrast to booming Europe, the US motorcycling situation was depressed. Post-war demand for increasing mobility was centered on the car, not the motorbike. Fast and light bikes were being imported in increasing numbers from Europe. The US motorcycle scene was also suffering with an image problem, partly caused by growing numbers of bike clubs, such as Satan's Slaves, Road Rats, and Gypsy Jokers. Members included World War II veterans who were having problems readjusting to civilian life.

Harley soldiered on, and in 1957 introduced a significant new model in the shape of the 883cc XL Sportster, featuring overhead valves in place of the side-valve layout of its predecessor the KH. The Sportster gained performance with bigger valves, and was good for 100mph (161km/h). It also featured two-tone paintwork, telescopic forks, chrome-covered twin shocks, and a single sprung saddle. The model was an instant hit, and would be successfully updated throughout the 1960s and far beyond.

Harley was badly in need of a high-performance twin because by 1957 the US market was proving fruitful for British firms. Triumph led the way, having established thriving agencies on both sides of the country: Johnson Motors on the West Coast and TriCor in the East. It was largely American enthusiasts' demands for extra performance and 'more cubes' that had led to the Brit manufacturers enlarging their parallel twin engines to 650cc. The leaders had predictably been Triumph, whose Thunderbird had been launched to great acclaim in 1950.

The original 'T-bird' was essentially a 649cc version of Triumph's popular Speed Twin. Its larger motor produced 34bhp, which was 4bhp up on the sporty 500cc Tiger 100's output. Although the top speed of just over 100mph (161km/h) was only a small improvement, the bigger motor had considerably more midrange punch. That helped the Thunderbird, which was barely heavier than the 500cc models, live up to Triumph's advertising claim that it was 'the most exciting motorcycle ever.' In 1954 Triumph unveiled a faster still 650, the Tiger 110, whose motor used hot cams, increased compression, and a larger Amal carburetor to produce 42bhp.

BSA also had a popular 650cc model, the A10 Golden Flash, which had been rushed into production in late 1950 to compete with the Thunderbird. Despite its name and claimed 35bhp

Harley-Davidson XL Sportster (1957)	
Engine:	Air-cooled ohv four-valve pushrod 45-degree V-twin
Capacity:	883cc (76.2 x 96.8mm)
Maximum power:	40bhp @ 5500rpm
Transmission:	Four-speed, chain final drive
Frame:	Steel twin downtube
Suspension:	Telescopic front; twin shocks rear
Brakes:	Drum front & rear
Weight:	463lb (210kg)
Top speed:	100mph (161km/h)

Above: Harley's Sportster provided '50s cool.

Below left: Triumph's T-bird had lots of muscle.

Triumph Thunderbird (1957)	
Engine:	Air-cooled ohv pushrod four-valve parallel twin
Capacity:	649cc (71 x 82mm)
Maximum power:	34bhp @ 6300rpm
Transmission:	Four-speed, chain final drive
Frame:	Steel cradle
Suspension:	Telescopic front; twin shocks rear
Brakes:	Drum front & rear
Weight:	385lb (175kg)
Top speed:	103mph (166km/h)

BSA Road Rocket (1956)

Engine:	Air-cooled ohv pushrod four-valve parallel twin
Capacity:	646cc (70 x 84mm)
Maximum power:	40bhp @ 6000rpm
Transmission:	Four-speed, chain final drive
Frame:	Steel twin downtube
Suspension:	Telescopic front; twin shocks rear
Brakes:	Drum front & rear
Weight:	418lb (190kg)
Top speed:	105mph (169km/h)

Above right: BSA's quick and stylish 646cc A10RR Road Rocket was launched in 1954.

Above: The Matchless G12 De Luxe.

Below: The AJS Model 16MCS was an off-road competition version of the 1954-model 350cc single, but also made a capable roadster.

maximum output, the Flash was not a racy sportster but a dependable all-rounder that was often used with a sidecar. The Birmingham firm added some performance with the short-lived Super Flash, which was sold in the US in 1953, and then with the A10 Road Rocket, whose 646cc engine featured aluminum cylinder head, hot camshaft, high-compression pistons, and 40bhp peak output.

The Road Rocket was good for 105mph (169km/h) and sold well both in Britain and the States, as did its similarly styled replacement, the Super Rocket. The BSA group also earned some extra sales from its 650cc twin when Ariel, which had been taken over by BSA in 1944, launched its own model, the Huntmaster, closely based on the Golden Flash. A slightly revised 35bhp engine was combined with a new gearbox and frame in one of the British industry's more successful attempts at 'badge engineering.'

The master of that particular practice was AMC (Associated Motor Cycles), which had been formed when Matchless of Plumstead in south London had taken over Wolverhampton firm AJS in 1931. From then on, bikes were often sold under both Matchless and AJS names, with few differences apart from color (typically red for Matchless, blue for AJS). Thus the original AMC 498cc parallel twin, launched in 1949, was both the Matchless G9 and AJS Model 20.

AMC followed the trend for increased capacity, enlarging the twin to 592cc to create the G11 in 1956, and three years later producing the 646cc G12, also sold as the AJS Model 31. In either guise it was a solid, reliable machine that handled well and was good for just over 100mph (161km/h). The G12 was also popular in De Luxe form, with uprated ignition and quickly detachable rear wheel. The sporty G12 CSR, with high-compression motor, siamesed exhaust, and alloy fenders, gave extra speed at the expense of vibration and unreliability.

The AMC empire also included Francis-Barnett and James, both of which had been successful before the war, and had later built Villiers-engined two-strokes before being taken over in 1947. Five years later Norton was also swallowed up by AMC, although production continued at Bracebridge Street in Birmingham, rather than moving to London (at least until 1962). Unlike AJS and Matchless models, Nortons retained a distinct identity. The marque belatedly joined the move toward increased capacity in 1956, when the Dominator 88's 500cc engine was enlarged to 597cc to create the Dominator 99.

Italy's All-Conquering Fours

The dominant racebikes of the 1950s were screaming 500cc fours from Italian factories Gilera and MV Agusta. The key figure was engineer Piero Remor, who had first designed a 490cc four-cylinder engine in 1923, and who in the 1930s had been involved with rider/engineer Piero Taruffi in building a supercharged four called the Rondine ('swallow'), on which Taruffi set several speed records.

Giuseppe Gilera, whose factory at Arcore near Milan was one of Italy's largest, had bought the Rondine project in 1936. Development of a supercharged 250cc four was abandoned after the war, when supercharging was banned by the FIM, but Remor used the engine as the basis for a dohc 500cc powerplant whose 55bhp output far exceeded those of singles including Gilera's own Saturno. Les Graham of AJS won the first

500cc world championship in 1949, but the following year Gilera's Umberto Masetti overcame his four's poor handling to win from Norton's Geoff Duke.

Duke gained his revenge in 1951 by winning on the slower but more agile Norton, but Masetti regained the title for Gilera in 1952. Duke was then signed by the Italian factory and won a hat-trick of championships between 1953 and '55. By this time Gilera had a new rival, because Remor had left for MV Agusta, taking chief mechanic Arturo Magni with him, and had designed a 500cc four for the Gallarate factory. This featured shaft final drive and a gearlever on each side of the engine, but after poor results it was redesigned with a more conventional layout.

Disaster struck when MV team leader Les Graham was killed at the TT in 1953. But the firm's fortunes changed with the signing of

John Surtees, who won the championship in 1956. Libero Liberati regained the title for Gilera in 1957 but at the end of that year the Arcore factory quit racing, largely for financial reasons, along with rivals Mondial and Moto Guzzi. That left the way open for Surtees, who added three more championships between 1958 and 1960, and especially for MV Agusta, who would rule the grand prix world for many more years.

Above: Gilera's mighty fours dominated 500cc grand prix racing in the early 1950s.

It was Triumph that ended the decade with the most significant arrival, when in 1959 the firm introduced a new high-performance, twin-carburetor version of its 649cc twin. Inspired by the exploits of Texan Johnny Allen, who in 1956 had ridden a Triumph streamliner to 214mph (344km/h) on the Bonneville salt flats in Utah, Edward Turner named the 46bhp twin the T120 Bonneville. The 'Bonnie' was an immediate hit, and its combination of performance, style, and competitive price would prove irresistible for years to come.

Below: At the 1954 Earls Court Show, James put the new 224cc Colonel alongside one of the firm's 225cc 2.25hp models from 1915.

Left: Triumph's original T120 Bonneville was launched hurriedly in 1959, complete with twin carbs and short-lived headlamp nacelle.

Empire in Decline
1960s

Above: By the early 1960s Soichiro Honda, the son of a Hamamatsu blacksmith, was on his way to becoming by far the most important figure in motorcycling history.

Previous page: Bridgestone's sophisticated 350 GTR two-stroke twin used disc valve induction.

Above: This 247cc Honda C71 was built in 1960, two years after the model's introduction. Its 1957 predecessor the C70, Honda's first twin, had similar styling, with frame, front forks, and big fenders made from pressed steel.

The British motorcycle industry began the 1960s on top of the world. The previous, increasingly affluent decade had ended with the UK manufacturers producing most of the best machines, and with a record number of over 350,000 registrations in Britain alone. Prime Minister Harold Macmillan's famous comment that 'You've never had it so good' seemed to apply particularly to a bike industry whose largest force, the BSA Group, posted record profits of over £3.5 million in 1960.

But already there were warning signs that the good times were drawing to a close. The 1950s had ended with the launch of two small, relatively inexpensive cars, the Austin Mini and Morris Minor. They and others would hit the UK motorcycle industry hard, just as Henry Ford's Model T had done in the USA decades earlier, and as the VW Beetle and Fiat's tiny Topolino were doing in Germany and Italy. Ordinary people now aspired to car ownership, and the motorcycle and sidecar combination that had provided British family transport for decades was regarded as distinctly second best.

Motorcycling was not helped by its downmarket image. In the USA, Hell's Angels were making headlines for violence and lawlessness (although Honda's 'You meet the nicest people...' advertising projected a contrastingly wholesome impression). Britain's relatively harmless 'leather boys' preferred burn-ups between cafés. But their resultant accidents led to bad publicity, which was partly responsible for provisional license holders being restricted to 250cc bikes in 1961. Many motorcycle dealerships, including the prestigious Kings of Oxford chain owned by Mike Hailwood's father Stan, began selling cars instead.

As early as 1960, many people realized that the biggest threat to the British motorcycle industry came from the east. In that year Edward Turner, head of the BSA Group's Automotive Division, visited several Japanese bike factories. His report to BSA's directors commented favorably that the Japanese firms had 'quality machine tool equipment, advanced techniques, scientific ability and keen commercial enterprise.'

By this time Honda's annual production of over 200,000 units exceeded the British industry's total. The large Japanese bike market was protected by import tariffs that were not reflected in Britain, where the market was much more vulnerable to foreign imports. Turner's report concluded that, rather than attempting to compete by building more and better small-capacity motorcycles, British manufacturers should concentrate their resources by building fewer different models. Turner and others believed that Japan's production of small bikes would be beneficial, as riders would graduate to larger British machines. For a while, some of them did …

Honda was already making an impression on motorcyclists outside Japan with a breathtaking arrival on the road-racing scene. Soichiro Honda had visited the Isle of Man TT back in 1954, while on a European trip to visit several car factories. In 1959 he returned with a five-man team of riders comprising four Japanese plus rider-manager Bill Hunt, the sales manager at Honda's recently established American office. Their bikes were 125cc parallel twins, inspired by the NSU Rennmax that had dominated the 250cc class before the German firm had quit racing in 1954.

Honda's inexperienced crew caused some amusement by arriving with knobbly tires, better suited to ash-covered home tracks than the Mountain circuit. Even when these were swapped for Avons, Honda couldn't match the pace of the winning MV Agusta ridden by Tarquinio Provini, but top-12 finishes by all four Japanese riders won the team prize. For the 1960 TT, Honda's team included Australian Bob Brown, who finished fourth in the 250cc race. Hondas took sixth to tenth places in the 125cc event.

Even that success didn't prepare the motorcycle world for the 1961 season. Helped by MV's withdrawal to concentrate on the bigger classes, Honda's riders Mike Hailwood and Australian Tom Phillis dominated the season, winning the 250 and 125cc world championships respectively. At the TT, Hondas took the top five places in both races. Even allowing for the limited factory opposition, it was a brilliant effort that confirmed the arrival of a major new force.

By this time Honda was also building twin-cylinder roadsters, having begun in 1957 with the 250cc C70, which also owed much to NSU. The 18bhp parallel twin had chain-driven overhead camshaft and unit construction (combined engine and gearbox). It was rather ungainly, with a pressed steel frame and front forks, big fenders and 16-inch wheels. Its successor, the C71, featuring an electric starter, was sold in small numbers in Europe in 1960.

Honda also built sporty and dual-purpose versions of some models, and it was the racier twins that helped establish the firm abroad in the early 1960s. First came the CB92, whose rev-happy and reliable 125cc engine gave a top speed of over 70mph (113km/h). With its flyshield, low handlebars, and big front drum brake, the little Honda looked the part too, though its pressed-steel frame and under-damped rear shocks did not match the aggressive image.

Increasingly sophisticated roadsters

The twin that did most to put Honda on the map was the 250cc CB72, whose twin carburetors helped give a maximum output of 24bhp and a 90mph (145km/h) top speed. Chassis layout was modern, with a tubular steel frame and telescopic forks in place of Honda's previous leading-link units. Many motorcyclists were still scornful of the revvy 'rice-burners,' but Honda's successful racers and increasingly sophisticated roadsters were gradually making an impression.

Above: This lightweight Honda line-up from the early '60s features (from left) the standard 50cc C110 and the C110 Sport, both from 1961, plus the 55cc C115 model from 1963.

Below: Honda's 125cc CB92 twin reached Europe in 1961, proving that the Japanese firm could build stylish, quick, and reliable bikes.

Honda CB72 (1962)

Engine:	Air-cooled sohc four-valve parallel twin
Capacity:	247cc (54 x 54mm)
Maximum power:	24bhp @ 9000rpm
Transmission:	Four-speed, chain final drive
Frame:	Steel spine
Suspension:	Telescopic front; twin shocks rear
Brakes:	Drum front & rear
Weight:	337lb (153kg) dry
Top speed:	90mph (145km/h)

Above right: Honda's influential 247cc CB72.

Below: Yamaha's 246cc YDS-2 two-stroke twin.

Yamaha YDS-2 (1963)

Engine:	Air-cooled two-stroke parallel twin
Capacity:	246cc (56 x 50mm)
Maximum power:	25bhp @ 7500rpm
Transmission:	Five-speed, chain final drive
Frame:	Steel twin cradle
Suspension:	Telescopic front; twin shocks rear
Brakes:	Drum front & rear
Weight:	313lb (142kg) dry
Top speed:	90mph (145km/h)

Suzuki, too, was gaining ground. The firm had begun by building looms for weaving, before moving into motorcycle production in 1954 with a 90cc four-stroke single called the Colleda. Suzuki entered the grand prix world and was boosted in 1961 when Ernst Degner, star rider of the East German MZ team, defected to the West, taking the tuning secrets of two-stroke engine genius Walter Kaaden with him. The following year Degner won the first 50cc world title for Suzuki. New Zealand's Hugh Anderson and Germany's Hans-Georg Anscheidt won a total of seven more 50 and 125cc titles for Suzuki in the next few years.

Yamaha, whose parent company Nippon Gakki had long been a leading producer of musical instruments, had also begun building motorbikes in the mid-1950s, as a way of utilizing machinery that had manufactured propellers in the war. Yamaha's first bike, the YA-1 'Red Dragon,' was one of several from different countries to be copied from German firm DKW's RT 125 two-stroke single. The YD-2, a two-stroke parallel twin, followed in 1957.

The models that launched Yamaha's reputation for rapid small-capacity two-strokes were the 250cc YDS-1 and especially its successor the YDS-2, which was exported successfully in the early 1960s. The YDS-2 produced 25bhp, was good for 90mph (145km/h), and captivated all who rode it. 'What a fantastic machine this is!' began the test in UK magazine *Motorcycle Mechanics* in 1963. 'The acceleration makes you gasp in sheer amazement because you only expect this sort of performance from a racing machine.' Yamaha's two-stoke racers were faster still, as they soon proved with the 250cc and 125cc world championships won by Britain's Phil Read and Bill Ivy.

Kawasaki, a giant corporation that built ships, planes, and locomotives among other things, had also been manufacturing motorcycle engines since 1949, and had formed a firm called Meihatsu to sell them in the 1950s. Kawasaki set up its own motorcycle factory, and in 1961 built its first complete bike, the B7, a 125cc two-stroke single based on a Meihatsu. The following year Kawasaki took over Meguro, a marque that dated back to 1928, and had previously built the Rikuo, a copy of a side-valve Harley-Davidson V-twin. Kawasaki thus became an established manufacturer almost overnight, with a range from 50 to 500cc.

By no means all the Japanese manufacturers were thriving, however. In the mid-1950s there had been more than 80 bike firms, but by the early '60s only a handful survived. Olympus had abandoned bikes to concentrate on cameras, Hosk and Showa had been bought by Yamaha, and Fuji by Bridgestone. One of the biggest firms, Marusho, was known for high-quality Lilac 250cc and 125cc transverse V-twins. The firm went bust in 1961, returned with a BMW-style 500cc flat-twin three years later, but by 1967 had ceased production for good.

While Japanese firms had been making their bikes faster and more sophisticated during the late 1950s, Triumph had tried a different approach with its Twenty-One, named after its capacity of 21 cubic inches or 350cc. The 18bhp parallel twin, launched in 1957, was significant in featuring Triumph's first unit-construction engine and gearbox. And the Twenty-One also introduced the 'bathtub' – a sheet-steel enclosure of the rear wheel, intended to give scooter-like cleanliness. By no means all riders were impressed, especially when the bathtub was used on larger models including the 650cc Tiger 110.

Triumph's star of the 1960s was the T120 Bonneville. After a slightly troubled start (early models' crack-prone frames led to a stiffer twin-downtube design, which caused vibration and fuel frothing, cured by another new frame) the 'Bonnie' was successfully tweaked to keep it hugely popular throughout the decade and beyond. Its basic format of 649cc pushrod engine with twin carburetors remained, as did its key attributes of good looks and lively acceleration, backed-up by reasonable smoothness, reliability, and handling.

If Triumph built what was widely regarded as the outstanding parallel twin engine of the 1960s, then Norton had the best chassis. The Dominator 99's Featherbed frame held a 597cc engine that was available in SS (Sports Special) trim, with twin carbs and higher compression. In 1961, the motor was enlarged to 646cc to power a US export model called the Manxman. The following year Norton created the Dominator 650SS, powered by a 646cc motor with SS

Above: Triumph's 1960-model T110 Tiger had controversial bathtub rear enclosure.

Left: Triumph's T120 Bonneville, here in 1961 form, was a star throughout the 1960s.

Triumph T120 Bonneville (1961)

Engine:	Air-cooled four-valve ohv pushrod parallel twin
Capacity:	649cc (71 x 82mm)
Maximum power:	46bhp @ 6500rpm
Transmission:	Four-speed, chain final drive
Frame:	Steel twin downtube
Suspension:	Telescopic front; twin shocks rear
Brakes:	Drum front & rear
Weight:	402lb (183kg) wet
Top speed:	110mph (177km/h)

Right: Struggling Norton produced one of its best ever bikes in 1962 with the Dominator 650SS, which combined a 49bhp parallel twin engine with Featherbed-framed chassis, and provided both speed and fine handling.

Below: Ariel gambled in 1960 by abandoning four-stroke production in favor of the futuristic Leader, featuring a 249cc two-stroke engine enclosed by pressed-steel bodywork. The gamble failed, and Ariel went bust.

Ariel Leader (1960)

Engine:	Air-cooled two-stroke parallel twin
Capacity:	249cc (54 x 54mm)
Maximum power:	16bhp @ 6400rpm
Transmission:	Four-speed, chain final drive
Frame:	Pressed-steel
Suspension:	Trailing-link front; twin shocks rear
Brakes:	Drum front & rear
Weight:	310lb (141kg) dry
Top speed:	70mph (113km/h)

specification plus a new downdraft cylinder head developed from engineer Doug Hele's Domiracer competition bike.

The 650SS was a superb machine that produced 49bhp, had a top speed of almost 120mph (193km/h), and handled in finest Norton tradition. The 650SS did not match the Bonneville's sales, partly due to a higher price and also to Norton's generally lower production numbers. But the model was a success on road and track, being voted *Motor Cycle News'* machine of the year in 1962 and '63, and winning two major long-distance production races within months of its launch. Those achievements were overshadowed when in 1963 struggling parent company AMC closed the famous Bracebridge Street works, and moved Norton production to the Matchless factory in Woolwich, south London.

Another popular marque gained a new home for the wrong reasons in 1963, when Ariel production was moved from the traditional Selly Oak base to parent company BSA's factory at Small Heath, Birmingham. Ariel's problems dated back to the 1950s, when Edward Turner, the autocratic Triumph boss, had taken control of the BSA group's bike division. Rather than developing Ariel's assets, Turner seemed to regard the marque as a threat to Triumph. Development of an updated Square Four was abandoned, and in 1960 the small Ariel Competition Department was closed down, although trials ace Sammy Miller was beating all comers on his legendary HT Red Hunter single with the number plate 'GOV132.'

In 1960 Ariel also controversially abandoned production of roadgoing four-strokes including the Red Hunter and the 650cc Huntmaster twin, in favor of the Leader. This was an innovative machine powered by a 250cc, two-stroke parallel twin with angled-forward cylinders, designed by Val Page and owing much to the German marque Adler. Its chassis combined a pressed-steel frame, trailing link forks, further pressed-steel bodywork sections, and a dummy tank that could hold an open-face helmet.

Ariel's advertising slogan 'Tomorrow's Design Today' promised much, and the Leader offered smooth cruising, a 70mph (113km/h) top speed, and light handling. But that was not enough to make it a lasting success, despite initially promising sales. The Leader's convenience and reasonable performance were offset by flaws including poor brakes, difficult starting, unreliable electrics, and inaccessibility for maintenance.

Two-stroke troubles

Ariel attempted to broaden the two-stroke's appeal with more conventional models. The unfaired Arrow and its racier derivative the Super Sports Arrow (known as the Golden Arrow) were used with some success in club racing. But when sales dropped, Ariel had nothing else to offer. Moving production across Birmingham to Small Heath merely delayed the inevitable, and the last two-strokes were produced in 1965. BSA later revived the Ariel name for two disastrous commuter machines, the 50cc Pixie and three-wheeled Ariel-3, but the once proud 'House of the Horse' was effectively dead.

Perhaps Ariel's attempt to create a machine with motorbike performance and scooter-style convenience had simply been ill-timed. The UK two-wheeled scene was polarizing into two rival groups: the bike-riding, leather-jacketed rockers; and the mods, who rode scooters and wore tent-like parka jackets over smarter clothes; and preferred 'Mersey beat' pop tunes to rock. Bank holiday weekends in the mid-'60s saw battles between the two groups on the beaches of coastal towns such as Brighton and Southend.

Rockers tended to gather at transport cafés, the most famous of which was the Ace, near Wembley in north-west London. As many as 1000 bikes were sometimes parked outside the Ace, most of them British singles and twins that were tuned and otherwise modified to boost performance. Favored sport of the 'café-race' crowd was the record run – 'record' as in gramophone recording – when a rider put a coin in the juke-box, rushed out to his bike and raced off in an attempt to complete a pre-set road course in time to hear the end of the song. Many didn't make it back at all.

Arguably the ultimate rocker bike of the era was the Triton, the unofficial blend of Triumph twin engine and Norton Featherbed frame that provided the best of British biking: the speed of the Bonneville or T110 with the handling of a Dominator or racing Manx. Tritons were constructed by individual riders and also by dealers, most notably by Dave Degens. The former Ace regular turned racer won numerous production events plus the Barcelona 24-hour race on Tritons. His Dresda firm also built more than 500 of the hybrids during the '60s, and would still be building them 30 years later.

Top: Rockers favored low, clip-on handlebars and badge-covered black leather jackets.

Above: Bikes are lined up at Regency Square in Brighton, the south coast city that was a popular destination for rockers' runs.

Left: The ultimate 1960s café racer was the Triton, a blend of Triumph twin-cylinder engine and Norton Featherbed frame that gave the best of British motorcycling.

Right: BSA built the Rocket Gold Star both in this US export version, with raised handlebars and twin exhausts, and home market spec with low, clip-on bars and siamesed pipes. In either form it was one of the fastest bikes on the road.

BSA Rocket Gold Star (1962)

Engine:	Air-cooled ohv pushrod four-valve parallel twin
Capacity:	646cc (70 x 84mm)
Maximum power:	46bhp @ 6250rpm
Transmission:	Four-speed, chain final drive
Frame:	Steel twin downtube
Suspension:	Telescopic front; twin shocks rear
Brakes:	Drum front & rear
Weight:	418lb (190kg)
Top speed:	115mph (185km/h)

Below: Royal Enfield's Constellation provided plenty of power from its big 692cc parallel twin engine, but the 'Connie' was too unreliable to become a big success.

BSA's most memorable production twin of this period also owed much to a hybrid. The Rocket Gold Star was inspired by a one-off special that Oxfordshire dealer Eddie Dow had created by fitting a Gold Star single with a twin-cylinder engine. In 1962, BSA was set to replace its long-running 646cc A10 twin engine with a new A65 unit-construction powerplant (and similar 500cc version, the A50). The familiar 'pre-unit' motor was given a fitting finale by being bolted into a slightly modified Gold Star frame, to create the 'Rocket Goldie.'

The Rocket Gold Star motor was a tuned version of the existing Super Rocket unit, and used higher compression, hotter camshaft, and racing style magneto ignition to produce 46bhp. The bike's look and specification generally mimicked that of the Gold Star, with silver-and-chromed gas tank, low 'Ace' handlebars (for the UK market; higher for the US), big front drum brake, and alloy wheel rims. With genuine 115mph (185km/h) performance plus handling to match, the Rocket Gold Star was a fine way to end the A10 line.

In a straight line, at least, the BSA had some worthy opposition from Royal Enfield, the small firm from Redditch, near Birmingham, that had long produced parallel twins of distinctive capacity and style. The Meteor, introduced in 1953, had a softly tuned 692cc engine because it was essentially two 346cc single-cylinder Bullet units. Three years later the Super Meteor increased peak output by 4bhp to 40bhp, but it was in 1958 with the launch of the Constellation that Enfield finally found some genuine performance.

The Constellation motor retained the 692cc capacity but was comprehensively overhauled and produced an impressive 51bhp, enough for a top speed of 115mph (185km/h). The big powerplant had plenty of low-rev torque too, but oil leaks and unreliability thwarted Enfield's hopes of success. Even fitting Ace bars and reworking the engine to make it more oil-tight didn't make the Constellation popular in the early '60s. Enfield then enlarged the motor again to create the 750cc Interceptor in 1962. Its extra size and pulling power were intended to appeal to the US market, but the Interceptor was not the hit that struggling Enfield desperately needed.

Since Indian had ceased production in 1953, Harley-Davidson had been the sole US manufacturer (although Enfield's Meteor had subsequently been given big fenders, and marketed as an Indian Chief). Harley's Sportster, designated the XL, had been popular since its launch in 1957, and reached new heights in following years with the high-performance XLCH. No official explanation was given for the extra initials, which some said stood for 'California' or 'Competition Hot.' The bike was developed from the stripped-down XLC that had been built in small numbers, mainly for Californian desert racers.

Whatever, the result was a lean, mean, hotted-up version of the 883cc pushrod V-twin; and one that fully lived up to the Sportster part of its name. With a tiny gas tank borrowed from Harley's single-cylinder Hummer (a 125cc two-stroke copied from the German DKW), single seat, relatively light weight, and enough power for a top speed of well over 100mph (161km/h) in standard form, the XLCH was fast enough to compete with British 650cc twins.

Harley also updated its big twin range through the 1960s, and introduced the 'full-dressed' touring style complete with factory-supplied windshield, panniers and other accessories. Early stages in the evolution had come in the late 1940s, with a new 1213cc (74ci), 55bhp V-twin engine whose smooth aluminum rocker covers prompted the nickname 'Panhead.' Hydraulically damped telescopic forks had replaced springers in 1949, resulting in the Hydra-Glide.

The Duo-Glide was created in 1958 with the introduction of twin-shock rear suspension. And in 1965, the addition of an electric starter resulted in the birth of the most famous big Harley of all, the Electra-Glide. It was huge, heavy, expensive, under-braked, and not very fast. But the Electra-Glide was also comfortable, smooth, and stylish enough to become not just a very successful tourer, but an icon whose name and character would survive several decades and numerous updates, albeit with its hyphen quietly dropped.

Harley struggled in the early 1960s, with a significant proportion of its business being police and other services, but there was plenty going on behind the scenes at Milwaukee. In 1960 the firm attempted to gain ground in the small-capacity markets by buying a 50 percent stake in Aermacchi, a financially struggling Italian marque. Aermacchi's sporty 250cc single the Ala Verde was sold in the US as the Sprint, and was raced with some success.

During the 1960s, Harley began to acquire something of a cult status with a section of the American biking public, and to attract customizers who bolted longer forks, hard-tail frames and

Above: Early-'60s versions of Harley's Sportster were respectably quick machines that were a match for many British rivals, but the Milwaukee firm's 883cc V-twin became less competitive throughout the decade.

Below: Harley created the Electra-Glide in 1965 by adding an electric starter to the Duo-Glide, launching a long-running legend.

Left: Windshield, footboards, and buddy seat gave the Electra-Glide a luxurious ride.

Above: The R69S was BMW's sportiest model for most of the 1960s, but the conservative German marque offered only white paintwork as an alternative to the standard black.

Below: Panther's traditional angled 'sloper' single-cylinder engine took the place of a frame downtube, doubling as a stressed member of the chassis. The Model 100 name came from the 598cc engine's long stroke of 100mm.

Right: The photo of this 1961 Model 100S is untypical, because the vast majority of Panther's big singles were fitted with sidecars.

custom-painted parts to bikes and also to the three-wheeled Servicar. The Servicar was far from the only non-two-wheeled Harley product, as the firm had diversified into the manufacture of golf carts and even boats, after taking over a boat-building firm called Tomahawk.

But sales and prospects were poor, and in 1965 Harley raised much needed capital by becoming a public company, with the Harley and Davidson families retaining a majority of shares. This allowed increased advertising but Harley failed to increase its feeble six percent share of the US market. (Exports accounted for less than five percent of production.) In 1969 the crippled company was bought by American Machine and Foundry (AMF), an industrial giant that was keen to expand its interests in the leisure market.

The situation was equally bleak in the European motorcycle industry. In Germany the downturn had begun in the late 1950s, resulting in Adler and Horex ceasing production, NSU turning from bikes to cars, and former giants DKW, Victoria, and Express merging to form the Zweirad Union. In 1966, Hercules joined the Union, which was taken over by the large Fichtel & Sachs group three years later. Many small bikes and mopeds would follow, but Germany's days as a major motorcycling force were over.

BMW had also struggled in the late 1950s, with bike production down to little over 5000 units, and the company at one stage under threat of being taken over by Mercedes-Benz. But BMW survived, and in 1960 launched a new range of bikes with more powerful engines. The peaky and unreliable 500cc R50S lasted only two years, but the standard R50/2, and the 600cc R60/2 and sporty R69S were built throughout the decade. They gained numerous detail updates along the way but kept their conservative look with big fuel tanks, huge seats, Earles forks, and black or white paintwork.

Many British bike builders were in far deeper financial trouble. After posting a profit in 1960, the Associated Motor Cycles group had begun losing money. In 1966 AMC was taken over by a firm called Manganeze Bronze Holdings, which had recently acquired Villiers, manufacturer of small engines. The new firm was named Norton Villiers, confirming that Norton was the prize asset among the AMC brands, and before long the other marques were discarded.

Left: *This Royal Enfield Continental GT dates from 1967, so was one of the last to be built before the Redditch factory was closed. Despite a capacity of just 248cc, the single's café-racer look was backed by a fair turn of speed.*

Below: *Although Velocette's 1960-model Viceroy gave reasonable performance from its 250cc two-stroke engine, it lacked the style of rival Italian scooters and failed to sell.*

Declining sales

James and Francis-Barnett, which had been building Villiers-engined lightweights of often similar design, were quickly closed down. AJS and Matchless were both famous old marques with much racing history. The Matchless G50, a 500cc single developed from AJS's famous 350cc racer the 7R or 'Boy Racer,' had won races into the 1960s. But sales of the badge-engineered and often near-identical AJS and Matchless singles and twins had been slow for years, and by the end of 1967 Norton Villiers had axed the lot.

Panther was another old name to be put to sleep in 1967, after several years of ill-health. The Yorkshire firm had been building its 598cc Model 100, known as a 'sloper' due to its angled-forward single cylinder, from 1928 to 1963 with relatively few changes. Even the more recent 645cc Model 120 produced only a slow-revving 27bhp. In 1960 the firm had estimated that 90 percent of Model 100s were attached to sidecars, so the rise of the Mini and its cohorts hit Panther particularly hard. There was a final attempt with a 250cc Villiers-engined twin, named the Red Panther after a model of that name whose success had rescued Panther in the 1930s. But when lightning failed to strike twice, the factory closed for good.

Royal Enfield survived to the end of the decade, but only just. Enfield made a brave fight, notably with its line of 250cc pushrod singles, which were repeatedly updated following the launch of the original Crusader model in 1956. That led to the tuned Crusader Sports, the Super 5 (named after its five-speed gearbox), and the Continental, which arrived in 1963 with a yet more powerful engine plus flyshield and dropped handlebars.

Below: *Triumph's TR6 Trophy combined a powerful 650cc engine with stylish high-level pipe, and was very popular in the US.*

The final fling was the following year's Continental GT, which was devised after Enfield contacted its dealers' young apprentices to ask what potential customers wanted. The result was an attractive bike that combined the flyshield and low bars with a long red gas tank, humped dual-seat, and perforated dummy cooling rims for the front drum brake. The GT's light weight, 85mph (137km/h) top speed and good handling more than made up for its unreliable gearbox, and the bike was popular with British provisional license holders who were limited to 250cc by the recent law change.

That was not enough to save Royal Enfield, which had come under the control of financiers who decided that the motorcycle firm was worth less than its traditional factory site in Redditch,

Velocette Venom Thruxton (1965)

Engine:	Air-cooled ohv pushrod two-valve single
Capacity:	499cc (86 x 86mm)
Maximum power:	40bhp @ 6200rpm
Transmission:	Four-speed, chain final drive
Frame:	Steel single downtube
Suspension:	Telescopic front; twin shocks rear
Brakes:	Drum front & rear
Weight:	390lb (177kg)
Top speed:	105mph (169km/h)

Above right: Velocette's Venom Thruxton was the last and raciest of the firm's singles, with clip-on bars, tuned 499cc motor, big front brake, humped seat, and firm suspension.

near Birmingham. Production of all singles was abandoned in 1967. The Interceptor 750 twin was built at Bradford-on-Avon in Wiltshire until 1970. After that, the only survivor was the humble Bullet single, which continued to be built in India where it had been produced under license since the 1950s.

Another sad story was that of Velocette, whose problems had begun in 1960 with an attempt to move into the scooter market. The Viceroy, powered by a 248cc, two-stroke horizontally opposed twin, was a smooth and sophisticated device that handled well and was good for 70mph (113km/h). But its unusual styling failed to catch on with riders who preferred fashionable Vespas and Lambrettas, and by the early '60s the scooter boom was over. After all Velocette's expensive development and tooling, fewer than 1000 Viceroys were sold, and the glass-fiber-bodied LE Vogue was no more successful.

Velocette did at least have time to produce one last development of the singles for which the marque was famous. Since the late 1950s, Velocette's sporty pushrod singles had been the 500cc

Norton Commando (1968)

Engine:	Air-cooled ohv pushrod four-valve parallel twin
Capacity:	745cc (73 x 89mm)
Maximum power:	58bhp @ 6800rpm
Transmission:	Four-speed, chain final drive
Frame:	Steel spine with twin downtubes
Suspension:	Telescopic front; twin shock rear
Brakes:	Drum front & rear
Weight:	420lb (191kg)
Top speed:	115mph (185km/h)

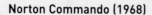

Left: BSA's standard 650cc parallel twin of the late '60s was the Thunderbolt, introduced in 1966 with single carb and 40bhp output.

Below: The Spitfire MkIV, released in 1968, was the fastest of BSA's 650 twins, and also featured a big front drum brake and new rear shocks. But like previous Spitfires its tuned 54bhp engine often gave problems when used hard.

Venom and 350cc Viper, both of which had become available in high-performance Clubman trim. After a Velo had won the prestigious Thruxton 500-mile (805km) race in 1964, the firm offered a race kit including big-valve cylinder head and Amal Grand Prix carburetor.

In 1965 these were incorporated into a new model, the Venom Thruxton, which also featured clip-on bars, rearset footrests, large gas tank, humped seat, firm suspension, and a big twin-leading-shoe front drum brake. Its 499cc engine produced 40bhp, good for genuine 90mph (145km/h) cruising and a top speed of about 105mph (169km/h). The Thruxton made a superb, if uncompromising, roadster, and a successful racer that won its class at the first Production TT in 1967. But by then Velocette's financial problems were deepening, and few bikes were built before production ended in 1970.

BSA was another victim of the scooter market in the early '60s, notably with a machine that was sold as both the BSA Sunbeam and the Triumph Tigress. Both were produced with 175cc two-stroke single (from the BSA Bantam) or new 250cc four-stroke twin engines. Like Velocette's Viceroy they lacked the style to attract the scooter crowd, and also suffered from overheating of the enclosed engines. This was by no means the only example of poor BSA engineering, as both Triumph's 200cc Tiger Cub and BSA's related C15 single had a string of problems.

BSA was nevertheless very profitable in the mid-'60s, largely due to the group's success in the United States. Exports accounted for 75 percent of production by 1966, earning both BSA and Triumph the Queen's Award for Industry. At that point production had increased by 40 percent in two years. New workers were employed, and BSA's Small Heath factory was modernized with an expensive, computer-controlled assembly system.

Lionel Jofeh, the former aircraft industry figure who took over as group motorcycle chief in 1967, based himself at a lavish, recently purchased new Research and Development center at Umberslade Hall, a grand country house with peacocks on its lawn, situated south of Birmingham midway between the BSA, Triumph, and Royal Enfield factories. It had a staff of 300 and cost an estimated £1.5 million per year to run, but would earn its nickname 'Slumberslade Hall' by producing little of value.

Opposite center: With its raised bars and twin high-level pipes, Norton's Commando 750S had a stylish and distinctive look.

Opposite below: Norton's Commando 750, seen here in Fastback style with 1972-model front disc, was a fast and smooth-running roadster.

Right: Kawasaki's 1967-model W2TT Commander was the dual-purpose version of the Japanese firm's British-style 624cc parallel twin.

Below: Honda produced many dual-purpose models in the late '60s, mainly for the US market, including this CL450 parallel twin.

Bottom right: The CB450 parallel twin, known as the 'Black Bomber,' arrived in 1965 to confirm that Honda was entering the big bike market.

There were still some great bikes to come from Britain, though, not least the Bonneville. By the late 1960s the T120 had arguably reached the peak of its development, thanks to improvements including a powerful twin-leading-shoe front brake, forks with two-way damping, a longer swingarm, and engine mods that improved reliability and oil retention. The Bonneville was lean and handsome, raced from zero to 100mph (161km/h) in the quarter mile, and handled better than ever.

'If you are a sporty rider and deem yourself a bit of a jockey, you know you are waiting for the day you can buy your Bonnie,' summed up an impressed tester from US magazine *Cycle World*. The Triumph backed up its performance on the track too, with four wins in the big 500-mile (805km) production race at Thruxton and Brands Hatch. John Hartle won the first Isle of Man Production TT in 1967, and two years later Malcolm Uphill set the first 100mph (161km/h) production lap of the island on the way to another victory.

Honda CB450 (1965)

Engine:	Air-cooled dohc four-valve parallel twin
Capacity:	445cc (70 x 57.8mm)
Maximum power:	43bhp @ 8500rpm
Transmission:	Four-speed, chain final drive
Frame:	Steel twin cradle
Suspension:	Telescopic front; twin shocks rear
Brakes:	Drum front & rear
Weight:	411lb (187kg)
Top speed:	102mph (164km/h)

The Bonneville gained a worthy rival in 1968 when Norton introduced the Commando 750. Its engine was the 745cc pushrod parallel twin from the Atlas, tuned slightly with increased compression to give 58bhp. The key Commando feature was its chassis, which incorporated the 'Isolastic' system of rubber mounting, designed to isolate the vibration that had traditionally plagued the Atlas and other larger-capacity twins. Provided its rubber bushes were well maintained, the Isolastic system, developed by a team headed by former Rolls-Royce engineer Dr. Stefan Bauer, worked well.

There was plenty more that was good about the Commando. Its styling, complete with streamlined 'Fastback' tailpiece, was dramatic, and the beefy motor provided plenty of low-rev torque along with enough top-end for maximum speed of 115mph (185km/h). Equally importantly the new frame, in conjunction with Roadholder forks and Girling shocks, gave handling that was up to Norton's high standard. The Commando was fast, stable, and comfortable, and became a big hit on both sides of the Atlantic.

BSA had great trouble convincing motorcyclists that its unit-construction 650cc A65 Star and 500cc A50 Star twins were an improvement on their A10 and A7 predecessors, following their launch in 1962. Interest picked up slightly in 1964 with the launch of the tuned A65 Rocket, whose good low-rev manners were matched by lively acceleration and a top speed of 105mph (169km/h). The following year's twin-carburetor A65 Lightning was faster still and, like its 500cc equivalent the A50 Cyclone, could also be ordered in Clubman trim with tuned and dyno-tested engine, clip-on bars, rearset footrests, and humped seat.

In 1966 BSA replaced the Star model with the 40bhp single-carb Thunderbolt, which made a useful tourer, and introduced a new high-performance 650: the Spitfire MkII. This was a stylish flyer with a bright red gas tank, new twin-downtube frame, and a Lightning Clubman spec engine that was further tuned with Amal GP carbs to give 54bhp. It looked great, raced to 120mph (193km/h) and handled well. But the tuned motor was horribly fragile, and often exploded in expensive fashion. Despite introducing Spitfire MkIII and IV versions in following years, BSA moved slowly to cure the problems.

Above: The XS-1, powered by a 654cc parallel twin engine, was Yamaha's first four-stroke roadster. Launched in the US market in 1969, it sold well and led to a string of successful twins including the XS-2 and various XS650 models.

Left: Suzuki's T500 two-stroke was called the Titan in the US and the Cobra in Britain. Launched in 1967, the 44bhp twin changed very little during eight years of production.

Honda challenges MV's reign

MV Agusta and Honda dominated grand prix racing in the 1960s, between them winning every 500cc and 350cc world title, plus six in the 250cc class. Honda's Jim Redman led the way with six 250 and 350cc titles, riding mainly four-stroke fours, before Yamaha's growing two-stroke challenge forced Honda to build one of its greatest ever bikes. The RC166, a compact and brilliantly engineered 247cc in-line six that produced 60bhp at 18,000rpm, took Mike Hailwood to the title in 1966 and '67. Hailwood also won both years' 350cc championships on a bored-out 297cc version.

MV were masters of the 500cc class, which the Gallarate firm dominated following the rival Italian marques' withdrawal from GP racing in 1957. John Surtees won his fourth title for MV in 1960, then Gary Hocking won one before Hailwood joined the Italian team to win four consecutive 500cc championships.

'Mike the Bike' then signed for Honda, to set up one of the great periods in motorcycle grand prix racing history.

Riding a powerful but ill-handling 500cc Honda four, Hailwood fought a series of epic battles with MV's new star Giacomo Agostini. In 1966, the Honda broke down in the final round at Monza, handing Ago and MV the title by just six points. In 1967 the championship race was even closer. In the penultimate round the British ace broke the lap record and was leading by half a lap when his Honda stuck in top gear. Hailwood won the last race but Ago retained the championship, not on

points or even race wins, which were equal, but on his greater number of second place finishes. Honda promptly quit GP racing, having made a huge impact but failed to lift the biggest prize.

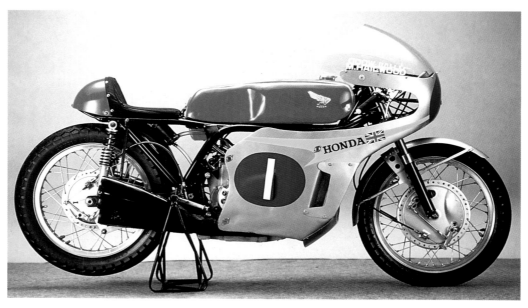

Above: *The great Mike Hailwood won the 250 and 350cc double for Honda in 1966 and '67, but just missed the 500cc title in both seasons.*

Above right: *Honda's brilliant six-cylinder RC166 produced 60bhp at 18,000rpm, and took Hailwood to the world championship in 1966.*

Top right: *Short-circuit ace Dave Croxford leads world champion Giacomo Agostini (right).*

By this time parallel twins were also being built in Japan by firms including Kawasaki, whose W2 Commander owed its design to BSA. In the 1950s Meguro, the firm taken over by Kawasaki, had copied the 500cc pre-unit A7 to create a model it called the M1. Kawasaki updated this, increased capacity to 624cc and renamed the bike the W1; then in 1967 released the tuned, twin-carburetor W2. This was built in both W2SS roadster and W2TT dual-purpose styles. It was good for 110mph (177km/h) and handled reasonably well, but suffered from typical parallel twin vibration. Although the W2 became the best-selling big bike in Japan, it made little impact abroad, where the Kawasaki name was still unfamiliar.

Honda introduced a more significant twin in 1965 with the CB450, which confirmed that the Japanese firm had set its sights on the big bike market. The 445cc Honda's style and layout echoed those of smaller models such as the 250cc CB72, but the CB450 differed by having twin overhead cams, and unusual torsion-bar valve springs. It had a humped gas tank, twin-cradle frame, and black paintwork that helped earn it the nickname 'Black Bomber' in Britain.

The CB450's 43bhp maximum gave an unexceptional top speed of just over 100mph (161km/h), but the motor was pleasantly smooth, flexible, and reliable. Despite being slightly heavy at 411lb (187kg) the Honda handled well too, and made a comfortable tourer. It lacked the style or speed to challenge home-built 650cc twins in Britain, but was reasonably popular in the US. The British firms had been warned.

The Japanese twin that made the biggest impact, especially in the US, was Yamaha's XS-1. The engine of Yamaha's first ever four-stroke was similar to BSA's Lightning in its 654cc capacity and internal dimensions, but differed in using a single overhead camshaft instead of pushrods, and in having a left-foot gearchange with a five-speed box. The maximum output of 53bhp gave respectable acceleration with a top speed of 105mph (169km/h), and vibration was reasonable for a big parallel twin.

Chassis performance was less impressive, due to a combination of thin-tube frame and under-damped suspension. But with its high bars and lean lines the XS-1 was an attractive machine, and its reliability and competitive price also contributed toward making it a hit when launched in the US in 1969. In subsequent years the twin was updated with XS-2 and XS650 models that did much to establish Yamaha worldwide.

Suzuki's two-stroke attack

Suzuki was also gradually making a name for itself with a parallel twin, although unlike most of its Japanese contemporaries the T500 was a two-stroke. The lively T500 was based on the T20 Super Six, a quick and agile 250cc twin that was launched in 1966. The bigger model arrived a year later, powered by a heavily-finned, 492cc air-cooled motor whose 44bhp peak output gave a maximum speed of over 100mph (161km/h).

Above: Handling was not the Suzuki T500's strongest point, but the quick and well priced two-stroke cornered reasonably well.

Left: Suzuki's T20 was a quick and light 250cc two-stroke twin whose six-speed gearbox earned it the name 'Super Six.' It was capable of 95mph (153km/h), handled well, was raced successfully, and did much to help make Suzuki popular following its launch in 1966.

Bridgestone 350 GTR (1966)

Engine:	Air-cooled two-stroke parallel twin
Capacity:	345cc
Maximum power:	37bhp @ 7500rpm
Transmission:	Six-speed, chain final drive
Frame:	Steel twin cradle
Suspension:	Telescopic front; twin shocks rear
Brakes:	Drum front & rear
Weight:	330lb (150kg)
Top speed:	95mph (153km/h)

Right: The 350 GTR was stylish, fast, and well built, but Bridgestone abandoned bike production in 1968 to concentrate on the tires for which the Japanese firm is still well known.

Below: Moto Guzzi's V7 Special, launched in 1969, helped earn the Italian marque a reputation for fast and comfortable roadsters, powered by transverse V-twin engines.

Like many Japanese bikes of the time the T500 made fewer friends with its spindly frame and crude suspension, which gave marginal high-speed handling. But the Suzuki was quick, well priced, and reliable, and it would remain in production until the mid-'70s, when it was updated with a disc brake and other modifications to create the GT500. The twin also formed the basis of the notoriously fast T500 racer, which was timed at over 150mph (241km/h) but earned the nickname 'Flexi-flyer' because of its scary handling.

The decade's other outstanding Japanese bike was another two-stroke parallel twin: the 350 GTR from Bridgestone, which built bikes as a sideline to its main business of tire production. Unlike Suzuki's reed-valve roadsters, the GTR used disc-valve induction, which helped give a peak output of 37bhp from its 345cc engine. The GTR was agile, well built, and offered lively acceleration plus a top speed of 95mph (153km/h). Many who rode the Bridgestone following its US launch in 1966 were impressed. Two years later the GTR became available in Europe but shortly afterward Bridgestone, under pressure from the rival Japanese manufacturers, quit bike production to concentrate on making tires.

While most British and Japanese firms concentrated on singles or parallel twins during the '60s, Italian manufacturers found alternative ways of combining more than one cylinder. Moto Guzzi came upon its now famous transverse V-twin format by accident, as the layout was first used in a three-wheeled mountain vehicle called the 3x3, produced for the Italian military. Few were built but Guzzi revised the motor and used it to power a 703cc bike called the V7, which was released in 1967 and became popular, largely due to the simplicity and reliability of its softly tuned 40bhp engine.

Guzzi's real impact came with the V7 Special, introduced two years later with an engine enlarged to 757cc to give 45bhp. In other respects the pushrod-operated V-twin motor – with car-style dry clutch, four-speed gearbox, and shaft final drive – was virtually unchanged. The Special was built for comfort and practicality, with high bars and a generous dual-seat. Nevertheless the

Easy Riders and Leather Boys

Two films highlighted the very different motorcycle cultures on opposite sides of the Atlantic in the 1960s. The decade's best and most influential movie was *Easy Rider*, the low-budget 1969 classic that portrayed Peter Fonda, Dennis Hopper, and Jack Nicholson riding across the USA toward the Mardi Gras in New Orleans on a pair of chopped Harleys.

Easy Rider was built around writer/producer Fonda's take on the way his country's spirit of freedom – represented by his character, Captain America – was being challenged. As well as featuring great bikes, good acting, excellent photography, and breathtaking scenery, *Easy Rider* pioneered the use of original recordings in a memorable soundtrack from artists including Steppenwolf and Jimi Hendrix.

By contrast, *The Leather Boys*, released in 1963, was a story of a young rocker in England. Many motorcyclists from London's Ace Café were used as extras, along with their Triumph and Norton bikes. While hardly a cinema classic, *The Leather Boys* had a better plot than 1968's psychedelic offering *Girl on a Motorcycle*, which starred Marianne Faithful and was also released with the title *Naked Under Leather*.

Best bike action in the movies came in *The Great Escape*, in which Steve McQueen memorably attempted to jump a barbed-wire fence on a bike that was supposed to be a captured German army BMW, and was in fact a lightly disguised Triumph Trophy 650. McQueen was a top rider who was picked to compete in America's International Six-Days Trial team. He did most of his own stunt riding

and also appears in the movie in a German uniform, chasing himself! But the big final jump was doubled by McQueen's friend and ISDT team-mate, Bud Ekins.

Guzzi handled well, was good for over 100mph (161km/h), and became highly regarded as an exotic grand tourer well suited to covering big distances in style.

Much of Ducati's production in the 1960s consisted of sohc singles, developed from the Gran Sport 100 of the mid-'50s. Among the best were the sporty models with low, clip-on handlebars, such as the 1962-model Diana 250 and its 1965 successor the Mach 1, which was capable of

Above: Clockwise from top right: The Leather Boys *starred rockers and their British twins;* Peter Fonda and Dennis Hopper on their Harleys in Easy Rider; *Steve McQueen prepares for fence-jumping action in* The Great Escape.

Right: Ducati's 350 Scrambler was launched in 1968 and was popular through the early '70s, especially in Italy and the US. The larger 450cc version of the Scrambler had a desmo engine, but many riders preferred the simpler 350.

Below: Ducati's Apollo prototype was good for over 120mph (193km/h), but the project was abandoned after the giant V4's excessive power and weight led to repeated tire problems.

Below: MV Agusta enthusiasts were disappointed in 1967 when the Italian marque's first four-cylinder roadster was a curiously styled and poorly performing 600cc tourer.

105mph (169km/h) when tuned with Ducati's accessory hot cam and straight-through pipe. The Mark 3 Desmo, launched in 1969, brought desmodromic valvegear to the street in a quick and fine-handling sportster. One of Ducati's biggest hits was the Scrambler, a stylish dual-purpose single that was launched in 1962, and updated in 1968 with Ducati's new 'wide-case' engine design, in 250cc, 350cc, and later 450cc capacities.

Ducati had suffered a very different outcome in 1964 when attempting to develop a 1257cc V4 cruiser, the Apollo. The giant bike was created at the request of the Italian firm's US importer, Berliner Corporation, which was very influential because it sold the majority of the factory's production in the early '60s. Fabio Taglioni's air-cooled sohc 90-degree V4 engine produced a phenomenal 100bhp in its original prototype form, but had to be detuned to 65bhp because no tires then produced could cope with its power and weight. That meant the Apollo was not viable, so the project was scrapped after only two bikes had been built.

MV finally builds a four

One four-cylinder Italian bike that did reach production was MV Agusta's 600cc tourer, introduced in 1967. Like Ducati, MV built mainly singles, but the Gallarate firm had long considered producing a four developed from its all-conquering racebikes. MV chief Count Domenico Agusta did not want to build a production bike that could be raced, so the four was a shaft-drive touring machine whose modest 52bhp output gave a top speed of barely 100mph (161km/h). Inevitably, given its ugly, angular styling and high price, the four was a flop.

Britain's most notable multi-cylinder machines also had controversial looks. In 1969, BSA Triumph finally released the three-cylinder model whose development had begun four years earlier. Due to pressure from BSA Triumph's American importers, the triple was launched both as the Triumph T150 Trident and BSA Rocket Three. The two bikes shared unusual, angular styling and a 740cc ohv pushrod engine that produced 58bhp and was very much a development of previous twins.

Left: Triumph's T150 Trident was fast and handled well, but its angular styling was unpopular and the British bike's 740cc three-cylinder engine gave many problems.

Triumph T150 Trident (1969)

Engine:	Air-cooled ohv pushrod six-valve triple
Capacity:	740cc (67 x 70mm)
Maximum power:	58bhp @ 7250rpm
Transmission:	Four-speed, chain final drive
Frame:	Steel single downtube
Suspension:	Telescopic front; twin shocks rear
Brakes:	Drum front & rear
Weight:	468lb (212kg)
Top speed:	120mph (193km/h)

The triples scorched to 120mph (193km/h) with a tuneful exhaust howl and acceleration to match any bike on the road. They used different chassis, with the twin-cradle BSA frame angling its motor forward more than the single-downtube Triumph equivalent. Both bikes handled well despite being quite heavy. But the three-cylinder engine was unreliable, and the bikes' specification, including kick-starter, four-speed gearbox, and drum brakes front and rear, confirmed they were very much machines of the 1960s. Few potential buyers liked either the slab-sided styling or the Trident's aquamarine color, and sales were poor.

Unfortunately for BSA Triumph, the triples' limitations were soon highlighted by the arrival of the outstanding motorcycle not merely of the decade, but of the century: Honda's CB750. When it was unveiled in 1968, the world's first mass-produced four-cylinder bike was clearly a uniquely refined roadster. Its 736cc engine produced 67bhp, and incorporated a chain-driven overhead camshaft and an electric starter. By this time many motorcyclists had grown up on smaller Hondas, and were rightly confident that the four would be reliable and oil-tight.

The CB750's twin-cradle frame was competent rather than outstanding. Despite firm suspension the high-handlebarred four could not match the high-speed stability of the British triples. But the Honda was smooth and fast, with a top speed of 120mph (193km/h). It also came with an efficient disc front brake and a very competitive price. The CB750 was a huge success both when launched in the US in mid-1969, and when it became available in Europe the following year. The first 'superbike' had ushered in a thrilling new era of performance and sophistication.

Below: With its reliable four-cylinder engine, electric starter, and disc front brake, Honda's CB750 revolutionized motorcycle design.

Superbikes Roar In
1970s

Honda CB750 (1970)

Engine:	Air-cooled sohc eight-valve four
Capacity:	736cc (61 x 63mm)
Maximum power:	67bhp @ 8000rpm
Transmission:	Five-speed, chain final drive
Frame:	Steel twin downtube
Suspension:	Telescopic front; twin shocks rear
Brakes:	Single disc front; drum rear
Weight:	506lb (230kg) wet
Top speed:	123mph (198km/h)

Previous page: Honda's stunning six-cylinder CBX1000, launched in 1978, showed how far technology had advanced during the decade.

Below: Honda's CB500 shared much of the larger four's speed and sophistication along with less weight and more agile handling.

Right: The original CB750 was a fast and stylish bike producing a throaty roar from its four pipes, but later versions were slower and quieter.

Modern motorcycling began in the 1970s. Honda's spectacular CB750 heralded a decade that saw an explosion of performance, sophistication, and mechanical variety, ending with the introduction of huge, six-cylinder machines that would have been unthinkable ten years earlier.

This revolution was led by the Japanese firms, especially Honda and Kawasaki, whose multi-cylinder 'superbikes' and high-performing smaller machines dramatically changed motorcyclists' expectations. The basic format of air-cooled engine, tubular steel frame, telescopic front forks, and twin rear shocks remained. The Japanese introduced features such as more powerful engines, electric starters, and disc brakes, plus much improved reliability and quality of construction.

Motorcycling was changing fast in more ways than just the machines and their country of origin. Outside the US many motorcyclists still did not own a car, and used bikes for everyday transport. But sidecars had almost disappeared, and the days of the motorcycle as a family vehicle were gone. In place of black leather jackets and waxed-cotton, the new breed of rider wore full-face helmets, colorful jackets, sometimes even racing-style one-piece leathers.

Although Japan quickly rose to become the dominant motorcycle manufacturing nation, by no means all the best bikes came from the East. Italian firms had long been leading producers of small-capacity machines, and turned to superbike manufacture with a variety of engine formats. The Italians could not match Japanese levels of reliability, but offered style plus superior chassis engineering that gave notably better high-speed handling.

Other countries' motorcycle industries struggled to compete. Harley-Davidson and BMW continued with their familiar twin-cylinder engine layouts, their erstwhile dominance by now a distant memory. The '70s would prove disastrous for the British motorcycle industry, recently the world's largest, as most of its remaining great names went out of business.

The bike that highlighted how far behind the British firms were, and did most to kill them off, was the CB750. On pure performance, Honda's four was not significantly ahead of the Trident and Rocket Three triples that Triumph and BSA had launched in 1969. The Japanese and British

bikes were closely matched on straight-line speed, and the triples generally handled better than the four, whose high bars revealed Honda's initial focus on the US market.

Where the CB750 scored was by backing up its smooth acceleration, throaty exhaust note, and top speed of over 120mph (193km/h) with an unprecedented degree of user-friendliness. The 736cc four had only a single overhead camshaft and two valves per cylinder, unlike Honda's dohc, 16-valve racing fours that preceded it. But it revved reliably to 8000rpm and beyond, didn't leak oil, and required far less maintenance than the British pushrod triples.

The CB750 was a huge success, not least in the US where it initially sold for more than the $1400 retail price, and where veteran racer Dick Mann gave Honda a further boost by winning the Daytona 200 on a modified four in 1970. The modern superbike had arrived, and motorcycling had taken a huge leap forward.

Yoshirou Harada, who headed the CB750 design team, had intended to uprate the model with a dohc engine after two or three years. That did not happen, and during the early '70s the four was detuned slightly to reduce emissions. Honda did, however, produce some excellent smaller-capacity fours, starting with the CB500, released in 1971, which combined 50bhp output with a lighter and more maneuverable chassis. The CB350, which followed two years later, was more compact and agile still. According to no less an authority than Soichiro Honda, it was the finest, smoothest Honda ever built.

Honda and his long-time business partner Takeo Fujisawa retired on the same day in 1973. The company they had built was by far the world's largest motorcycle firm and had also moved successfully into car production. Unusually, both men had prevented their sons from joining the company, and retained only honorary positions after retirement, rather than becoming directors as was normal in Japan.

Honda had plenty of competition when it came to building light, revvy roadsters, not least from Yamaha. Alongside its XS-2 and later XS650 four-stroke twins, developed from the XS-1, the firm built fast and popular two-strokes. The 350cc YR5, released in 1970, was the biggest of a

Top: Suzuki's T250 Hustler was an updated version of the T20 Super Six two-stroke twin, and was more stylish as well as more powerful.

Above: The CB350 four handled superbly and was reasonably successful in the US, but was too expensive to be sold in many European markets.

Left: Yamaha's YR5 provided plenty of performance thanks to its revvy 350cc twin-cylinder engine and light weight. It was the first in a long line of superb two-stroke middleweights.

Kawasaki H2 (Mach IV) (1972)

Engine:	Air-cooled two-stroke triple
Capacity:	748cc (71 x 63mm)
Maximum power:	74bhp @ 6800rpm
Transmission:	Five-speed, chain final drive
Frame:	Steel twin downtube
Suspension:	Telescopic front; twin shocks rear
Brakes:	Disc front; drum rear
Weight:	454lb (206kg)
Top speed:	120mph (193km/h)

Above: Kawasaki's 500cc H1 triple had earned a
fearsome reputation for high performance and evil
handling by the time this disc-braked model was
produced in the early 1970s.

family of 250, 200, and 125cc parallel twins. The bigger model produced 36bhp, screamed to
over 90mph (145km/h), and weighed just 330lb (150kg). The YR5 and its RD350 successors were
fast, fun, and brilliant value for money.

The firm that made an even bigger impression for fast and exciting two-strokes was Kawasaki.
The line had started in the late 1960s with the H1, also known as the Mach III, a 498cc air-cooled
triple that was very popular in the US. Three key figures ensured the Mach III's success there: it
made 60bhp, weighed barely 400lb (182kg), and cost under $1000. It could beat almost anything
away from the lights, and sold in huge numbers.

Owners soon found that the Mach III's highly tuned motor ran feebly until its power suddenly
arrived at 5000rpm, when the bike often leapt forward with enough force to lift its front wheel or
overwhelm its relatively simple and insubstantial chassis. Stories of the triple's scary performance
earned it a fearsome reputation. In 1972 Kawasaki reacted in the spirit of the times – by
launching a bigger, even more powerful follow-up, the 748cc H2, or Mach IV.

The H2 produced 74bhp at 6800rpm, 14bhp more than the smaller triple, and accelerated even
harder to a top speed of 120mph (193km/h). Despite a slightly wider power band it was barely
more practical than the Mach III. Few owners minded that, as they gripped the high handlebars
tight while the H2 streaked to 100mph (161km/h) from a standstill in less than 13 seconds.

Kawasaki had done little to improve the original triple's chassis, and the H2 was also prone to
wobbles. It did at least have not only a friction steering damper but also a frame lug for fitment of
a hydraulic damper, a useful addition. Many owners were prepared to accept those chassis
failings, because for generating speed and excitement, few bikes could even approach the H2.

Suzuki also made an impact with a 750cc two-stroke triple, but the GT750 was a much bigger,
softer all-rounder, with bulbous styling and a liquid-cooled engine that produced 67bhp at
6500rpm. The GT750's initials stood for Grand Tourer, and the bike lived up to its name. It was
built more for flexibility and comfort than outright performance, and despite a respectable
110mph (177km/h) top speed was best suited to cruising in leisurely fashion as its weight, chassis
design, and upright riding position did not reward aggressive riding.

Right: The 748cc H2 triple's raw power, high bars,
and relatively light weight combined to make the
hydraulic steering damper, visible below the tank,
a very useful accessory.

Left: Suzuki's original 1972-model GT750J was admired for its water-cooled two-stroke triple engine's smoothness and flexibility, rather than its outright performance. Pink paintwork and drum front brake were quickly revised.

Below: The final GT750B of 1977 was slightly more powerful than the original model, and had a twin disc front brake. The triple earned a loyal following, being known as the 'Water Buffalo' in the US and the 'Kettle' in Britain.

Decline of the two-strokes

Suzuki developed the triple over the years before eventually it became a victim, like other two-strokes including the firm's own quick and capable air-cooled GT550 triple, of tightening emissions regulations, especially in the US. Last in the line was the GT750B of 1977. By then Suzuki had all but abandoned its alternative attempt at a luxury bike, the RE-5, powered by a 497cc liquid-cooled Wankel rotary engine. The 62bhp RE-5, launched in 1975, was smooth and sophisticated; but also far too heavy, complex, and expensive.

A rival rotary, Sachs-DKW's air-cooled 294cc W2000, was simpler and lighter – but slower, barely cheaper and equally unsuccessful. By contrast, fellow German firm BMW stuck to its simpler air-cooled boxers, production of which was moved from Munich to Berlin. BMW had introduced its 745cc R75/5 back in 1969, along with smaller R60/5 and R50/5 siblings. These retained the familiar pushrod-operated flat twin engine layout, but abandoned the Earles fork front suspension system used during the 1960s.

The German firm even made an attempt to liven up the appearance of its traditionally black or white roadsters. Other colors were introduced, and in 1972 the R75/5 came in 'toaster tank' form with a smaller, chrome-sided fuel tank. That option did not last long but the shaft-drive twin's smooth cruising ability, stable handling, refinement, and reliability made it popular in some markets, despite a high price.

Those attributes also applied to the striking flagship that BMW introduced in 1973. The R90S was the sports version of the standard R90/6 boxer, launched at the same time, and used a tuned, 67bhp version of the new 898cc motor. It featured a steering damper, larger fuel tank, and second front brake disc. The R90S also incorporated the novelty of a headlamp fairing which, along with a striking smoked paint scheme, gave a unique look.

More importantly, the fairing allowed the BMW's rider to make full use of the impressive performance. The German bike's blend of 125mph (201km/h) top speed, relaxed cruising ability, excellent handling, reliability, and high-quality finish put it in a league of its own in 1973. The BMW was very expensive, costing twice as much a Honda's CB750 in many markets, and was

BMW R90S (1973)	
Engine:	Air-cooled ohv pushrod four-valve flat twin
Capacity:	898cc (90 x 70.6mm)
Maximum power:	67bhp @ 7000rpm
Transmission:	Five-speed, shaft final drive
Frame:	Steel twin downtube
Suspension:	Telescopic front; twin shocks rear
Brakes:	Twin discs front; single disc rear
Weight:	474lb (215kg) wet
Top speed:	125mph (201km/h)

Top right: BMW attempted to give its 1972-model R75/5 more style with a chrome-sided fuel tank, but the 'toaster tank' was not popular with the marque's generally conservative customers.

Above: With its headlamp fairing, smoked paint scheme, and blend of high cruising speed and fine handling, the R90S was one of the outstanding superbikes of the 1970s.

outsold by the cheaper R90/6. But as well as being an outstanding bike, it showed the way forward for motorcycle design. The boxer even made a useful racer, as Reg Pridmore's victory in the 1976 US Superbike championship proved.

The era's other most memorable German bike was more expensive still, and very different. Friedel Münch had begun developing his Mammut (Mammoth) back in the mid-'60s, around a 1085cc NSU car engine. During the '70s he built small numbers, refining the design along the way. The fuel-injected version of the Mammut produced over 100bhp, and had unbeatable straight-line performance despite its vast weight. Production would continue until the early 1980s, with capacities of up to 1500cc.

By contrast, Spain's bike manufacturers had concentrated on small-capacity machines since the country's motorcycle industry had been established after the war. While Sanglas stuck to four-stroke singles, Montesa, Derbi, Bultaco, and Ossa produced a wide variety of on- and off-road machinery, mostly with two-stroke engines of less than 250cc. The Spanish firms were successful in road-racing, with Ossa's Santiago Herrero and Derbi's Angel Nieto prominent.

The best known Spanish roadster was Bultaco's Metralla, a two-stroke single that was repeatedly updated through the 1960s and 1970s. But the Spanish firms, whose home market had been protected by import restrictions, struggled in the more competitive climate that followed General Franco's death in 1975. By the end of the decade, they would be crippled by falling sales and workers' disputes. That would leave them vulnerable to take-over by the Japanese giants, especially Honda and Yamaha, which were increasingly adopting a policy of 'globalization' by establishing factories all over the world.

Kawasaki continued to concentrate mainly on large capacity motorcycles, but the other three Japanese firms built a huge variety of small bikes and scooters. Most were forgettable but one that stood out was Yamaha's popular FS1-E, a 49cc moped that was introduced in Britain in 1973, after 16-year-olds had been restricted to machines with 'pedal assistance.' Once its pedals were locked in place, the 'Fizzy' provided its teenage rider with a top speed of over 40mph (64km/h) and excitement out of all proportion to the bike's capacity. Rival 'Sixteener Specials' included Honda's SS50, Suzuki's AP50, and Italian flyers from Garelli and Fantic.

Trail bike heritage

Yamaha's success with small-capacity dual-purpose bikes dated back to the '60s, and included the early-'70s DT175 two-stroke on which many people had experienced trail riding for the first time. The 1977-model XT500, whose 30bhp sohc four-stroke single engine gave generous amounts of low-rev torque, initiated a new era of larger dual-purpose motorcycles. Two years later it faced new competition from Honda's XL500S, developed from the XR500 enduro single.

Meanwhile the British industry, which had turned from the single to the parallel twin, had been struggling to modernize that engine layout. BSA Triumph had been in deep financial trouble from the start of the decade, and had needed its redesigned 1971 twins to be a big success. But the BSA Lightning 650 and Triumph Bonneville 650 were a disaster. Developed at the expensive Umberslade Hall research and development facility, they had new frames that gave a much higher seat, and were so unpopular that the chassis had to be hastily redesigned.

The firm hit further problems with another twin, the Edward Turner-designed dohc 350 that was due to be sold as the BSA Fury and Triumph Bandit. Turner's prototype ran so poorly that it was abandoned. The racing triples campaigned successfully in Formula 750 races at Daytona and elsewhere showed that British bikes could still be competitive, but their days were numbered. At the end of 1971, BSA announced that the group had lost £8 million during the year. Chairman Eric Turner resigned, and the competition department was closed.

After a further big loss the following year, the BSA/Triumph group was merged with Norton Villiers to form Norton Villiers Triumph. The aim was to create a stronger company backed by government finance, but NVT ran into problems almost immediately when attempting to rationalize by moving Triumph production from its traditional Meriden factory to BSA's old Birmingham plant, which built Trident engines. The Triumph workers objected and occupied the Meriden factory for 18 months, delaying Trident production because components were kept there.

Triumph did at least manage to produce one more outstanding bike in the X-75 Hurricane, an eye-catching version of the 750cc triple that was conceived by the firm's US agent and designed

Above left: This 1978-model Bultaco Metralla 250 GTS was the last of the Spanish firm's simple but effective Metralla two-stroke singles.

Above: Future world champion Barry Sheene discusses a Bultaco TSS350 with his father Frank and the marque's boss, Don Paco Bulto.

Below: This BSA 650 Lightning was built in 1971, the first year of the controversial 'oil-in-frame' twins with their much taller seats.

Kawasaki Z1 (1973)

Engine:	Air-cooled dohc eight-valve four
Capacity:	903cc (66 x 66mm)
Maximum power:	82bhp @ 8500rpm
Transmission:	Five-speed, chain final drive
Frame:	Steel twin downtube
Suspension:	Telescopic front; twin shocks rear
Brakes:	Single disc front; drum rear
Weight:	542lb (246kg) wet
Top speed:	132mph (212km/h)

Above and top right: Triumph's X-75 Hurricane was a uniquely stylish version of the triple.

Below: As well as a powerful four-cylinder engine, the Z1 boasted very attractive looks.

in the States by Craig Vetter, a custom bike builder and fairing manufacturer. With its wasp-waisted tank-seat unit, kicked-out front forks, and a trio of mufflers on its right side, the Hurricane looked stunning. As arguably the first 'factory custom' it made a lasting impression, although fewer than 1200 were built.

There was only one multi-cylinder machine at the top of most motorcycle enthusiast's wish list in 1973, however. Kawasaki's Z1 blasted onto the scene, its 903cc dohc four-cylinder engine producing 82bhp – fully 15bhp more than Honda's CB750. That was enough to give the Kawasaki a top speed of over 130mph (209km/h), making it a clear 10mph (16km/h) faster than any other bike on the road. The eight-valve motor was also smooth, flexible, and outstandingly reliable, and earned a reputation for being bulletproof even when tuned.

The Z1 was also very good-looking, with rounded lines and a compact rear duck-tail that neatly offset the muscular air-cooled engine. But the Kawasaki's combination of power and 542lb (246kg) of weight was at times too much for its relatively ordinary chassis. To combat high-speed instability many owners fitted steering dampers and aftermarket rear shock units, built by specialists such as Marzocchi of Italy.

Such was the Z1's performance lead that Kawasaki did little to change it, merely altering cosmetic and minor details before adding a second front brake disc in 1976, when the bike was renamed the Z900. By that time it had become known as the King, and had earned Kawasaki a lasting reputation for power and strength.

Harley-Davidson was also laying the foundations of a dynasty of its own, in a very different way. In 1971, the US firm's styling chief, Willie G. Davidson, had created the Super Glide, using a collection of styling cues including a large 'boat-tail' rear end. The Super Glide was not a particularly strong seller, but it earned Harley plenty of attention, and provided a platform for future models.

Meanwhile, Milwaukee's V-twins were attracting a new breed of custom builders, led by Arlen Ness. The 'Bay Area' style (Ness and others were based around San Francisco) was longer and lower than the traditional chopper look. Radical customs such as Ness's Accel Bike and Strictly Business inspired many Harley owners to modify their own bikes, using components from both Milwaukee and aftermarket specialists.

Meanwhile Italian manufacturers were establishing their own distinctive styles and engine formats. Laverda, based at Breganze in north-eastern Italy, had begun producing parallel twins in the late 1960s, in 654cc and then 744cc capacities. The most famous twin was the SFC, introduced in 1971. Designed primarily for endurance racing and painted orange, it featured a half-fairing, clip-on bars, rearset footrests, and single seat. The SFC's tuned, sohc engine produced 70bhp, enough for a top speed of 125mph (201km/h). The SFC was produced in small numbers until 1976, gaining power and an uprated chassis along the way.

Laverda also launched the format for which it would become best known when in 1973 an additional cylinder was added, creating the 981cc triple that was initially called simply the 3C. The bigger dohc motor produced a claimed 80bhp, and the 3C combined simple but attractive styling with a competent chassis. Relatively few were exported but the 135mph (217km/h) triple was already making an impression.

Italy's most famous racing marque remained MV Agusta, which had dominated 500cc grand prix racing for more than a decade, without releasing a roadgoing replica. Finally MV's autocratic boss Count Domenico Agusta relented, and in 1972 the firm introduced the 750 Sport, a stylish roadburner with a 743cc dohc four-cylinder engine and high quality chassis.

Like the racebikes, the Sport used gears to drive its overhead camshafts, though it also retained the tourer's shaft final drive, reportedly because Count Agusta did not want owners to race it. The tuned motor produced 65bhp, enough for a top speed of 115mph (185km/h) plus impressive acceleration. 'In a straight drag with a Kawasaki Z1 it lost only a few yards up to 100mph [161km/h],' reported British magazine *Bike*.

Handling was generally good, too, although the MV's heavy drive shaft gave the rear suspension a difficult time. Early models had a Grimeca front drum brake, which was replaced by twin discs in 1973. The exotic Sport could be ordered with a full- or half-fairing, or a flyshield. But despite its high price the bike cost so much to make that it was not profitable for MV, which was also making little money on its small-capacity singles.

Above: The Z1's handling did not match the performance of its magnificent 82bhp engine, leading to much work for aftermarket frame specialists and shock absorber manufacturers.

Above: Harley's Super Glide featured an unusual 'boat-tail' rear end that was removed by many dealers, but the eye-catching V-twin played an important part in the firm's revival.

Left: Laverda's raw and single-minded 750 SFC parallel twin was a street-legal production racer, and was painted orange to help factory lap-scorers spot it during an endurance race.

MV Agusta 750 Sport (1973)	
Engine:	Air-cooled dohc eight-valve four
Capacity:	743cc (65 x 56mm)
Maximum power:	65bhp at 7900rpm
Transmission:	Five-speed, shaft final drive
Frame:	Steel twin downtube
Suspension:	Telescopic front; twin shocks rear
Brakes:	Twin discs front; drum rear
Weight:	506lb (230kg) dry
Top speed:	115mph (185km/h)

Above right: MV Agusta's 750 Sport was the race-replica four the Italian firm's fans had hoped for, although very few could afford one.

Below: Ducati's Desmo 250 produced only 30bhp but had styling and handling in abundance.

Opposite below left: The 900SS provided storming performance and superb handling.

Opposite below right: British ace Paul Smart's victory in the prestigious Imola 200 race in 1972 gave the Bologna factory a huge boost.

Ducati also progressed from building singles to superbikes, starting when chief engineer Fabio Taglioni combined a pair of cylinders at 90 degrees to form a V-twin. The basic single-pot engine design had been uprated over the years, notably when being given desmodromic valvegear in 1969. In 1973 the Desmo range of 250, 350, and 450cc singles was restyled and given a distinctive yellow finish by Leopoldo Tartarini, the former Ducati works racer who would later found Italjet.

Taglioni's first V-twin was the 750GT, launched in 1971. Its 748cc sohc engine used conventional valve springs, produced 50bhp, and was a softly tuned all-rounder. Two years later came the 750 Sport, which provided extra performance from a hotted-up, 56bhp motor. The Sport was slim, light and racy, with clip-on handlebars, rearset footrests, single seat, and bright yellow paintwork. With a top speed of 125mph (201km/h) it was fast enough to show a clean pair of Conti pipes to most rival roadsters.

Ducati's most significant event was its victory in the prestigious 1972 Imola 200-mile (322km) race. Factory riders Paul Smart and Bruno Spagiarri finished first and second on rapid 750cc V-twins fitted with desmo valvegear. Ducati then produced a roadgoing replica, which was popular so more were built, named the 750 Super Sport instead of Imola Replica as before. The sleek half-faired roadster was silver, like the fully-faired racer, and featured a tuned 748cc desmo motor. It provided a unique blend of raw performance, stable handling, and minimalist style.

Ducati built only about 200 units of the 750SS, but in 1975 used it as the basis of the bike for which the firm would become best known: the 900SS. This was powered by an enlarged 864cc version of the bevel-drive desmo V-twin, which produced 79bhp. Like the smaller model the 900SS was a single-minded street racer, with unfiltered 40mm Dell'Orto carbs, booming Conti pipes, half-fairing, clip-on bars, rearsets, single seat, firm suspension, and twin Brembo front discs. In many respects it was the quintessential Italian superbike.

The uncompromising 900SS had no electric starter or anything else that was not needed for pure performance. It thundered to a top speed of 135mph (217km/h), and handled superbly thanks to a combination of rigid chassis, relatively light weight, long wheelbase, and taut suspension. Although expensive, demanding of maintenance and too extreme for many riders, it had few rivals as a pure-bred sporting superbike for road or production racing use.

Ducati's softer V-twin

Ducati introduced another significant model in 1975 with the more versatile 860GT. Angular styling by car designer Giorgetto Giugiario was matched with a softly tuned motor that produced 70bhp. High handlebars did little to boost handling or high-speed comfort. But the following year's 860GTS, featuring lower bars, an electric starter, and second front brake disc, was a capable sports-tourer with plenty of character.

Ducati was not the only Bologna-based firm producing V-twins. Alfonso Morini had begun making bikes under the name MM in the 1920s, and had ridden one to a class win in the 1927 Italian Grand Prix. After the war he built single-cylinder roadsters and some successful racers under his own name. In 1974, Moto Morini introduced a pair of roadsters, the 3¹/₂ Strada and 3¹/₂ Sport, powered by an air-cooled, 72-degree pushrod V-twin engine.

The standard Strada model's raised handlebars and dual-seat made for a practical all-rounder. But it was the stylish Sport, with its low bars and humped seat, that attracted more attention. Higher compression and a hotter camshaft provided extra power, and little V-twin's 39bhp output gave a top speed of just over 100mph (161km/h). With firm suspension and just 337lb (153kg) of weight the Morini handled superbly, too. Although impractical and too expensive to sell in large numbers, it earned a loyal following.

The Italian firm best known for long-distance bikes was Moto Guzzi, which found a profitable niche in 1971 with a US export version of its 757cc V7 Special. The California featured higher bars plus the screen and panniers with which the Special was commonly fitted, and was well received. For 1972 Guzzi enlarged its pushrod V-twin engine to 844cc, added a five-speed gearbox and made the shaft-driven California more freely available, confirming the arrival of a tourer that would be a mainstay of the range for decades to come.

In 1971 Guzzi had also introduced an important high-performance model, the V7 Sport. This used a more compact and powerful version of the firm's transverse V-twin engine, with capacity reduced slightly to 748cc to allow entry in 750cc races. Peak output was rated at 52bhp, roughly

Above: Ducati's 1973-model 750 Sport did not have desmodromic valvegear, but the V-twin's performance and racy look made it popular.

Ducati 900SS (1975)	
Engine:	Air-cooled sohc four-valve 90-degree V-twin
Capacity:	864cc (86 x 74.4mm)
Maximum power:	79bhp at 7000rpm
Transmission:	Five-speed, chain final drive
Frame:	Steel ladder
Suspension:	Telescopic front; twin shocks rear
Brakes:	Twin discs front; single disc rear
Weight:	414lb (188kg) wet
Top speed:	135mph (217km/h)

Right: *Ducati launched its sports-touring V-twin line in 1975 with the GT860. Its softly tuned 864cc engine was impressively flexible, but the angular GT's performance was marred by its exposed riding position, marginal high-speed stability, and lack of an electric starter – though one could be ordered as an accessory.*

Below: *A racy riding position, bold styling, and superb handling helped earn Moto Morini's 3¹/₂ Sport many admirers, even though the little 344cc V-twin produced a mere 39bhp.*

Opposite below: *Moto Guzzi's original Le Mans 850 offered a unique blend of styling, V-twin performance, and stable handling.*

70bhp at the crankshaft. An alternator on the front of the crank allowed engineer Lino Tonti to design a lower frame with top rails between the cylinders, where the old dynamo had been.

The V7 Sport was an elegant bike, with lime-green paintwork plus, on the first 150 units, a red frame. Its motor required revving hard, and responded with smooth cruising and 125mph (201km/h) top speed. The Sport was stable, and cornered well despite the heavy shaft-drive system. For 1974 it was replaced by the 750S, featuring twin front discs instead of the Sport's twin-leading-shoe drum. Then came the 750S3 which, like the 850cc T3 tourer introduced at the same time, also featured a rear disc. Guzzi's linked system used the handlebar lever to work one front disc, with the foot pedal operating the other front plus the rear disc, and was highly rated by most riders who tried it.

Guzzi's most famous model followed in 1976, when the 750S3 was enlarged to 844cc and revamped to create the 850 Le Mans. With its small headlamp fairing, distinctive lipped seat, and its transverse V-twin engine's cylinders on display, the Le Mans was arguably the most beautiful of the great Italian superbikes of the 1970s. Increased compression ratio, unfiltered 36mm Dell'Orto carbs, and a free-breathing exhaust gave a peak output of 80bhp, 8bhp up on the 750S, plus stronger midrange.

Top speed was 130mph (209km/h), and the Le Mans' fairing and racy riding position meant the performance was very usable. Firm suspension helped give stable handling, and ensured the Le Mans' status as one of the most desirable machines on the road. But Alejandro de Tomaso, the Argentinean car baron who had bought both Guzzi and Benelli in the early '70s, was reluctant to invest in the firm, and the Le Mans' appeal gradually faded.

The most powerful and fastest of the era's great Italian superbikes was Laverda's Jota. This was a tuned version of the 3CL triple, created by Slater Brothers, the firm's British importer. Laverda had produced the 3CL in 1976 by modifying the 3C with cast wheels, triple discs, and a tail fairing. Brothers Roger and Richard Slater tuned its 981cc dohc engine with high-compression pistons, factory endurance race cams, and a free-breathing exhaust. They also added rearset footrests and a humped seat.

Laverda's snarling triple

The result was the Jota: a snarling, 90bhp brute that ran roughly below 4000rpm, then came alive with vicious acceleration and a soulful exhaust bellow as it charged toward a 140mph (225km/h) top speed that made it the world's fastest roadster in 1976. Handling was good provided the rider was prepared to manhandle the big, heavy triple. One who did was Slaters' racer Pete Davies, who dominated the British production series. Although the tuned triple was officially a UK-only model, it was sold elsewhere. When Laverda enlarged the motor to 1116cc to create the 1200 model in 1978, Slaters again produced a tuned version, the Mirage. The name was later used by Laverda for the standard 1200.

Like Laverda, Benelli entered the big-bike market with a parallel twin, the Tornado 650, before moving on to multi-cylinder superbikes. The Tornado, which entered production in 1971, was a torquey but unexceptional roadster. It was followed three years later by the more glamorous 750 Sei, powered by motorcycling's first transverse six-cylinder engine.

Ironically, the Sei (Italian for Six) was not particularly fast, as its softly-tuned, 71bhp sohc engine meant the broad Benelli ran out of speed at 115mph (185km/h). The 748cc engine, which resembled one-and-a-half Honda CB500 units, was flexible and smooth, if not particularly reliable. For a bike that weighed 484lb (220kg) the Sei handled well, and made a pleasant all-rounder. But that wasn't enough to make it popular given the inevitably high price. The same was true of Benelli's four-cylinder models, the 500 Quattro and the diminutive 254, whose capacity was just 231cc.

Another glamorous superbike whose performance didn't live up to its price was Harley-Davidson's 1977-model XLCR1000 Café Racer, a big, black V-twin with a headlamp fairing and plenty of aggressive attitude. Such a sporty-looking V-twin was a departure for Harley, although the American firm had a road-racing pedigree of sorts. Following parent group AMF's purchase of Aermacchi, Italian ace Walter Villa had won four 250 and 350cc world titles on Harley-badged two-stroke twins from the former Aermacchi factory at Varese in northern Italy. Harley's roadgoing range also included small-capacity two-strokes from the same source.

Top: *The first high-performance Guzzi was the 750 Sport, launched in 1971 with adjustable bars, 70bhp output, and big front drum brake.*

Above: *Guzzi's 1975-model 750 S3 was notable for its striking paintwork and the linked triple disc brake system that gave the bike its name.*

Moto Guzzi Le Mans 850 (1976)

Engine:	Air-cooled ohv pushrod four-valve 90-degree transverse V-twin
Capacity:	844cc (83 x 78mm)
Maximum power:	80bhp @ 7300rpm
Transmission:	Five-speed, shaft final drive
Frame:	Steel spine
Suspension:	Telescopic front; twin shocks rear
Brakes:	Twin discs front; single disc rear (linked system)
Weight:	476lb (216kg) wet
Top speed:	130mph (209km/h)

Laverda Jota (1976)

Engine:	Air-cooled dohc six-valve triple
Capacity:	981cc (75 x 74mm)
Maximum power:	90bhp at 8000rpm
Transmission:	Five-speed, chain final drive
Frame:	Steel twin downtube
Suspension:	Telescopic front; twin shocks rear
Brakes:	Twin discs front; single disc rear
Weight:	521lb (236kg) wet
Top speed:	140mph (225km/h)

Above: Laverda's most famous models, the 1200cc Mirage (left) and 1000cc Jota, began their existence as standard triples that were tuned by the Italian firm's British importer.

Right: Benelli's 650 Tornado parallel twin was launched in 1971, with this 750S following two years later, featuring a new front brake. Many parts were rubber-mounted against vibration.

The XLCR was built in Milwaukee and was powered by the 998cc pushrod-operated V-twin engine from the Sportster, unchanged except for black finish and a siamesed exhaust that maintained its 61bhp peak output. A new frame, box-section swingarm, alloy wheels, and triple discs gave a sporty specification. The Café Racer's fairing and flat bars made it a useful bike for highway cruising, but its high-rev vibration, 115mph (185km/h) top speed, and four-speed gearbox confirmed that this was no sports bike, and sales were poor.

Harley had proved it could build a rapid V-twin with the XR750 dirt-track racer. Introduced unsuccessfully in 1970, the XR was revamped with a new aluminum engine two years later, and took Mark Brelsford to the first of the bike's many championships, which included a hat-trick for Jay Springsteen from 1976-78. Another XR750-mounted star was Evel Knievel, the stunt rider

who became a legend for the number of cars and buses he jumped over, and for the number of bones he broke.

Harley's most significant roadster was the laid-back Low Rider, launched in 1977. Developed relatively inexpensively using parts from several other models, the Low Rider derived a new look from its short suspension, long wheelbase, and low, stepped seat. The bike was harshly suspended, but it had plenty of character and appealed to many Harley enthusiasts, for whom style was far more important than performance.

Harley was still struggling financially but the situation was even worse in Britain, where the recently formed Norton Villiers Triumph group, handicapped by the Meriden workers' sit-in, had lost several million pounds in 1974. There was one final fling for Triumph, in the following year's T160 Trident, which combined handsome new styling with significant improvements over the T150 triple. The 740cc motor's peak output was unchanged, but it finally gained an electric starter and left-foot gearchange.

The motor was angled forward in a new frame that improved handling and ground clearance, in conjunction with new forks and a longer swingarm. The Trident was heavy, at over 500lb (227kg), but cornered well. It was also fast, with a 125mph (201km/h) top speed plus stirring top-end acceleration. Despite a high price and some unreliability, it was popular, with roughly 7000 being sold in 1975.

NVT advertised the Trident alongside Norton's Commando, highlighting the 'Power Choice' between three or two cylinders. In 1973 the Commando motor had been enlarged to 830cc, adding to its already strong mid-range. But although both bikes had their supporters, the end was approaching for NVT. By late 1975 the group was in receivership, the Small Heath factory was about to be closed, and NVT had turned its attention to the humble Easy Rider moped, assembled using parts bought from abroad.

Ironically the only NVT factory still building big bikes was the Triumph plant at Meriden, where the much publicized workers' sit-in had led in 1975 to the creation of the Meriden Co-operative, backed by government subsidies. Triumph had enlarged its 649cc parallel twin engine to 744cc, creating the T140 Bonneville, which had more mid-range torque, albeit with more

Above: The Benelli 750 Sei's six shiny exhaust pipes emphasized its unique engine layout, but the softly tuned Italian multi lacked the power and speed to justify its inevitably high price.

Below left and right: Harley's XLCR Café Racer had the long, low look of a racy V-twin sports machine, but its modest 61bhp output and heavy handling told a different story.

Racing's Two-stroke Takeover

In the early '70s, MV Agusta's domination of 500cc grand prix racing came under increasing threat from two-strokes, led by Yamaha. The Italian factory's most successful rider was Giacomo Agostini, who won seven consecutive 500cc titles on the roaring red 'Gallarate fire engines' before Britain's Phil Read took over, retaining the championship for MV in 1973 and '74. Ironically it was Italian idol Agostini who became the first two-stroke

500cc champion, when he won on a straight-four Yamaha in 1975.

MV, its 17-year winning streak ended, had no answer to the more powerful two-strokes, and Barry Sheene won the next two championships on a square-four RG500 Suzuki. Yamaha's Kenny Roberts then began a US takeover of grand prix racing when he arrived in 1978 to win the first of three consecutive titles, pioneering a power-sliding riding style adapted from dirt-track racing.

Roberts also won many races on arguably the most famous two-stroke of all, Yamaha's TZ750. The straight-four TZ, whose engine was essentially a pair of TZ350 twins side-by-side, won many big races including the Daytona 200, and in 1977 it was ridden to the first Formula 750 world championship by Canadian Steve Baker.

Ironically the TZ's most memorable victory was not a road-race, but Roberts' dirt-track

triumph at the Indianapolis Mile in 1975. Yamaha's four-stroke twin was uncompetitive against Harley-Davidson's XR750, so 'King Kenny' rode a bike built around the 120bhp two-stroke four, fitted with a button to kill the power from one cylinder in turns. Roberts mastered the vicious bike to score a remarkable last lap win, after which the TZ dirt-tracker was promptly banned for being too fast and dangerous. Even the iron-hard Roberts didn't complain.

Above: Giacomo Agostini won 13 world titles for MV, then two more on two-stroke Yamahas.

Top right: Kenny Roberts rode the fearsome TZ750 to a famous victory before it was banned.

Below: Harley's XR750 V-twin dominated US dirt-track racing for much of the 1970s.

vibration too. The Co-op began building the Bonneville and its single-carb derivative the TR7 Tiger, both of which already traded on retro appeal.

This was emphasized by the success of the 1977-model Silver Jubilee Bonneville, built to celebrate Queen Elizabeth II's 25 years on the throne. The Jubilee combined an unchanged 52bhp motor and near-standard chassis with silver paintwork, extra chrome, and a blue seat. Like the standard Bonnie it vibrated at high revs and was less sophisticated and reliable than Japanese rivals. It was also light, handled well and had lively performance, best used well short of the 110mph (177km/h) top speed. The Co-op sold more than the planned 2000 units before the weakening US dollar caused a slump in that vital market. Debts rose, and more workers were laid off.

Low-volume production

By this time the rest of the British industry's output was limited to machines built by hand in small numbers, such as the Silk 700S, a 653cc two-stroke parallel twin. The bike's creator, Derbyshire-based George Silk, was a Scott enthusiast, and his 47bhp liquid-cooled 700S engine was a development of the Scott unit. The Silk handled well, thanks to a rigid Spondon Engineering frame and good suspension, but was expensive and ran poorly at low speed. More than 100 were built but the 700S would not survive the decade.

An even more ambitious British project was the Quasar, the futuristic roofed machine intended to provide its rider with the weather protection and comfort of a car. Designer Malcolm Newell's wedge-shaped glass-fiber bodywork enclosed a tubular steel frame. The Quasar's 848cc

Left: *Triumph's T160 Trident arrived in 1975 with new styling, plus an electric starter and left-foot gearchange for its 740cc three-pot motor. But although reasonably successful, it could not save Norton Villiers Triumph.*

liquid-cooled four-cylinder engine came from a Reliant three-wheeler. Although it produced only 40bhp, the excellent aerodynamics allowed 90mph (144km/h) cruising. But at £3500 ($6125) in 1976 the Quasar cost twice as much as a Japanese superbike, and fewer than 20 were built.

The design of more conventional touring bikes had by this time taken a step forward with the launch in 1977 of BMW's R100RS, which combined a new 980cc flat twin engine with a full fairing that provided unprecedented weather protection. The pushrod boxer motor's 70bhp output gave a top speed of over 120mph (193km/h), but the BMW's key asset was its rider's ability to use that performance for long distances with minimal fatigue. Stable handling, optional panniers, and shaft final drive added to the R100RS's long-distance ability. A year later BMW followed it with the R100RT, whose taller fairing, more upright riding position, and larger dual-seat made for an even more relaxed and comfortable ride.

Ironically a model that would eventually have far more impact on the motorcycle touring world had arrived in 1975 to a very mixed reception. Honda's GL1000 Gold Wing was not specifically a tourer; it was a giant, unfaired bike powered by a liquid-cooled, 999cc sohc flat four

Above: *The futuristic and streamlined Quasar, built in England's West Country, offered effortless cruising and a reclined, fully enclosed riding position. But it was too unusual and expensive to be a commercial success.*

Left: *By 1977 Triumph's T140 Bonneville was notable more for its character than for the performance of its 744cc parallel twin engine. That year's Silver Jubilee special edition was a success for the Meriden factory co-operative.*

Right: BMW's R100RS brought a new dimension to long-distance riding in 1977 with its efficient and streamlined full fairing, which allowed the 980cc boxer engine's performance to be used in unprecedented comfort.

Above: Honda's CX500 was built for the US market with high bars, but in Europe the efficient shaft-drive V-twin was regarded as a long-distance workhorse, and was the most popular choice of city dispatch riders.

engine that made 80bhp. The Wing had bulbous styling, a dummy fuel tank (fuel lived under the seat), and weighed a massive 639lb (290kg) with gas. It was smooth, flexible, and softly sprung. Its specification included shaft final drive and Japan's first triple disc brake system.

Some motorcyclists in Europe, especially, disliked the Gold Wing, notably the tester at *Bike* magazine, which slated the bike under the headline: 'Two Wheeled Motor Car.' The GL1000 certainly had faults, as its upright, exposed riding position prevented the engine performance from being exploited, and the bike's weight inevitably gave soggy handling. As a long-distance machine the Wing was compromised by its hard seat and small fuel tank.

But the response was positive in the US, where many older riders appreciated the Gold Wing's assets: power, flexibility, smoothness, and effortless cruising ability when heavily loaded. This it

Right: The R100RT tourer featured higher handlebars and a taller, less streamlined fairing than its BMW stablemate the R100RS, giving a more upright riding position. Many owners also fitted accessory hard panniers.

Honda GL1000 Gold Wing (1975)	
Engine:	Liquid-cooled sohc eight-valve flat four
Capacity:	999cc (72 x 61.4mm)
Maximum power:	80bhp at 7500rpm
Transmission:	Five-speed, shaft final drive
Frame:	Steel twin cradle
Suspension:	Telescopic front; twin shocks rear
Brakes:	Twin discs front; single disc rear
Weight:	639lb (290kg) wet
Top speed:	125mph (201km/h)

often was, because many owners added accessories, from fairings and luggage to extra chrome and lights. Honda was slow to produce a fully equipped Wing, so the accessory makers also loved the model. By the end of the decade, more than 200,000 had been sold and the cult of the Gold Wing was firmly established.

Another of Honda's most popular bikes was the contrastingly compact CB400F, whose lean good looks and sweet-running four-cylinder engine made an attractive combination on its introduction in 1975. The 408cc sohc four's flat handlebars and rearset footrests gave a sporty riding position, and the four-into-one exhaust system's four downpipes swept across the engine in eye-catching fashion.

The four's maximum output of 37bhp made it competitive with rival two-strokes such as Suzuki's GT380 triple and Yamaha's RD400 twin, giving a top speed of 100mph (161km/h) provided the rider crouched down low. Good fuel economy, reliability, agile handling, and a keen price made the CB400F popular in Europe, though less so in the US. Many riders were disappointed when in 1977 Honda replaced it with the CB400T, a twin that was slightly faster and cheaper, but lacked the four's character and style.

Honda developed its range of fours fairly successfully during the '70s, without reproducing the excitement or all-conquering performance of the original CB750. That model was taken in two directions, the sporty CB750F and a bulkier, four-piped touring model, the CB750K. Honda's best effort came in the 1977 with the CB750F2. This was a revamped version of the previous year's 750F1, featuring tuned, 73bhp engine, strengthened frame, new suspension, innovative alloy-rimmed 'Comstar' wheels, flat bars, and a four-into-one pipe. It was good for 120mph (193km/h) and handled well, but Honda's sohc 750cc line had been allowed to continue for too long, and had lost its performance lead.

That was clear from the simultaneous arrival of hot new rivals from each of the other Japanese manufacturers. Kawasaki's Z650 gave away almost 100cc to the F2, but the dohc four produced 64bhp and was good-looking and robust. Kawasaki's US advertising screamed that 'Right out of the crate it will out-perform any 750 in the world!' It wasn't quite true, but the Z650 still sold well.

Above left: The original GL1000 Gold Wing was a large but relatively normal looking unfaired roadster. Its bulbous dummy tank contained electrical components, a kickstart lever, and some storage space; fuel lived under the seat.

Below: Honda's CB400F combined a revvy, reliable four-cylinder engine with fine handling and a competitive price. But arguably its best feature was the unique exhaust system, with four downpipes curving across the motor.

Yamaha's troubled triple

Yamaha's three-cylinder XS750 was the firm's first four-stroke superbike, and looked impressive with its 747cc dohc engine, featuring 64bhp output and shaft final drive. Initial reports were favorable. The Yamaha was smooth, flexible, and powerful, with a top speed of 120mph (193km/h) and effortless cruising ability. It also handled well and was comfortable. But the promise turned to disappointment when the engine proved unreliable, and sales did not recover despite numerous modifications and the arrival of the more powerful XS850 in 1980.

Suzuki had no such problems with the GS750 four that was launched in 1977, and which shared the reliability of the Kawasaki Z900 from which its dohc engine design was clearly derived. The 748cc Suzuki unit produced 68bhp, making it the most powerful 750 on the market, and the GS had a chassis to match, with a strong twin-downtube frame and excellent suspension. Top speed was over 120mph (193km/h); handling was precise and stable. The GS750 was an outstanding machine that instantly established Suzuki's four-stroke credentials, as did the capable GS550 four that was introduced at the same time.

Suzuki scored again a year later with the GS1000. Like the smaller GS models, the 997cc newcomer was an air-cooled dohc four with pleasant but unimaginative styling. The difference this time was that the GS1000's maximum output of 87bhp was 4bhp up on Kawasaki's rival Z1000, making the GS the world's most powerful four-cylinder superbike.

The GS1000's frame was a stronger version of the GS750's, and the bigger bike also featured air-assisted forks, damping-adjustable shocks, and a second front brake disc. The Suzuki stormed to a top speed of 135mph (217km/h), and was reasonably smooth and very reliable. Equally importantly the GS's handling was notably superior to that of its rivals. Here at last was an open-class Japanese superbike that could be ridden hard without weaving or wobbling. Suzuki followed it with the attractive, bikini-faired GS1000S, plus a pair of shaft-drive touring models, the GS850 and GS1000G.

Yamaha's first four-cylinder superbike, the XS1100, also came with shaft final drive. The 'Excess Eleven,' introduced in 1978, was a huge machine whose 1101cc dohc engine produced an

Above: Kawasaki's Z650 four resembled the Z1000 in styling and engine layout. The smaller model's 110mph (177km/h) performance and competitive price made it a hit.

Right: Yamaha's XS750 triple promised much with its powerful and smooth-running three-cylinder engine, but was hit by unreliability of parts including its ignition and primary chain.

<table>
<tr><td colspan="2">Suzuki GS1000 (1978)</td></tr>
<tr><td>Engine:</td><td>Air-cooled dohc eight-valve four</td></tr>
<tr><td>Capacity:</td><td>997cc (70 x 64.8mm)</td></tr>
<tr><td>Maximum power:</td><td>87bhp @ 8000rpm</td></tr>
<tr><td>Transmission:</td><td>Five-speed, chain final drive</td></tr>
<tr><td>Frame:</td><td>Steel twin downtube</td></tr>
<tr><td>Suspension:</td><td>Telescopic front; twin shocks rear</td></tr>
<tr><td>Brakes:</td><td>Twin discs front; disc rear</td></tr>
<tr><td>Weight:</td><td>533lb (242kg) wet</td></tr>
<tr><td>Top speed:</td><td>135mph (217km/h)</td></tr>
</table>

Above left: With its rigid steel frame and firm, damping-adjustable suspension, Suzuki's GS1000 was the best-handling open-class superbike yet from a Japanese manufacturer.

Above: Suzuki's GS750 became the firm's first four-stroke superbike when it was launched in 1977, and its brilliant all-round performance made the 68bhp four an instant success.

impressive 95bhp, and which weighed more than 600lb (272kg) when its big fuel tank was full. The Yamaha had unbeatable low-rev acceleration and a top speed of over 130mph (209km/h), but it was built for distance rather than speed, with soft suspension and a big seat.

Attempts to make full use of the XS's engine performance inevitably ended in disappointment, as the big four's power and weight overwhelmed its chassis, producing wobbles. Predictably the Yamaha flopped in Europe, but it was more popular in the US, where its standard-fitment fairing mounts were utilized by many touring riders. Yamaha even produced a fully-faired Martini version with an innovative full fairing whose top section turned with the handlebars.

Kawasaki's Z1000, which had succeeded the Z900 and featured a bored-out, 1015cc engine, was joined in 1978 by the sportier Z1-R. This featured angular styling, silver-blue paintwork, and a matching bikini fairing. Bigger carbs and a four-into-one exhaust system increased maximum output to a claimed 90bhp, and the chassis was modified with a strengthened frame and new suspension. The Z1-R was stylish and good for 130mph (209km/h) but its handlebar-mounted fairing hindered high-speed stability, and firm shocks gave an uncomfortable ride. Even so, this was the fastest and best big Kawasaki so far.

Honda's most successful newcomer of 1978 was a very different bike: the CX500, a plump, liquid-cooled transverse V-twin with shaft final drive. Its 50bhp pushrod engine allowed comfortable 80mph (129km/h) cruising and was very robust once some early mechanical problems had been cured. That plus good brakes and fuel economy made the 'plastic maggot' popular with dispatch riders, who tolerated its curious styling and heavy handling.

The Japanese twin that made the biggest impact in the US was Yamaha's XS650 Special, a revamped version of the familiar parallel twin featuring high bars, small tank, and short mufflers. By 1979 the Special was on sale in Europe alongside a restyled, high-barred Z650SR version of

Action Movies

Some of the best motorcycling movies of the 1970s feature racing of one sort or another. *On Any Sunday*, the most famous bike sport film of all, covers US dirt-track, motocross, desert racing, and the notoriously steep Widowmaker hillclimb. Stars including Mert Lawwill, Malcolm Smith, and Steve McQueen help make director Bruce

Brown's 1971 documentary very watchable. Ten years later, Don Shoemaker and Ed Forsyth co-directed a competent sequel, *On Any Sunday 2*.

Robert Redford stars in *Little Fauss and Big Halsy*, a 1970 movie centered on a pair of motocross racers. The decade's other biggest bike-sport film is 1979's *Silver Dream Racer*, based on the road-racing exploits of actor/pop

star David Essex. Although not totally convincing, it includes some neat bikes and genuine racing action along with the story of a privateer racer's struggle to the top. The decade's other best-known biking movie, the 1973 release *Electra Glide in Blue*, is a less spectacular story of a US cop with a Harley and an attitude problem.

Above: The dirt-track action in On Any Sunday *included plenty of spectacular crashes.*

Top center: Silver Dream Racer *included action sequences shot at British race circuits.*

Above right: The star of Electra Glide in Blue *poses with chief actor Richard Blake.*

Right: This Yamaha XS1100 is the US spec model with high bars and short pipes. The huge shaft-drive four was a successful touring model in the US, but sold poorly in most other countries.

Kawasaki's four. The Japanese factory custom had arrived, and future years would see similarly adapted versions of many other models.

Honda finally introduced a twin-camshaft four in 1979, ten years after the CB750. The CB900F and similarly styled CB750FZ owed much to Honda's mighty RCB four-cylinder endurance racers, and differed from their rivals by containing 16 valves. They also shared an angular 'Eurostyle' shape that was similar to that of Honda's humble 400 and 250cc Super Dream

Left: The 1978-model Kawasaki Z1-R's angular styling incorporated a handlebar-mounted fairing that gave the rider useful wind protection, but hindered high-speed stability.

twins. The larger 901cc unit produced an impressive 94bhp, and the CB900F also had a sophisticated chassis, with air-adjustable forks and damping-adjustable shocks. With strong mid-range performance, top speed of over 130mph (209km/h) and handling to match, the CB900F was Honda's best big four yet.

Japanese bikes' chassis performance was finally starting to match their engines. But the old failings had inspired numerous specialists, who had built bikes around Japanese engines, most commonly Kawasaki's fours. Nico Bakker in Holland, Georges Martin in France, Fritz Egli in Switzerland, and various British specialists including the Rickman brothers, Colin Seeley, Spondon Engineering, and Harris Performance, had created fast, exotic specials that were generally much lighter and handled far better than mass-produced superbikes.

The outstanding chassis specialist was Bimota. Inspired by co-founder and design genius Massimo Tamburini, Bimota had already created advanced chassis with which Yamaha and

Below: Honda's CB900F was a significant because it was designed mainly for the European market, with a notably sportier nature than previous US market-led machines.

Left: Honda's factory RCB fours dominated endurance events including the Le Mans 24 Hours and Bol d'Or during the late 1970s.

Above: Bimota's SB2 was in a different league to mass-produced superbikes in 1977, from its streamlined full fairing, via its supremely rigid chassis to its self-supporting aluminum seat.

Right: The Magni MV Agusta, built in small numbers by former race team boss Arturo, resembled the factory racers with its full fairing, twin-cradle frame, and curved pipes.

Opposite top left: Honda's stunning CBX1000 made do without frame front downtubes to make its 24-valve engine more visible. For a big, heavy bike it handled very well.

Opposite center right: Kawasaki's liquid-cooled Z1300 required a large radiator that hid the front of its engine, but the huge, slab-sided six still looked like nothing else on two wheels.

Harley-Davidson had won road-race world championships. The first Bimota streetbike, the HB1, had been built in small numbers around a Honda CB750 engine in the mid-'70s. But it was with the Suzuki GS750-powered SB2 that the firm from Rimini made its mark.

The SB2 was a stunningly advanced machine, with a curvaceous tank-seat unit that was made from glass-fiber lined with aluminum, so required no rear subframe. The sophisticated tubular steel frame was hugely rigid, and held a vertically mounted rear shock unit, operated via a rising-rate mechanism. Other features included lightweight alloy wheels, triple Brembo discs, and numerous machined alloy parts. The streamlined Bimota was good for over 130mph (209km/h), weighed 60lb (27kg) less than the GS750 and handled far better than any mass-produced superbike. Only 70 were built, mainly because the SB2 cost three times as much as a standard GS750, but it had provided a glimpse of motorcycling's future.

Another Italian specialist was former MV Agusta race team manager Arturo Magni. MV had updated its four-cylinder 750S to produce the 790cc America, and in 1977 enlarged the dohc engine to 837cc to create the Monza. Prepared by Magni, who had set up a tuning business near the factory, the Monza produced 85bhp and thundered to a top speed of 140mph (225km/h). Few of these sublime but unprofitable bikes were built before, in 1978, MV abandoned bikes to concentrate on its main business of producing helicopters. Magni also built a small number of an even more exotic MV, featuring a chain-drive conversion plus his own frame, based on the stronger, twin-loop design of the works racebikes. Finally MV's four had a chassis worthy of the marque's racing heritage.

Benelli provided a late flourish when the Pesaro firm enlarged its 750 Sei's six-cylinder engine to 906cc, creating the 900 Sei. But even this produced only 80bhp and the Sei was outshone by another six: Honda's CBX1000. The 1047cc, dohc engine contained 24 valves and produced 105bhp, making the Honda the world's most powerful production bike when it was launched in 1978. The CBX looked superb, too, with the view of its wide, air-cooled engine unhindered by frame downtubes.

Honda CBX1000 (1978)	
Engine:	Air-cooled dohc 24-valve six
Capacity:	1047cc (64.5 x 53.4mm)
Maximum power:	105bhp @ 9000rpm
Transmission:	Five-speed, chain final drive
Frame:	Tubular steel
Suspension:	Telescopic front; twin shocks rear
Brakes:	Twin discs front; disc rear
Weight:	573lb (260kg) wet
Top speed:	135mph (217km/h)

The sporty CBX was shaped by Honda's former multi-cylinder racebike designer Shoichiro Irimajiri. It provided ferocious and smooth acceleration toward a top speed of 135mph (217km/h), with a stirring exhaust howl. Despite Honda's innovative use of magnesium and plastic the CBX was heavy, at 573lb (260kg), but it handled and braked very well. Most who rode the CBX loved it, and the six boosted Honda's staid image. But it was far more expensive than fours of equivalent performance, and was not a sales success.

The CBX was one of the first models to be built at Honda's new US factory in Maryville, Ohio, which began producing bikes in 1979. By this time the Japanese giant had been using foreign production for almost two decades, after establishing a Belgian base to assemble mopeds back in 1962. Honda plants in Asian countries including Thailand began production in the mid-'60s, followed by factories in countries including Mexico, Brazil, and Nigeria in the '70s.

Motorcycling's final act of the decade was another six-cylinder machine, Kawasaki's Z1300, which was even bigger, heavier, and more powerful than the CBX. The slab-sided Kawasaki's 1286cc dohc liquid-cooled engine produced 120bhp, fully 15bhp more than the Honda, and the Kawasaki weighed more than 660lb (300kg) with fuel. With its upright riding position, sheer size, and shaft final drive, the Z1300 was intended as a grand tourer.

Although its exposed riding position limited its practical cruising speed, the big Kawasaki was stunningly fast, whirring smoothly to 135mph (217km/h). It also handled and braked very well for such a big machine. Despite that it failed to sell in large numbers, partly because, like the CBX, it was more expensive than rival fours. The big, thirsty six also arrived in the wake of an oil crisis, just as the West German government had introduced a 100bhp power limit. Some reports suggested that the Z1300 would lead to bikes being banned. As the 1970s drew to a close, the giant Kawasaki seemed to some people to be a warning that after a decade of many highlights and much progress, motorcycling was spiraling out of control.

Kawasaki Z1300 (1979)	
Engine:	Liquid-cooled dohc 12-valve transverse six
Capacity:	1286cc (62 x 71mm)
Maximum power:	120bhp @ 8000rpm
Transmission:	Five-speed, shaft final drive
Frame:	Steel twin cradle
Suspension:	Telescopic front; twin shocks rear
Brakes:	Twin discs front; disc rear
Weight:	672lb (305kg)
Top speed:	135mph (217km/h)

Fire and Water
1980s

If motorcycling as most current riders know it began in the 1970s, then it was the following decade that did most to shape the modern bike. The race toward ever-larger and more powerful unfaired machines ended in 1979 with Kawasaki's Z1300 six. From then on, development continued in more diverse and generally more practical directions. By the end of the decade, most of the key features of today's bikes would be in place.

At the start of the '80s, even the most sophisticated bikes were generally unfaired and had air-cooled engines, tubular steel frames, and twin rear shock absorbers, just like their predecessors of ten years earlier. All that quickly changed. By the second half of the decade, many large and even some smaller bikes had fairings, liquid-cooled engines, aluminum frames, and single rear shock units with rising-rate linkages.

They also incorporated some less visible developments, including engines with four or even five valves per cylinder. Wider, smaller-diameter wheels increasingly wore tubeless radial tires. Most tires and disc brakes worked as well as could be expected in wet weather, unlike many of their dangerously rain-affected predecessors. Not all the decade's technical developments were positive, however. Poorly designed bodywork and needlessly complex features, such as Honda's enclosed brake discs, increased the cost of parts and servicing.

Japan's grip on the worldwide motorcycle market was stronger than ever, but even the big four suffered when sales in many key markets fell dramatically in the early '80s. Yamaha had grown quickly until that point, and was firmly established as the second largest manufacturer, but the firm's attempt to close the gap with Honda proved ill-timed. The sales slump resulted in huge over-production and a price war that was damaging to both companies. By fall 1982, it was estimated that well over a million unsold Japanese bikes were being stored in the US and Canada, stacked in crates inside huge warehouses.

Yamaha survived, after making heavy losses and producing some notably mediocre and under-developed bikes, especially V-twins such as the XV550 and 981cc TR1. Honda reduced its range and emerged with status reinforced but with problems of its own. Mechanical failures suffered by

Above: The top superbike at the start of the 1980s was Suzuki's GSX1100, an old-style naked machine with air-cooled four-cylinder engine, twin rear shocks plus lots of bulk and weight.

Right: Kawasaki's GPz1100 arrived in 1981 with a traditional twin-shock chassis format and even a two-valves-per-cylinder engine, but its fuel-injection system added a futuristic touch.

Previous page: The VFR750F did much to restore Honda's reputation for top quality engineering.

Left: Yamaha's RD350LC was one of the great bikes of the early '80s, and became a cult machine thanks to its unbeatable blend of outrageous performance and value for money.

Yamaha RD350LC (1981)

Engine:	Liquid-cooled two-stroke parallel twin
Capacity:	347cc (64 x 54mm)
Maximum power:	47bhp @ 8500rpm
Transmission:	Six-speed, chain final drive
Frame:	Steel twin downtube
Suspension:	Telescopic front; single shock rear
Brakes:	Twin discs front; drum rear
Weight:	331lb (150kg)
Top speed:	110mph (177km/h)

models including the VF750F were an embarrassment to the firm that had introduced reliable motorcycling to the world.

Manufacturers in other countries were even more vulnerable. The British industry finally faded away almost completely, and Italian firms including Ducati, Moto Guzzi, and Laverda suffered from low production levels and lack of finance for investment. Harley-Davidson survived, with the help of a controversial US government tariff on large-capacity imported bikes.

Demand for motorcycles had fallen partly because in the major markets bikes were by now regarded mainly as 'luxury' items, so might be dispensed with in a financial downturn. Once the economies recovered, so did bike sales. Meanwhile the riding experience was getting better as riders benefited from improvements in clothing and accessories, as well as machinery. The best 'waterproof' clothing really did keep out the rain; full-face helmets gained anti-scratch visors that dramatically improved night-time visibility. Sports bike riders increasingly wore color-matched leathers, though only racers got to ride on a track.

Bikes became increasingly specialized during the 1980s, epitomized by the arrival of fully equipped luxury tourers, and at the other extreme by Suzuki's light and racy GSX-R750, which began the race-replica revolution in 1985. But there were also plenty of capable machines of various capacities for riders who needed versatility or economy. For those who found the technology race too much, the growing interest in classic bikes provided a welcome alternative.

The top superbike of 1980 would be the last of the old-style unfaired, air-cooled fours to hold that position. Suzuki's GSX1100 looked ungainly but was a fine example of the type. Its 1075cc engine, enlarged from that of the GS1000, incorporated Suzuki's first 16-valve cylinder head. The GSX combined a peak output of 100bhp with storming mid-range delivery, and could run at over 135mph (217km/h) for as long as its rider could hang on to the bars. Its traditional twin-shock chassis gave excellent handling, too, despite 551lb (250kg) of weight.

Honda finally responded to demands for weather protection when in 1980 it upgraded the Gold Wing. The basic model became the GL1100, with a more powerful, 1085cc flat four engine plus a new chassis incorporating air suspension. But the year's more important arrival was the

Below: Yamaha's 1982-model XS650 Heritage Classic was a typical 'factory custom,' built for the US market with high bars, stubby exhaust pipes, plus fat dual-seat and rear tire.

Honda CB1100R (1981)

Engine:	Air-cooled dohc 16-valve four
Capacity:	1062cc (70 x 69mm)
Maximum power:	115bhp @ 9000rpm
Transmission:	Five-speed, chain final drive
Frame:	Steel twin downtube
Suspension:	Telescopic front; twin shocks rear
Brakes:	Twin discs front; disc rear
Weight:	518lb (235kg) dry
Top speed:	142mph (229km/h)

Above: Honda's CB1100R outclassed all comers.

Right: Suzuki's Katana 1100 combined high performance with sharp and original styling.

Suzuki GSX1100S Katana (1982)

Engine:	Air-cooled dohc 16-valve four
Capacity:	1075cc (72 x 66mm)
Maximum power:	111bhp @ 8500rpm
Transmission:	Five-speed, chain final drive
Frame:	Steel twin downtube
Suspension:	Telescopic front; twin shocks rear
Brakes:	Twin discs front; disc rear
Weight:	545lb (247kg) wet
Top speed:	140mph (225km/h)

fully-dressed GL, called the Interstate in the US and the De Luxe in Europe, which featured a large fairing, hard luggage, and crash-bars as standard.

The big machine was immediately popular, and two years later was followed by the Aspencade, which added a sound system, passenger backrest, and an on-board compressor to adjust its suspension. The Aspencade, named after a US rally popular with Gold Wing riders, weighed a massive 766lb (347kg) with fuel, but was fast, smooth, and supremely comfortable. The age of the luxury tourer had arrived, as Yamaha confirmed in 1983 with its XVZ1200 Venture, a smooth-running V4 with under-seat fuel tank and similarly lavish level of equipment.

At the other end of the scale, the most popular arrival was Yamaha's RD350LC two-stroke, which screamed onto the scene in 1981, except in the US where it failed to meet emissions regulations. The LC initials stood for Liquid Cooled, and the parallel twin was descended from the lively air-cooled RD400 roadster and Yamaha's all-conquering liquid-cooled TZ250 and 350 racebikes. Its 347cc engine produced 47bhp (a near-identical RD250LC made 35bhp), enough to send the rev-happy 'Elsie' to a top speed of 110mph (177km/h).

The LC's race-developed chassis featured a cantilever rear suspension system, with a single shock unit mounted diagonally under the seat. At just 331lb (150kg) with fuel the Yam was light, and despite slightly soft forks it handled superbly. It was also reliable, well braked, and reasonably priced. In Britain its sales were boosted still further by the televised RD350 Pro-Am race series, which pitted professional riders against top amateurs on identical standard bikes, and produced memorably close and spectacular racing.

Kawasaki's GPz1100 arrived in 1981 to challenge for the title of best naked, air-cooled superbike. Unlike Suzuki's GSX1100 the GPz's new 1089cc engine used two valves per cylinder, and a fuel-injection system that helped give a maximum of 108bhp – enough for fearsome acceleration and a top speed of 140mph (225km/h). The Kawasaki's twin-shock chassis featured air-assisted forks and gave reasonable handling, despite the bike's weight. The GPz was very much a superbike of the old school, but it restored Kawasaki's reputation for high performance. Similarly styled GPz750 and GPz550 fours added style and speed in their respective classes.

Left: The last of Ducati's long line of bevel-drive
V-twins was the 973cc Mille Replica that was
produced only in 1985, the year in which the
Bologna firm was taken over by Cagiva.

Below: Ducati's 1981 star was the Pantah 600.
Like the original Pantah 500 of two years earlier,
the 583cc V-twin used belts instead of bevel shafts
to drive its overhead cams.

But the unfaired fours were blown away by the sophisticated star of 1981, Honda's CB1100R.
This was not a mass-produced superbike, it was Honda's first 'homologation special' – a purpose-
built production racer of which only 1000 units would be built. The 1100R sold for twice as much
as the CB900FZ from which it was developed, and was created to win big production events in
Australia (especially the famous Castrol Six Hour) and South Africa.

Honda enlarged the 901cc 16-valve engine to 1062cc, and tuned it with increased compression
ratio to give 115bhp, also adding numerous strengthening modifications. The chassis featured a
more rigid frame and the most sophisticated cycle parts yet seen, including air-assisted, damping
adjustable forks, and twin-piston front brake calipers. The 1100R looked racy, with a half-fairing
and single seat, and it delivered on the track, winning numerous endurance events and dominating
the UK Superstock championship.

The CB1100R also made a superb road bike. Its big motor was flexible and smooth, and the
fairing allowed effortless high-speed cruising toward a 142mph (229km/h) top speed. Suspension
control, braking, and ground clearance were all outstanding, although the fairing triggered a slight
high-speed weave. Honda cured that with the following year's fully-faired CB1100R-C, which
was further ahead of the pack than ever.

Suzuki sharpens its attack

The most significant new superbike of 1982, however, was a machine that would be built in much
greater numbers than Honda's flagship – and which was even more visually striking. Suzuki's
Katana 1100, named after a Samurai warrior's sword, was a single-minded sportster with a pointed
nose, small flyshield, low clip-on bars, and a swooping tank-seat section. Based on the GSX1100,
it was styled by German firm Target Design, which had previously shaped BMW's R90S.

Suzuki tuned the 1075cc 16-valve motor with new carburetors, airbox, camshafts, and
alternator, adding 11bhp to give a maximum of 111bhp. The unchanged frame held new
suspension parts including forks equipped with a hydraulic anti-dive system borrowed from

Suzuki's grand prix racers. The result was a memorable bike that provided style, 140mph (225km/h) performance, and stable handling at a sensible price. It was also firm and uncomfortable at slow speed, but few owners minded that and the Katana became a long-running success. Suzuki followed the original model with a 1000cc Katana for production racing, watered-down middleweight Katanas, and even tiny 250 and 400cc replicas for the Japanese market.

While Suzuki was bringing aggression and flair to the so-called 'Universal Japanese Motorcycle' four-cylinder format, most Italian manufacturers were having a difficult time. Ducati's most notable bikes of the early '80s had both been launched in 1979. The 900SS Hailwood Replica was built to commemorate 'Mike the Bike' Hailwood's heroic comeback victory, aged 38, in the previous year's Isle of Man Formula One TT. The green, white, and red painted, fully-faired V-twin was even less practical than the standard 900SS, but it looked great, sold well and would remain in the range, through several updates, until 1985. Tragically Hailwood, arguably the greatest motorcycle racer of all, was killed in a car crash in 1981.

Ducati's other newcomer was more significant because the 499cc air-cooled V-twin engine of the Pantah 500, with belt drive to single desmodromic camshafts, would form the basis of the marque's engines for several decades to come. The Pantah's two-valves-per-cylinder motor produced 52bhp, had no kick-starter and was notably quieter and more sophisticated than its predecessor. The bike was good for 120mph (193km/h), and handled and braked very well. With its tall fairing and efficient exhaust system the Pantah lacked the style and raw appeal of the old V-twins, and it was expensive. But it showed the way forward for Ducati, and in 1981 its engine was enlarged to 583cc to create the Pantah 600, with an extra 6bhp and reshaped bodywork.

While Ducati was developing a new generation of engines in its familiar V-twin format, BMW was planning a move away from its traditional flat twins. The K100 arrived in 1984, powered by a completely new longitudinal four-cylinder, shaft-drive engine designed to take the German firm into the 21st century. The 987cc liquid-cooled engine's cylinders were arranged horizontally, with the crankshaft on the right. Peak output was 90bhp, with the emphasis on low-rev torque.

That helped make the K100 easy to ride, but the bike disappointed in other areas. Top speed was close to 130mph (209km/h) but the high bars and hard seat meant its performance could not

Above: With its 987cc in-line four-cylinder engine with cylinders arranged horizontally, the K100 was a radical departure for BMW, which was planning to abandon its flat twins.

Right: In typical BMW fashion the K100 was soon followed by a K100RS sports-tourer with a streamlined fairing. Equally predictably, a more relaxed K100RT tourer was not far behind.

The Turbo Craze

The most vivid examples of Japanese manufacturers' obsession with complex engineering in the early 1980s were the turbocharged bikes released by each of the 'Big Four.' Honda began in 1982 with the CX500 Turbo, a striking, fully-faired machine powered by a turbocharged version of the firm's transverse V-twin engine. Turbos are best suited to large, multi-cylinder engines that give a smooth exhaust flow, so the 497cc CX unit made Honda's job especially difficult.

Nevertheless the CX500 Turbo produced 82bhp, well up on the standard CX500's 50bhp, and proved reliable. The rest of the bike was almost as high-tech, with fuel-injection, anti-dive forks, Pro-Link rear suspension, and twin-pot brake calipers. As well as suffering from turbo lag, the delay between throttle opening and acceleration, the Honda was far too complex, heavy, and expensive to sell in serious numbers. The CX650 Turbo, launched a year later, had less lag plus more power and a top speed of 135mph (217km/h).

Honda's rivals opted for the more obvious in-line four engine layout. Yamaha was first to respond. Its XJ650 Turbo featured a stylish and efficient full fairing but the bike's 125mph (201km/h) performance was disappointing. The same was true of Suzuki's XN-85, whose 673cc engine produced 85bhp and gave performance no better than that of a normally aspirated 750cc four.

Fastest and best of the bunch was the last, Kawasaki's Z750 Turbo, which arrived in 1984 with scorching acceleration and a top speed of almost 140mph (225km/h). But the Turbo was competing with Kawasaki's own GPZ900R, which offered similar performance and price, plus no turbo lag and less chance of expensive mechanical problems. While the 900R became a lasting hit, the turbo bikes were quietly abandoned by all four manufacturers.

be used for long. The K100 was also a big, heavy machine whose soft front suspension did not encourage hard riding. BMW had more success with the K100RS, whose full fairing gave good weather protection. Combined with the relaxed riding position, the result was a competent sports-tourer. Touring-oriented K100RT and 'luxury' LT models further broadened the four's appeal, although many riders still preferred the boxers.

While BMW was preparing to abandon flat-twin engines, the layout was still being enthusiastically utilized elsewhere, notably in the Soviet Union. After the war, several Soviet factories had begun producing bikes based on captured BMW twins, and had carried on doing so with few modifications. Four decades later the crude but cheap boxers were being imported to the West, to be sold with added chromework and sometimes with sidecars attached. Similarly outdated BMW replicas were also being built in China, alongside the huge numbers of smaller two-strokes that were emerging from that nation's growing motorcycle industry.

Like BMW, Honda made a dramatic move to a new engine layout: the V4. When it was introduced in 1982, the V4 seemed so well suited to motorcycle use that some thought it would lead bikes away from in-line fours for ever. Honda's 748cc 90-degree, 16-valve motor produced

Above: Honda's CX500 Turbo was too complex and expensive to be a commercial success, but the V-twin was stylish, fast, and comfortable.

Below: Many people were surprised when Honda debuted its 748cc V4 engine in the heavy and strangely styled VF750S, or Sabre in the US.

an impressive 79bhp, was compact, and had perfect primary balance plus space in the Vee for carburetors. Liquid-cooling prevented traditional problems of overheating rear cylinders. Surely the V4's time had finally come?

Honda's first mistake was to debut the V4 in 1982 both in a cruiser variant, the US-market V45 Magna, and a sportier machine called the VF750S, or Sabre in the US. The Sabre included TRAC anti-dive and Pro-Link single-shock rear suspension, as well as shaft final drive. The motor was smooth and powerful, though the VF's high handlebars meant its 120mph (193km/h) performance could not be used for long. More importantly the bike weighed over 500lb (227kg) with fuel, and had curious styling and vague handling.

Honda answered most of the criticisms a year later with the VF750F, called the Interceptor in the US. This was a much more stylish and sporty machine with a half-fairing, belly-pan, and a new chassis that combined a frame of square-section steel with 1983's racing-inspired fashion item, a 16-inch front wheel. Power was up to 90bhp, pushing top speed to 130mph (209km/h), and the V4 had looks and handling to match. It quickly became very popular, only for Honda's delight to turn to embarrassment when the engine suffered a series of mechanical problems. In some markets Honda responded by doubling its engine warranty to 24 months, but the firm's reputation would take years to recover.

Above: Honda's VF750F, known as the Interceptor in the US market, was fast, handled well, looked good, and was set for huge success – until its engine proved unreliable.

Alternative V-twin layout

Fortunately for Honda there were fewer problems with its new V-twin, the VT500, which unlike the popular CX500 and later CX650 had its cylinders arranged in line with the bike. The softly tuned VT produced 50bhp and echoed the CX in its use of liquid-cooling and shaft drive, but had a narrower, 52-degree cylinder angle. The VT was a slimmer and more stylish bike that was also comfortable, reliable, and handled well. It took over from the CX as a dispatch riders' favorite.

Most of Honda's efforts remained concentrated on its V4 range, which grew quickly with a string of models. The VF400F, also launched in 1983, was rev-happy, quick, agile, and reliable, albeit also complex and expensive. The following year saw the VF500F, complete with stylish full

Right: The 1984-model VF1000R was a homologation special, with exotic chassis parts and tuned V4 engine, but was surprisingly uncompetitive in production racing.

fairing and 120mph (193km/h) performance, plus two 998cc V4s. The VF1000F looked like the 750F and combined fine handling with a flexible and reliable 116bhp powerplant.

Top of Honda's 1984 range was the VF1000R, a fully-faired super-sports machine which, like the CB1100R before it, was a street-legal production racer built in small numbers. Its engine held gear-driven cams and was tuned to give 122bhp, its fairing was reinforced with lightweight carbon-fiber, and its chassis featured fully adjustable suspension and four-piston front brake calipers. The 1000R was comfortable, stable, and good for 150mph (241km/h). But it was too heavy and slow-steering to be outstanding on the track, and as a roadster it was far too expensive.

Kawasaki created contrasting superbikes in 1984, by refining the in-line four-cylinder layout for which it had been best known since the Z1 of 11 years earlier. At the end of that line of high-performance air-cooled fours came the Z1100R. With its bikini fairing, green paintwork, high bars and gold remote-reservoir shocks, the 1100R was a replica of the factory racer on which Eddie Lawson had won the US Superbike championship in 1981 and '82. The 1089cc four produced 114bhp and the Z1000R was stylish, fast, and flexible, if rather crude and not particularly stable at high speed.

Kawasaki's more important and successful newcomer began a new generation of liquid-cooled, 16-valve fours. The GPZ900R was a sophisticated machine whose 908cc engine also featured a balancer shaft and six-speed gearbox. Its peak output of 113bhp was slightly below that of the old GPz1100 and the Z1100R, but the 'Ninja' had an aerodynamic full fairing that helped increase its top speed to over 150mph (241km/h). The bike also had a sturdy steel frame that used the motor as a stressed member, plus firm suspension that helped give excellent handling.

The GPZ900R was a stunningly fast bike that was also compact, reliable, smooth, and comfortable, thanks to its flat bars and efficient fairing. At over 500lb (227kg) it was no lightweight but it was raced very successfully in production events as well as becoming a hugely popular roadster. It was later updated with a 17- instead of 16-inch front wheel, and remained in Kawasaki's range into the 1990s in a sports-touring role, outlasting its intended replacements the GPZ1000RX and ZX-10.

Kawasaki GPZ900R (1984)

Engine:	Liquid-cooled dohc 16-valve four
Capacity:	908cc (72.5 x 55mm)
Maximum power:	113bhp @ 9500rpm
Transmission:	Six-speed, chain final drive
Frame:	Steel spine
Suspension:	Telescopic front; single shock rear
Brakes:	Twin discs front; disc rear
Weight:	502lb (228kg) dry
Top speed:	155mph (249km/h)

Above: Kawasaki's Z1100R copied Eddie Lawson's US Superbike championship-winning racer in its headlamp fairing, lime green paintwork, and 'sit-up-and-beg' riding position.

Left: The modern era began for Kawasaki with the brilliant GPZ900R, which hid a powerful 908cc liquid-cooled 16-valve four-cylinder engine behind its streamlined full fairing.

Above: Yamaha's FJ1100 was intended as an out-and-out sports bike but was outperformed by the GPZ900R on its launch in 1984, and made its mark as a fast and comfortable sports-tourer.

The other outstanding large-capacity sports machine of 1984 found itself relegated to the role of sports-tourer almost immediately because it could not compete with the GPZ on pure performance. But Yamaha's FJ1100 became such a success as a long-distance roadburner that, following a capacity increase that produced the FJ1200 in 1986, it too would remain in production with few changes well into the following decade.

The FJ's appeal was built on its relatively simple air-cooled four-cylinder engine, which differed from the old XS1100 unit by having 16 valves, and final drive by chain rather than shaft. The original 1097cc motor produced 125bhp and was more notable for its storming low-rev performance, which was further boosted by the increase to 1188cc that resulted in the FJ1200. The chassis, based on a square-section steel tube frame, gave sound handling with the emphasis on stability. A half-fairing, large fuel tank, and broad dual-seat were other features that helped make the FJ popular for long-distance travel.

The other outstanding Yamaha of 1984 was far less successful than the FJ, ironically because it was too focused a sports machine. In fact the RD500LC was as close as any recent bike to a grand-prix-winning racer, as its look and 499cc liquid-cooled two-stroke V4 engine were inspired by the factory YZR500 that Eddie Lawson was riding to victory in that year's world championship. With a peak output of 90bhp, a top speed of almost 140mph (225km/h), and a dry weight of just 392lb (178kg), the V4 had the figures to back up its racy appearance.

The RD500LC also handled brilliantly, thanks to a high quality chassis that combined a square-section tubular steel frame with a single rear shock located under the engine. Along with the rev-happy engine, which came alive at 6000rpm with a fierce burst of acceleration and a high-pitched scream from the exhaust, it made the Yamaha superbly entertaining on the right road, as well as very fast on a racetrack. But drawbacks including excessive vibration, poor fuel consumption, and a high price prevented the two-stroke from selling in big numbers.

Much the same was true of the rival that the RD faced in 1985, when Suzuki launched its RG500 Gamma, a follow-up to the previous year's superbly agile RG250 Gamma twin. Like the

Above and right: In 1986 Yamaha enlarged the FJ's air-cooled 16-valve engine to 1188cc to create the FJ1200, which remained a popular long-distance roadburner well into the '90s.

Left: Yamaha's eagerly anticipated RD500LC was a faithful replica of the YZR500 grand prix racebike, with revvy 499cc liquid-cooled V4 engine and high-pitched exhaust note.

Below: The Suzuki RG500 roadster copied its works racer namesake not only in its square-four engine layout, but also with its aluminum frame construction and liking for wheelies.

bikes on which Barry Sheene, Marco Lucchinelli, and Franco Uncini had recently won world titles, the RG500 was a square four two-stroke. At just 433lb (196kg) it was even lighter than the RD, thanks to a frame which, like that of the works RG500 racebike, was made from aluminum. The fully-faired, 95bhp Gamma was every bit as stylish, fast, agile, and impractical as its Yamaha rival. Unfortunately for Suzuki, it was more successful.

Honda's two-stroke challenger, the NS400R, was subtly different. Its 387cc two-stroke motor was a V-triple, like that of the NS500 on which the outrageously talented young Louisiana star 'Fast Freddie' Spencer had won Honda's first 500cc world title two years earlier. With a claimed 72bhp the NS couldn't match the straight-line speed of its 500cc rivals, despite weighing just 365lb (169kg) wet. But the compact triple handled brilliantly, thanks partly to the first aluminum frame that Honda had used on a streetbike. Despite that, the NS was no more commercially successful than the RD and RG, and the two-stroke race-replica revolution faded.

Instead, motorcycle design took a giant leap forward in a different direction, due to an even faster and equally purposeful Suzuki released at the same time: the GSX-R750. With the exception of Honda's CB750, the original GSX-R was arguably the most influential machine of recent decades, as it introduced the concept of the ultra lightweight, aluminum-framed four-cylinder race-replica, and so is the bike to which most modern sports machines owe their design. The Suzuki was also hugely popular in its own right, and started a GSX-R dynasty that grew to include smaller models plus the larger GSX-R1100 and, later, the GSX-R1000.

The original GSX-R750 was based on Suzuki's 998cc endurance race bikes of the previous year, with its twin-headlamp fairing and use of 18-inch wheels instead of the fashionable 16-inchers. Its 749cc dohc 16-valve engine was cooled by oil rather than either water or the air of its GSX750 predecessor, and produced a competitive 100bhp. The motor was compact and very light, with its cam-cover cast in magnesium instead of aluminum.

The GSX-R's chassis was even more radically light, based on an aluminum frame which at 18lb (8kg) weighed half as much as the GSX's steel equivalent. That helped give stunning

Above: Honda's NS400R was a dead ringer for Freddie Spencer's 500cc world-championship-winning triple, but produced only 72bhp and was no more successful than its two-stroke race-replica rivals from Yamaha and Suzuki.

Below right: Suzuki's GSX-R750 rocked the motorcycle world on its introduction in 1985, with a combination of high-revving power, light weight and aggressive attitude that led to a new breed of super-sports machines.

acceleration to a top speed of 145mph (233km/h), provided the peaky motor was kept between 7000rpm and its 11,000rpm limit. The lack of weight was just as beneficial under braking and in corners, where the racy Suzuki was equally outstanding. The GSX-R was also uncomfortable, impractical, and sometimes unstable, until calmed with a longer swingarm a year later. Its success proved that plenty of riders were happy to ignore such details when the performance and image were so right.

Suzuki waited only a year before unleashing an even more complete superbike in the near-identical shape of the GSX-R1100, which added blistering mid-range power to the original model's many attributes. At 433lb (196kg) dry the 1100 was 45lb (20kg) heavier than the 750, due to many apparently identical parts being slightly larger and stronger. But not only was the GSX-R1100 faster still and easier to ride, it also handled and braked superbly and was by some distance the world's fastest and most exciting sports bike.

Yamaha's poor timing

It was Yamaha's misfortune that its impressive FZ750 had been released in 1985 to compete with the GSX-R750. In most other years the spotlight would have been on the FZ, whose 749cc liquid-cooled four-cylinder engine introduced the angled-forward cylinders and five-valves-per-cylinder layout that would form the basis of Yamaha's big-bike range for years to come.

The FZ was a less focused and more practical bike than the GSX-R, and its engine was as notable for mid-range output as for its 105bhp maximum. Top speed equalled the Suzuki's 145mph (233km/h), and although the Yamaha couldn't quite match the lighter bike for acceleration, it was easier to ride. It also handled very well, thanks to a strong frame of square-section steel tubes. But the half-faired FZ750 was not the sales success that its performance and innovative design deserved.

Yamaha did, however, have an unlikely hit in 1985 with the V-Max, the unique and supremely powerful V4 that would become a long-lived legend. The V-Max, designed in the US, was the two-wheeled equivalent of a V8 muscle car, and featured fake alloy air-scoops jutting out of the

Suzuki GSX-R750 (1985)	
Engine:	Oil-cooled dohc 16-valve four
Capacity:	749cc (70 x 48.7mm)
Maximum power:	100bhp @ 10,500rpm
Transmission:	Six-speed, chain final drive
Frame:	Aluminum twin downtube
Suspension:	Telescopic front; single shock rear
Brakes:	Twin discs front; disc rear
Weight:	388lb (176kg) dry
Top speed:	145mph (233km/h)

Left: The GSX-R1100, which followed the 750cc model in 1986, had similar twin-headlamp styling. Its storming mid-range performance and stronger five-speed gearbox helped make an even faster and more accomplished bike._

**Below:** Although Yamaha's FZ750 four handled superbly and had a powerful and flexible four-cylinder engine, its sales were disappointing. But the FZ's 20-valve cylinder head layout would be used by Yamaha's for years to come.

side of its dummy fuel tank. The Max's performance was real enough, however. Its 1198cc liquid-cooled motor was a highly tuned version of the V4 from the Venture tourer, and incorporated a system called V-boost that linked the four carburetors, providing extra power at high revs.

The result was a snarling, aggressively styled 143bhp beast that stormed away from the line faster than anything else on wheels. The Yamaha's poor aerodynamics limited top speed to 140mph (225km/h) but the heavy, crudely suspended chassis meant that was quite exciting enough for most riders. The V-Max's performance and brutal image earned it a cult following, though it was initially detuned in markets including Britain. The bike would barely be updated while remaining in production well into the 21st century.

By coincidence 1985, the centenary of the first ever motorcycle journey by Daimler's Einspur, was an outstanding year for new bikes. Kawasaki provided another with the GPZ600R. The fully-faired, liquid-cooled Kawasaki was based on the GPz550, one of several popular air-cooled 550s. The GPZ was the first 600cc four, and its aggressive style and specification set the standard for the class that would become motorcycling's most popular and competitive.

The Kawasaki's 592cc dohc 16-valve engine produced a maximum of 75bhp and needed revving toward its 11,000rpm redline to give of its best. Compact dimensions, a rigid steel perimeter frame, and 16-inch wheels gave agile handling. Ridden hard, the GPZ delivered 130mph (209km/h) top speed and thrilling all-round performance that inspired the rival Japanese firms to develop rival fours of their own.

Harley-Davidson would also come to regard 1985 as very important. The company narrowly avoided having to file for Chapter 11 (bankruptcy) protection in December of that year, when vital extra finance was agreed within hours of a deadline set by its banks. In 1981 Harley had been bought from parent company AMF by a group of 13 managers, headed by Vaughan Beals and including design ace Willie G. Davidson and future Chairman Jeff Bleustein. After losing $30

Yamaha V-Max (1985)

Engine:	Liquid-cooled dohc 16-valve 72-degree V4
Capacity:	1198cc (76 x 66mm)
Maximum power:	143bhp @ 8000rpm
Transmission:	Five-speed, shaft final drive
Frame:	Steel twin downtube
Suspension:	Telescopic front; twin shocks rear
Brakes:	Twin discs front; disc rear
Weight:	560lb (254kg) dry
Top speed:	140mph (225km/h)

Above: The V-Max's brutal styling, enhanced by fake air-scoops on each side of the dummy tank, helped make the V4 a long-running sales success despite – or perhaps partly because of – its mediocre handling and scary reputation.

Right: Harley-Davidson took a big step forward in the mid-'80s when it fitted its Softails with the new generation Evolution V-twin engine. Many owners added extras such as tassels and custom pipes, adding to Harley's profit.

million that year, the revitalized firm had broken even in 1983, and was set to benefit from President Ronald Reagan's five-year protection scheme, which initially put a tariff of 49.4 percent on imported bikes of over 700cc capacity.

The Japanese manufacturers responded by increasing production in their US factories, and by introducing 699cc versions of their most popular 750cc models. But the tariff helped Harley to survive, and to continue production of models powered by the recently introduced, new-generation 1340cc V-twin engine known as the Evolution. This retained the familiar air-cooled, 45-degree layout but was a notably more powerful, sophisticated, reliable, and cool-running unit.

Introduced in seven models including the much improved Electra Glide giant tourer, the Evo motor set Harley on course for a period of sustained success that few people would have believed possible. The 1985-model Heritage Softail, with its hidden rear suspension giving a 'hard-tail' look, emphasized the focus on traditional styling. In 1986 Harley became a public company once again, and made a profit on sales of 36,000 bikes. The firm would increase sales, turnover, and profit every year consistently into the 21st century.

A comeback was also under way in Italy, where in 1985 Cagiva took over struggling Ducati, then state-owned and building only a few thousand bikes annually. Cagiva, based at the former Aermacchi Harley-Davidson factory on the banks of Lake Varese, had been founded in 1978 by brothers Claudio and Gianfranco Castiglioni (whose father, CAstiglioni GIanni of VArese, gave his name to the firm). It had quickly become successful in the Italian 125cc market. After reaching an agreement to build Ducati-engined bikes in 1983, Cagiva bought the Bologna firm two years later, and began its recovery with a stylish 750cc V-twin called the F1 Replica whose full fairing bore the names of both Ducati and Cagiva. During the next two years Cagiva also bought Husqvarna, the Swedish off-road specialist, and Moto Morini, whose ageing 350cc V-twin engine found a new home in the striking, fully-faired Dart.

Other struggling Italian marques were less fortunate. Moto Guzzi had suffered from lack of investment for years, and reached a low point in 1985 with an updated version of its Spada II, a sports-tourer powered by the Mandello firm's 949cc transverse V-twin engine. Guzzis had long

Racing's V4 Revolution

The world's fastest bikes during the 1980s were the 500cc two-stroke V4s that dominated grand prix racing from 1984. Until then, the winning layout changed repeatedly. Yamaha's Kenny Roberts won on a straight four in 1980, followed by victories for Suzuki's RG500 square four, ridden by Italians Marco Lucchinelli and Franco Uncini, in 1981 and '82; and Honda's NS500 V-triple, by Freddie Spencer, in 1983.

Once Eddie Lawson had won the 1984 championship on Yamaha's 140bhp YZR500, there was no doubting the powerful and compact V4 two-stroke layout's superiority. Yamaha's design used twin crankshafts, geared together and spinning in opposite directions. Honda's NSR500, introduced the same year with an unsuccessful chassis layout that put its fuel tank under the engine, had a single crank that reduced friction at the expense of extra width.

Spencer proved the redesigned, more conventional NSR500's speed in 1985 when he rode it to half of his 500 and 250cc world championship double. From then on the 500cc

title was swapped between factories: Yamaha's Lawson, Honda's Wayne Gardner, then Lawson again. When 'Steady Eddie' joined Honda in 1989, the aluminum-framed NSR produced over 160bhp but handled horribly. The Californian tamed it to win his fourth and last 500cc crown.

been famed for stable handling but when fitted with the current fashion item of a 16-inch front wheel, without geometry changes to compensate, the Spada was prone to frightening wobbles. Meanwhile Benelli, also owned by Argentinean Alejandro de Tomaso, had built small numbers of the six-cylinder 900 Sei, and four-cylinder 654, 504, and 304 models. But the unprofitable firm was producing mainly small-capacity bikes when in 1989 it was bought by the Biesse industrial group, which planned a range of bikes all with capacities of just 50cc.

Above left: Californian Eddie Lawson retained his yellow 500cc champion's No.1 plate on a Honda NSR500 in 1989, becoming one of only a handful of riders to have won the 500cc world title for two different manufacturers.

Above: Honda's single-crankshaft NSR500 went through several major revisions following its introduction in 1984. The NSR was generally the most powerful of the factory V4s, but its chassis performance was often less impressive.

Left: Bimota's 1982-model HB2, powered by the 16-valve motor from Honda's CB900F, proved that small specialist firms could still provide cutting-edge chassis design. But mass-produced Japanese superbikes were closing the gap.

Right: The success of the stylish DB1, designed by Federico Martini, rescued Bimota from financial problems in 1986. Beneath the all-enveloping glass-fiber were a 750cc Ducati V-twin engine and steel ladder frame.

Below: Laverda's long line of air-cooled triples came to an end with the SFC1000, a characterful sports-tourer that produced 90bhp and handled well, but which struggled to compete with more modern and cheaper machines.

Above: The Meriden factory workers' co-operative continued producing Triumph twins into the 1980s, and introduced many updates while lacking the finance for a major redesign. This 1981-model TR7 Tiger 750 features electronic ignition, left-foot gearchange, and smoother-running crankshaft, but not the electric starter that was an optional extra.

Bimota, too, had hit financial problems despite starting the decade with some fine bikes including the HB2, powered by the four-cylinder engine from Honda's CB900F. Japanese advances in chassis technology had reduced the demand for the Rimini firm's expensive, hand-built bikes. In 1986 Bimota bounced back with an all-Italian creation, the DB1, which combined a 750cc Ducati V-twin engine with a steel ladder frame and a striking, all-enveloping fairing/tank/seat unit. The 76bhp Bimota's 130mph (209km/h) top speed was modest for such an expensive bike. But its style, light weight, and agility made the DB1 a sales success that put Bimota back in the black, at least for a while.

Laverda in decline

Laverda, another famous old Italian marque, was in deeper trouble. The Breganze firm had tried hard to modernize its famous air-cooled triple, with some success. The Jota 120 of 1982, with a smoother, 120-degree firing order instead of the old 180-degree arrangement, was a fine superbike of the old school. In the same year Laverda introduced the RGS1000, which combined more modern styling with a softer, more flexible three-cylinder engine whose more restrictive exhaust system enabled the bike to pass stricter noise regulations. But the RGS lacked the raw appeal and competitive speed of the old triples.

In 1984 Laverda created the RGS1000 Corsa by tuning the 981cc engine to give 90bhp, and the following year used this motor to power a new model, the SFC1000. This had reshaped bodywork and many new chassis parts, and was a stylish and charismatic sports-tourer with a top speed of 140mph (225km/h) and good handling. But the SFC was far too expensive to sell in big numbers, and Laverda lacked the finance to develop its planned range of three-cylinder middleweights. The final batch of SFC1000s left the Breganze factory in 1987, and Laverda production came to an end.

By this time the British motorcycle industry, too, had all but disappeared. There had been glimmers of hope during the decade, not least with the high-profile unveiling in 1980 of the Hesketh V1000, a V-twin sports-tourer developed by Northamptonshire-based aristocrat Lord

Alexander Hesketh, who had previously owned a successful Formula One car racing team. The 992cc 90-degree dohc engine, designed and built by speedway specialists Weslake, used four valves per cylinder and produced 86bhp. The high-quality chassis combined a tubular steel frame with Marzocchi suspension and Brembo brakes from Italy.

The exotic Hesketh was billed as a 'two-wheeled Aston Martin.' Its engine was smooth and flexible, and the small fairing allowed leisurely cruising plus a top speed of 120mph (193km/h). Despite weighing over 500lb (227kg), the V1000 handled and braked well, too. But its gearbox was poor and the expensive, hand-built Hesketh was horribly unreliable. Only 149 bikes had been built when the firm went bust in 1982. Lord Hesketh formed a new company and began production of a fully-faired touring model, the Vampire, but few had been built when Hesketh abandoned bikes for good.

Triumph's final fling

Of the great old British marques, only Triumph had started the decade still producing bikes. The Meriden workers' co-operative continued to build 744cc parallel twins in fairly small numbers, and in 1980 introduced an optional electric starter to the Bonneville and its single-carb sibling the

Above and below: The Hesketh V1000 promised much when launched in 1980, but its 992cc V-twin engine proved unreliable. Although the firm soon folded, a handful of updated V1000s would be built on the same premises years later.

Right: *The VFR750F was one of the most important bikes that Honda had ever introduced. By the time this V4 was built in 1989, the VFR had been updated with a 17-inch front wheel plus an adjustable screen, and had done much to restore Honda's reputation for high-quality engineering.*

Honda VFR750F (1986)

Engine:	Liquid-cooled dohc 16-valve 90-degree V4
Capacity:	748cc (70 x 48.6mm)
Maximum power:	105bhp @ 10,500rpm
Transmission:	Six-speed, chain final drive
Frame:	Aluminum twin spar
Suspension:	Telescopic front; single shock rear
Brakes:	Twin discs front; disc rear
Weight:	436lb (198kg)
Top speed:	145mph (233km/h)

Below: *The gigantic GL1500 Gold Wing brought a new dimension to long-distance motorcycling, with its smooth 1520cc flat-six engine and unprecedented level of luxury.*

TR7 Tiger. Both were pleasant enough machines that handled well and had a certain nostalgic appeal, but their build quality and reliability, as well as performance, were far behind Japanese levels, and demand was limited.

Production of the Tiger ended in 1981, when it was replaced by a short-lived dual-purpose model, the Tiger Trail 750, which performed poorly both on- and off-road. In 1982 Triumph introduced the TSS, whose eight-valve cylinder head increased peak output by 7bhp to 57bhp, and top speed to 120mph (193km/h). But without the finance to develop more modern alternatives to the old pushrod twin the co-operative was doomed. Production was halted at the end of 1982, and Triumph went into liquidation shortly afterward.

The Triumph name was bought from the liquidator by a Midlands builder named John Bloor, who kept a very low profile. Bloor allowed Les Harris, the boss of Devon-based Triumph parts specialist Racing Spares, to restart production of the Bonneville under license. Harris had built about 1200 bikes when in 1988 he was told that the license would not be renewed, and that production of the pushrod twin was over for good. Harris instead tried to revive the Matchless name with a model called the G80, powered by a 494cc sohc single engine from Rotax of Austria, but few were built.

Mighty Honda had meanwhile faced difficulties of its own in the mid-'80s, as rushed development had resulted in engine problems for models including the VF750F and the CBX550, a lively in-line four that had been plagued by camchain trouble. Several other Honda models had suffered with less serious ailments such as poor gearshifting and weak clutches, and the marque's reputation for quality and reliability had suffered. When in 1986 Honda unveiled a new generation V4, the VFR750F, it arrived to an unprecedented level of scrutiny.

Thankfully for Honda, the VFR proved a magnificent bike that would earn a lasting reputation for exceptionally high build quality. Its 748cc engine retained not only the VF's 90-degree, 16-valve V4 layout but also its compression ratio and internal dimensions. Lighter components, gear-driven cams, and larger carbs helped boost peak output by 15bhp to 105bhp. The new aluminum frame held air-adjustable forks and a rear shock whose preload could be set using a remote knob behind a sidepanel.

Fully faired and subtly finished in single color paintwork, the VFR was a classy sports-tourer whose blend of performance and comfort won praise from almost everyone who rode it. Its flexible and smooth V4 motor gave a top speed of over 140mph (225km/h). The VFR handled very well and was comfortable, well equipped and – most importantly of all, in the circumstances – supremely reliable. By the time the VFR was updated with a reshaped fairing and a 17-inch front wheel in 1988, the model had become known for unmatched versatility and refinement, and had done much to restore faith in Honda's engineering.

Honda had found its Gold Wing tourer simpler to develop than its V4 line, notably when enlarging the flat-four engine to 1182cc, to create the GL1200. But the extra weight of the fully-dressed Wing had taken its toll on performance, and the 1987-model Gold Wing was slightly slower than the original GL1000 of 12 years earlier. Finally Honda abandoned the four-cylinder motor altogether, and created the GL1500 Gold Wing around a new flat-six powerplant with a capacity of 1520cc.

The huge, liquid-cooled sohc six produced a maximum of 100bhp at 5200rpm, along with vast reserves of smooth torque at almost any revs. The GL1500 was gigantic, with a wide fairing, long wheelbase, plus luggage and sound systems that contributed to a dry weight of almost 800lb (363kg). Its starter motor even doubled as a reverse gear to help when parking. The Wing was fast, comfortable, and handled well considering its size. It was also very expensive, but as a motorbike for stress-free long-distance travel, it was in a class of its own.

Top and above: Honda's CBR600F, known as the Hurricane in the US, represented a significant change of direction for the world's largest motorcycle firm: away from V4s to a new line of liquid-cooled 16-valve straight fours. The fast, fine-handling, and competitively priced CBR was an immediate worldwide success.

Left: Yamaha entered the open-class super-sports battleground with the FZR1000, whose blend of powerful 20-valve four-cylinder engine and aluminum 'Deltabox' frame would remain popular for many years to come. This 1989 model incorporated Yamaha's EXUP exhaust valve to boost mid-range performance.

Above: Bimota's exotic YB6 EXUP, also known as the YB8, housed a Yamaha FZR1000 engine in an aluminum beam frame of the Italian firm's own manufacture. The roadster was closely based on Virginio Ferrari's 1987 Formula One world-championship-winning YB4 racer.

Below right: The sublime RC30, or VFR750R to give the V4 its full name, was the spitting image of Honda's all-conquering RVF factory racebike. Fast, agile, and rewarding to ride, the RC30 was a hit despite its high price, and was almost unbeatable in production-based racing.

Honda RC30 (1988)

Engine:	Liquid-cooled dohc 16-valve 90-degree V4
Capacity:	748cc (70 x 48.6mm)
Maximum power:	112bhp @ 11,000rpm
Transmission:	Six-speed, chain final drive
Frame:	Aluminum twin spar
Suspension:	Telescopic front; single shock rear
Brakes:	Twin discs front; disc rear
Weight:	407lb (185kg) dry
Top speed:	155mph (249km/h)

The GL1500's high specification and price contrasted with the more prosaic design of an important pair of 1987 Hondas: the CBR600F and CBR1000F. The CBRs represented a move away from V4s, back to the in-line layout that Honda had popularized with the CB750. The new Hondas shared rounded, all-enveloping styling that hid their liquid-cooled four-cylinder engines from sight. The motors themselves were more conventional, incorporating chain-driven twin camshafts, 16 valves, and six-speed gearboxes.

Only the Honda engines' liquid cooling, compact size, light weight, and impressive power outputs revealed their modernity. The CBR1000F produced 133bhp, shot smoothly to 160mph (257km/h), handled well for a 488lb (221kg) motorbike, and was a capable and comfortable sports-tourer. And the CBR600F was a real star. Its 85bhp motor was smooth, revvy, reliable, and capable of powering the compact four to 140mph (225km/h). The 600F's fine handling, versatility, and competitive price added to its appeal, and soon the Honda was the best-selling bike in many markets. Numerous updates would help the CBR remain at or near the top of the competitive middleweight sports bike sector for years to come.

The other most significant arrival in 1987 was Yamaha's FZR1000, an eagerly anticipated sportster that introduced the twin-spar aluminum Deltabox frame, based on that of Yamaha's 'Genesis' factory racebike. The FZR's 989cc engine was an enlarged version of the liquid-cooled, 20-valve unit that had been introduced two years earlier in the FZ750. It produced generous mid-range delivery and a maximum of 125bhp, which matched the output of Suzuki's GSX-R1100, the Yamaha's main rival.

The FZR was an aggressive super-sports machine, and proved more popular than the versatile FZ. Its motor delivered smooth power from as low as 2000rpm, and kicked hard at the top end to send the Yamaha to a top speed of almost 160mph (257km/h). The chassis gave a brilliant blend of stability and agility. On performance, style, and price the FZR was very competitive, and it brought Yamaha to the forefront of superbike design. Two years later the motor was enlarged to 1002cc, increasing peak output to 140bhp. The FZR also gained an electronically operated exhaust valve whose acronym led to the model often being known as the 'EXUP.'

Spanish engineer Antonio Cobas had designed the first twin-spar aluminum frame for a 250cc, Rotax-engined racing machine in 1982, leading a revolution in chassis design. Bimota

Trail Bike Twins

BMW discovered a successful new format in 1980 with a dual-purpose version of its boxer twin, the R80G/S. With a torquey, 37bhp engine, striking looks, and a rugged, versatile chassis, it was an entertaining bike that surprised many riders with its ability both on- and off-road. Three victories in the grueling Paris-Dakar Rally in the early '80s, by Frenchman Hubert Auriol and Belgian's Gaston Rahier, enhanced the boxer's appeal. When the updated, 980cc R100GS was launched in 1987 it became the best-selling bike in Germany. By the end of the decade, more than 50,000 units of the GS had been sold.

The Japanese manufacturers joined in with a variety of dual-purpose twins. Honda's Transalp, developed from the VT500 roadster in 1987, combined a 587cc in-line V-twin engine with an integrated fairing/tank unit. That in turn led to the XRV650 Africa Twin, with Paris-Dakar style twin-headlamp fairing, big tank, tall seat, and rugged image. By 1989 the Africa Twin had gained a more powerful,

742cc V-twin engine to compete against Yamaha's equally large and rally-influenced XTZ750 Super Ténéré, whose parallel twin motor was developed from that of the quirky but versatile TDM850 roadster.

Above left: Gaston Rahier won the Paris-Dakar Rally on this much modified BMW R80G/S.

Top center: Yamaha's XTZ750 Super Ténéré twin was better off-road than many owners realized.

Top right: BMW's R80G/S inaugurated the twin-cylinder dual-purpose bike's rise in 1980.

Above: Honda revised their versatile Africa Twin several times during the decade.

Left: Californian Fred Merkel, pictured riding with a misted screen at Donington Park in 1989, won the first two World Superbike titles for Honda on a factory-supported RC30.

Ducati 851 (1988)	
Engine:	Liquid-cooled dohc eight-valve 90-degree V-twin
Capacity:	851cc (92 x 64mm)
Maximum power:	100bhp @ 8250rpm
Transmission:	Six-speed, chain final drive
Frame:	Tubular steel ladder
Suspension:	Telescopic front; single shock rear
Brakes:	Twin discs front; disc rear
Weight:	396lb (180kg)
Top speed:	140mph (225km/h)

Above right: In 1989 Ducati introduced the relatively simple air-/oil-cooled four-valve 900SS (left), as well as comprehensively revamping the liquid-cooled eight-valve 851.

Below: Buell's RS1200 emphasized its Harley engine by leaving the V-twin unit on display. It handled well, thanks to an innovative frame with rear shock located under the motor.

adopted the twin-spar format for its YB4 racer, with which Virginio Ferrari won the Formula One world title in 1987. Ferrari's factory YB4 was powered by Yamaha's FZ750 engine, as was the YB4 IE roadgoing replica launched a year later. Bimota quickly followed this with a similar YB6 model using the engine from the FZR1000.

Both the YB6 and its successor the YB8, which used Yamaha's exhaust-valve equipped 1002cc engine, were fast and fine-handling bikes. The YB8 was more compact and 50lb (23kg) lighter than the standard FZR. Bimota also claimed extra power from its less restrictive muffler, taking peak output to 147bhp. The YB8 was a success for Bimota, which built more than 650 of the exotic machines over the next few years.

Honda's race-replica V4

By contrast Honda's annual production was about three million bikes, but the outstanding machine of 1988 was the similarly exclusive RC30. Like its CB1100R and VF1000R predecessors, the bike also known as the VFR750R was a homologation special; created as a basis for competition success with little regard for cost. It was closely based on Honda's mighty RVF, the V4 factory racer that had dominated world championship endurance and Formula One racing in the mid-'80s. The compact RC30 was almost a carbon copy, with its twin-headlamp fairing, single seat, and a rigid twin-spar aluminum frame that was rumored to be cast using the same dies as the RVF's. It had a single-sided swingarm, as used on Honda's endurance racers to speed wheel changes.

Power came from a tuned and lightened version of the VFR750F sports-tourer's 748cc liquid-cooled 90-degree V4 engine, modified with an RVF-style 360-degree crankshaft, instead of the 750F's 180-degree set-up. Bigger carbs, titanium conrods, and a complex single-muffler exhaust system combined to give 112bhp output with impressive reliability. The RC30 was uncomfortable and impractical in town, with its racy riding position and tall first gear. But on the open road or racetrack it stormed toward a top speed of 155mph (249km/h) at a thrilling rate.

The RC30 was equally brilliant in the bends, where its light weight, lavishly equipped chassis, and compact dimensions helped give outstanding handling and braking. Honda's exotic race-replica cost almost twice as much as rival 750s, but it made a fine road bike as well as a hugely successful racer. Britain's Carl Fogarty rode a race-kitted RC30 to the Formula One world championship in 1988 and '89, and America's Fred Merkel achieved a similar double victory in the new World Superbike class, which quickly displaced F1 to become the leading four-stroke race series.

Ducati would eventually rise to dominate World Superbikes in the 1990s, basing its success on the ground-breaking 851 that was launched in 1988. With its powerful dohc eight-valve V-twin engine the 851, named after its capacity, was the bike that brought Ducati thundering into the modern era under Cagiva control. Chief engineer Massimo Bordi retained the Bologna firm's trademark 90-degree V-twin layout and desmodromic system of positive valve closure, and added four-valve heads, liquid cooling, and fuel-injection to create a powerplant that produced 100bhp with greatly increased refinement and tuning potential.

The 851 retained Ducati's familiar steel ladder frame construction, and featured high quality suspension and brakes. But ironically the original 'tricolore' model, finished in patriotic red, white, and green, was fitted with 16-inch wheels and handled poorly. Revamped a year later with restyled red paintwork, an extra 4bhp and most importantly with the 17-inch wheels it should have worn all along, the 851 was transformed into a fast and fine-handling sportster.

In 1989 Ducati also introduced another important model, a 904cc air-cooled V-twin that was named the 900 Super Sport after its famous forebear of the '70s. Its softly tuned, sohc two-valves-

Above: British road racing enjoyed an upsurge of spectator interest in 1989 when Norton team-mates Steve Spray and Trevor Nation (pictured) rode to numerous victories on the powerful, flame-spitting rotary racer.

Below: Norton had begun work on a Wankel rotary-engined bike in the mid-'70s, and developed the 588cc machine in conjunction with several UK police forces before releasing the limited-edition Classic roadster in late 1987.

Right: In 1989 Norton updated the rotary engine with liquid cooling to power the Commander tourer, featuring big fairing and built-in panniers. This bike is being used by a motorcycling paramedic in central London.

Below: Kawasaki's ZXR750 produced a relatively modest 105bhp and was heavy by super-sports standards. But striking styling and a competitive price, plus some enthusiastic brochure copy, made the ZXR a big success.

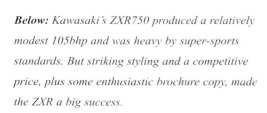

per-cylinder desmo motor produced a modest 83bhp, and the 900SS also had a simple chassis with no rising-rate rear suspension system. But it combined a 135mph (217km/h) top speed and strong mid-range performance with stable handling and plenty of V-twin charm. A competitive price also helped to make the 900SS a success, founding a Super Sport dynasty that would grow to include 750, 600, and 400cc models.

The year's other new air-cooled V-twin sportster came from the small town of Mukwonago, Wisconsin. Erik Buell was a former racer and Harley-Davidson engineer who had started a firm building sports bikes powered by the V-twin motors from nearby Milwaukee. His RR1000 and RR1200 Battletwin models featured all-enveloping bodywork that was good for aerodynamics but disguised the Harley connection. So Buell created a half-faired model, the RS1200, that left its 1203cc Sportster V-twin motor in view.

Buell's key feature was his Uniplanar engine mounting system, which used rods and joints to restrict engine vibration to the vertical plane. This allowed the engine to be rubber-mounted while also adding rigidity to the tubular steel ladder frame. Other innovative touches included a horizontal rear shock, located under the engine and working in tension rather than compression. Buell also designed the brake calipers, anti-dive system, and bodywork. Inevitably the hand-built RS1200 was expensive, and with its 60bhp Sportster engine it was not particularly fast. But it rumbled up to 120mph (193km/h), handled well and put Erik Buell's innovative, American-built bikes on the map.

Norton's Classic was an equally unusual bike that provided an unlikely success story. The Classic, an unfaired roadster with a 588cc 79bhp rotary engine, was the result of more than a decade of low-budget development work by the small firm, now based at Shenstone in Staffordshire. Norton sold a limited run of 100 Classics, and also developed a faired touring version, the Commander. Interest snowballed when a handful of employees, led by engineer Brian Crighton, built an aluminum-framed rotary racer. In 1989 Steve Spray rode the fire-spitting, 135bhp Norton to two major UK championships, to the delight of huge crowds.

Style, speed, and value for money

Kawasaki's ZXR750 scored a more predictable sales success in 1989. With its race-team-inspired paint scheme and a big pair of air ducts leading from its fairing nose toward a powerful in-line four-cylinder engine, the ZXR750 looked as though it belonged on a world championship race grid. Its 748cc engine was a tuned version of the rather bland GPX750 roadster's liquid-cooled 16-valve unit, and its chassis was based on that of Kawasaki's aluminum-framed ZXR-7 racer.

But the ZXR was no limited-edition race-replica like Honda's RC30 and Yamaha's similarly exotic but less successful rival, the 749cc OW01 in-line four. The ZXR was a mass-produced machine whose competitive price was as important a figure as its 105bhp peak power output. The Kawasaki screamed toward a top speed of 150mph (241km/h) at a thrilling rate, feeling suitably racy thanks to its stretched-out riding position and firm suspension. The ZXR750 won few races but was a worthy rival to Suzuki's GSX-R750, which had been comprehensively redesigned with more rounded styling, a new chassis, and a reworked engine.

Even the ZXR750 looked ordinary alongside 1989's most striking new bike, BMW's K1. With its brightly colored, all-enveloping bodywork, the 987cc longitudinal four was a striking machine by any manufacturer's standards, let alone those of the German firm that was known for efficient but unexciting tourers. In conjunction with the huge front fender, the K1's fairing and large rear section gave a wind-cheating shape unmatched even by Japanese race-replicas.

BMW had shaped the K1 that way both to highlight the firm's new, more adventurous approach, and to improve performance because the engine's peak output was being kept to 100bhp, the voluntary German limit. The bike's unmatched aerodynamics meant that it managed a top speed of 145mph (233km/h), and the softly tuned motor was also impressively flexible. Despite its racy looks the K1 was no sports bike. Its shaft drive system contributed to a weight of no less than 570lb (259kg), and the conservative steering geometry and long wheelbase added to the bike's slow-steering, ultra-stable feel.

Flaws included annoying vibration above 5000rpm, and the rear bodywork's broad storage pockets, which held little and made panniers impossible to fit. But in other respects the K1 was a capable sports-tourer that rivaled Yamaha's FJ1200 for fast and comfortable long-distance travel, and it signified the start of a new era at BMW. As the 1980s came to a close it was clear that, with motorcycles regarded by many buyers as leisure purchases rather than mere transport, all manufacturers were under pressure to develop innovative and exciting machines.

BMW K1 (1989)	
Engine:	Liquid-cooled dohc 16-valve in-line four
Capacity:	987cc (67 x 70mm)
Maximum power:	100bhp @ 8000rpm
Transmission:	Five-speed, shaft final drive
Frame:	Tubular steel space frame
Suspension:	Telescopic front; monoshock rear
Brakes:	Twin discs front; disc rear
Weight:	570lb (259kg)
Top speed:	145mph (233km/h)

Below: Aerodynamic, all-enveloping bodywork, which incorporated the large front fender, helped give BMW's K1 high cruising and top speeds, even though its 987cc engine's maximum output had been limited to 100bhp.

Weekend
Warriors
1990s

Above: A mildly customized Harley was the ideal bike for the new breed of American enthusiast.

Previous page: The updated 1998-model 900SS was one of many new models from rejuvenated Ducati toward the end of the decade.

Below: Kawasaki's 750cc Zephyr was the middle of three naked retro fours of the same name.

Below right: Honda's CB750, known as the Nighthawk in some markets, was a budget 'standard' built initially for the US market.

M otorcycling came of age in the 1990s. The days when a motorbike was a poor man's alternative to a car seemed long ago, as increasingly bikes were the toys of affluent middle-aged men – ironically, often the same people who had fueled a biking boom as impecunious youths two decades earlier. The new breed of motorcyclist often rode not to go anywhere in particular, but simply for fun on a sunny Sunday morning.

If there was one firm riding on top of the new wave, it was Harley-Davidson. The dark days of the company's fight for survival in the '80s seemed far away as Harley's sales and share price soared to new heights every year. Newspapers and general interest magazines ran features on Rich Urban Bikers (or 'RUBs' as they were known), each noting that beneath the mean-looking black leather most riders were well-educated professionals, in their 40s or above.

Harley's growth was concentrated in the US, where the Milwaukee firm had captured half of the market for large-capacity machines. Success came from targeting rising middle-class disposable income, with bikes that combined traditional American styling, large-capacity V-twin engines, non-threatening performance, and much improved build quality and finish. Equally important was the clever marketing that emphasized Harley's cool image, and the fostering of the Harley Owners Group, which strengthened brand loyalty and provided owners with places to ride.

Elsewhere, especially in Europe, Japanese manufacturers continued to dominate, and the focus was much more on performance. On summer weekends, twisty roads from England's Peak District to the Alpine foothills echoed with the exhaust notes of bikes of a wide variety of capacities and styles. Riders of many of the sportier machines wore one-piece leathers containing body-armor, and with removable knee-pads whose scuff marks confirmed the dramatic cornering angles possible on sticky radial tires.

Transverse four-cylinder engines remained the normal choice for large-capacity bikes of most types, but other layouts, notably the V-twin, would continue to be successful. Engine performance had increased to the point where the fastest bikes' top speeds were more than double most

Kawasaki ZX-11 (ZZ-R1100) (1990)	
Engine:	Liquid-cooled dohc 16-valve four
Capacity:	1052cc (76 x 58mm)
Maximum power:	145bhp @ 9500rpm
Transmission:	Six-speed, chain final drive
Frame:	Aluminum twin spar
Suspension:	Telescopic front; single shock rear
Brakes:	Twin discs front; disc rear
Weight:	502lb (228kg) dry
Top speed:	175mph (282km/h)

countries' national limits. That created political problems, not least the early-'90s threat of a Europe-wide 100bhp limit. After determined opposition from increasingly well organized and co-ordinated riders' pressure groups, the 100bhp limit would be defeated in most countries, France being a notable exception.

Such had been the advance in chassis engineering during the 1980s that despite their unprecedented straight-line speed, most bikes had handling, brakes, and tires to match. Frames were generally very rigid, whether made from steel or the increasingly popular aluminum. Suspension on many bikes, especially sports machines, was adjustable for hydraulic damping. This gave potential for better handling but demanded correct setting-up, and a higher level of rider skill.

In many countries, that increased knowledge and experience was available via high-speed riding, both on 'track days' and through more formal, circuit-based riding or racing schools. The track school format, pioneered in the US in the '80s by former racer Keith Code's California Superbike School, was widely copied and adapted. With motorcycles' performance becoming increasingly at odds with roadgoing speed limits and traffic density, and speed cameras becoming an added threat in some countries, track days were welcomed by riders and the motorcycle industry alike.

While sports bikes' performance raced ahead, manufacturers also strove to find lucrative niches that could be filled with a purpose-designed model and a slick marketing campaign. Japanese firms began to acknowledge their heritage, with 'retro-bikes' such as Honda's CB750 Nighthawk and Kawasaki's Zephyr range of naked fours in 1100, 750, and 550cc sizes. All were designed to tempt 'born-again bikers,' returning to two wheels after a break for kids or careers, with memories of the 1970s.

But there was only one four-cylinder Kawasaki dominating the headlines in 1990. The ZX-11 (ZZ-R1100 in the Europe) ripped onto the superbike scene with a stunning 1052cc 16-valve four-cylinder engine whose 'ram-air' system of forced induction, developed from Formula One car racing, helped give a peak output of 145bhp. Combined with bulbous but aerodynamically efficient bodywork, that sent the ZX-11 screaming to a 175mph (282km/h) top speed that made it by some distance the world's fastest streetbike.

Above left: Kawasaki's mighty ZX-11 was a searingly fast 16-valve four whose 145bhp output was delivered with the help of motorcycling's first 'ram-air' induction system, as used in F1 car racing.

Below: For crossing continents in high-speed comfort few bikes came close to matching Honda's ST1100. The transverse V4's peak output was limited to 100bhp, but the 'Pan European' was fast, smooth, and civilized.

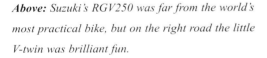

Above: Suzuki's RGV250 was far from the world's most practical bike, but on the right road the little V-twin was brilliant fun.

Above right: Honda successfully revamped the CBR600F every couple of years through the '90s, improving performance and retaining the versatility on which its popularity was based.

Below: Honda's ultra-racy, Japanese-market NSR250R was one of the most advanced bikes of the early '90s.

There was much more to the Kawasaki than straight-line performance. The ZX-11 was big and quite heavy but its rigid twin-spar aluminum frame, which like the engine was based on that of the previous ZX-10, held firm suspension that gave excellent stability even at high speed. The full fairing made that phenomenal performance very usable, as did a comfortable seat and such details as good mirrors and a strong pillion grab-rail. The ZX-11 was refined, handled well, and proved superbly reliable. Most important of all, it was blindingly fast.

Honda produced a sports-tourer of contrasting style and focus in 1990 with the ST1100, whose emphasis was on distance rather than speed. Its 1084cc liquid-cooled engine was a V4, but unlike previous Honda layouts this one placed its cylinders across the frame, facilitating the shaft final drive. The Pan European, as the ST was also known, was developed by Honda's German subsidiary, and its engine's 100bhp output remained within that country's voluntary power limit.

The big, softly-tuned V4 motor was very smooth and flexible, giving the Honda effortless performance to a top speed of 135mph (217km/h). Along with its large fairing, huge fuel tank, broad seat, and built-in panniers, that made the ST an excellent long-haul machine, albeit one whose conservative steering geometry and 614lb (279kg) of weight produced ponderous handling. The Pan European was more efficient than fun but hit its intended target, and would become a lasting success.

Kawasaki had also introduced a four-cylinder ZZ-R600 alongside the larger ZX-11, to compete in the popular middleweight sports division against Yamaha's FZR600 and Honda's CBR600F. The Kawasaki's revamped 599cc liquid-cooled 16-valve engine produced a class-leading 95bhp, good for over 140mph (225km/h), and was held by a frame made from aluminum, rather than steel like that of its GPZ and GPX600 predecessors.

The ZZ-R's closest rivals also had steel frames, but both were sportier than the large and roomy Kawasaki. Yamaha's FZR600, which had been launched in 1989, was a rev-happy and rapid 90bhp machine with crude suspension. It provided little practicality or comfort, but lots of high-revving entertainment. Honda's versatile and hugely successful CBR600F got better still in 1991 when it was revamped with fresh styling and a more powerful, 100bhp engine.

Small bikes, big thrills

While many European riders regarded 600cc as the perfect compromise between performance and cost, in Japan the hot class for high-tech sports machines was 400cc. Honda's CBR400RR and Suzuki's GSX-R400R, both in-line fours, and their V4 rival the VFR400R were tiny, high-revving bikes that handled superbly thanks to ultra-light chassis, but were too expensive to be sold outside Japan. Super-sports 250cc two-strokes were also popular in Japan. Some, notably Kawasaki's KR-1 and Suzuki's RGV250, were sold in Europe.

Honda's 1994 NSR250R race-replica was notably high-tech, as it featured a 'smart-card' that slotted into the steering head. Alternative cards could be used to alter the two-stroke V-twin's engine management system, giving instant tuning. The NSR and other exotica reached Europe in

Below: Harley revitalized its Sportster 1200 in 1991 with a mildly tuned V-twin engine, five-speed box, and belt final drive. It was slow, vibrated, and had mediocre handling. But it also looked great and sold well – as did the similarly styled, budget-priced Sportster 883, whose capacity echoed that of the original 1957 model.

Above: Suzuki updated the GSX-R750 with a liquid-cooled engine in 1992, by which time the 16-valve four's storming performance and aggressive, wheelie-happy personality had earned it a cult following around the world.

Below: For British bike enthusiasts the decade's best surprise was the rebirth of Triumph, with a range of modular three- and four-cylinder superbikes. This prototype 900 Trophy was painted in contrasting colors for evaluation.

Below right: Norton's expensive rotary-engined F1 sportster, left, was inspired by Steve Spray's championship-winning racebike.

small numbers when enterprising dealers began trading in 'gray' models ignored by official importers. More worrying for some countries' importers were 'parallel imports,' familiar models sourced independently from abroad and sold cheaply. Some importers were forced into big price reductions to overcome the problem.

Honda had suffered a more serious setback when in 1990 it had attempted to reverse falling US sales and market share with a bold new machine, the PC800 Pacific Coast. This was a large, rounded device, designed by Honda's car division to entice a new generation of non-motorcyclists onto two wheels. Beneath its expanse of plastic the Pacific Coast held an 800cc, in-line V-twin engine from the VT800 Shadow cruiser. It produced 50bhp and gave quiet running with a top speed approaching 120mph (193km/h). The Coast was lighter than it looked, and handled reasonably well. But few people bought one, despite an expensive TV advertising campaign.

Honda's US slump contrasted with the rise of Harley-Davidson, whose Sportster was the top-selling bike of 1990. That year saw the introduction of the Fat Boy, whose blend of 1950s-inspired styling and disc wheels would prove a hit. In 1991 the Sportster 1200 was updated with a more powerful, 50bhp engine, five-speed gearbox, and final drive by belt, as already used by the firm's 1340cc 'Big Twins.' The Sportster was still crude and not very fast, but it looked as cute as ever and continued the success story.

While cruisers dominated the US market, elsewhere attention was focused on the open-class super-sports battle between Suzuki and Yamaha. Suzuki had blundered in 1989 by updating its original GSX-R1100 with the ill-handling GSX-R1100K. That model was followed a year later by the 1100L, which replaced the K model's stiff front forks with a new pair whose 'upside-down' design, derived from road-racing, was claimed to give increased rigidity.

The GSX-R1100L shared its predecessor's uprated 1127cc 141bhp four-cylinder engine, and combined searing straight-line speed with much improved handling. In 1991 it faced fresh opposition from Yamaha's FZR1000RU, an uprated version of the old favorite with sharper styling, unchanged 140bhp 20-valve 1102cc powerplant and a pair of upside-down forks of its own. The two rivals were good for about 165mph (266km/h) and were closely matched in every way. Suzuki also revised its popular GSX-R750 to good effect.

Triumph Trophy 1200 (1991)

Engine:	Liquid-cooled dohc 16-valve four
Capacity:	1180cc (76 x 65mm)
Maximum power:	125bhp @ 9000rpm
Transmission:	Six-speed, chain final drive
Frame:	Steel spine
Suspension:	Telescopic front; single shock rear
Brakes:	Twin disc front; disc rear
Weight:	529lb (240kg)
Top speed:	153mph (246km/h)

At the opposite end of the scale to the mass-produced fours was Norton's F1, a compact rotary sportster derived from the marque's British championship-winning racer. The F1's 588cc liquid-cooled engine produced 95bhp, and was held by a high-quality aluminum frame, based on the racer's and built by local specialists Spondon Engineering. The F1's power and 422lb (191kg) weight figures matched those of a typical Japanese 600, as did its 145mph (233km/h) top speed.

The rotary felt very different, thanks to its smooth mid-range power surge and unique exhaust howl. But the expensive F1 had rough edges including snatchy low-rev response, poor fuel economy, and a tendency to overheat. In 1991 Norton introduced the cheaper F1 Sport, featuring simpler bodywork and less expensive cycle parts. Few were sold, despite another burst of Norton glory when Steve Hislop rode the rotary racer to victory in the 1992 Senior TT.

By this time the British motorcycle industry was celebrating the sensational rebirth of Triumph, which in 1991 had appeared with a range of three- and four-cylinder superbikes. When the old Triumph firm had gone into liquidation in 1983, the name had been bought by John Bloor, owner of a Midlands-based building firm. Bloor was worth over $175 million but was unknown in the bike world, and most people assumed Triumph had died.

But Bloor and his small team spent the next eight years developing a range of modern bikes amid great secrecy at a purpose-built plant at Hinckley in Leicestershire, not far from Triumph's old Meriden works. The dohc, liquid-cooled engine layout owed much to Japanese practice (notably Kawasaki's GPZ900R) but incorporated a unique modular concept that echoed plans that BSA-Triumph's Bert Hopwood had produced back in 1973, but which had been abandoned after the company's financial collapse.

Bloor's Triumphs used either three or four cylinders, plus a choice of short- or long-stroke crankshafts, to create four engines that powered six models. All combined the same steel frame with Japanese-made suspension parts of varying specification. The basic roadster was the Trident, a naked triple of 749 or 885cc capacity. It was stylish and handled well, and the larger model combined generous mid-range torque with a 130mph (209km/h) top speed.

Top left: Top of reborn Triumph's initial six-model range was the Trophy 1200. The fast and fine-handling sports-tourer was remarkably competitive with its Japanese rivals.

Above: Triumph's modular system meant that the larger-engined naked roadster, the Trident 900, shared its 885cc engine, plus its frame, tank, seat, and many other parts, with the fully-faired Trophy 900 sports-tourer.

Above: The NR750 was beautiful, and crammed with technology that only Honda could have developed. But the V4 was very heavy, and its oval pistons were of little benefit on a roadster.

Honda CBR900RR (1992)

Engine:	Liquid-cooled dohc 16-valve four
Capacity:	893cc (70 x 58mm)
Maximum power:	123bhp @ 10,500rpm
Transmission:	Six-speed, chain final drive
Frame:	Aluminum twin spar
Suspension:	Telescopic front; single shock rear
Brakes:	Twin discs front; disc rear
Weight:	407lb (185kg) dry
Top speed:	160mph (257km/h)

Above right: The initial 1992-model CBR900RR, called the FireBlade in most markets, took super-sports performance to a new level thanks to its unprecedented blend of powerful 893cc engine and light, compact chassis.

Impressive sports tourer

Triumph's two Daytona sports bikes, handicapped by the modular concept, were less impressive. But the four-cylinder Trophy 1200 was a fine sports-tourer that matched its Japanese rivals in almost every area. Its 1180cc 16-valve motor produced 125bhp, giving smooth acceleration to a top speed of over 150mph (241km/h). The Trophy also handled and braked well, and was comfortable and competitively priced. Equally importantly, all the new Triumphs proved oil-tight and very reliable. The firm soon became established in the UK market, and began exporting a growing number of bikes, initially to France and Germany, as Triumph's 200-strong workforce aimed for an annual target of 10,000 units.

In the year that one reluctant new industry hero emerged, motorcycling's greatest figure of all passed away. Soichiro Honda died in August 1991, aged 84. The motorcycle firm that he had started in a Tokyo shed in 1948 now had over 80,000 employees, and factories in more than 40 countries. With bike production growing steadily toward a 1996 peak of over five million units, Honda remained by far the industry's largest and most influential force.

Honda launched one of its fastest and best ever bikes in 1992, in defiance of the lingering threat of a 100bhp limit in Europe, the new bike's intended main market. The CBR900RR, known as the FireBlade in most countries, was relatively conventional in its liquid-cooled, four-cylinder engine layout and its twin-spar aluminum frame. But this was a gloriously sharp-edged machine whose unprecedented performance resulted from a combination of big-bike horsepower and light weight. The contrast with its heavier super-sports rivals was striking.

The FireBlade's 893cc 16-valve engine produced a maximum of 123bhp, and equally importantly was barely bigger or heavier than Honda's CBR600F powerplant. The frame held thick 45mm diameter forks that were not the fashionable upside-down design, and which held a 16-inch front wheel instead of the 17-inch norm. The CBR's steering geometry was racy, and it weighed just 407lb (185kg), comparable with a middleweight four rather than its open-class rivals.

Performance was addictively thrilling. The Honda couldn't match its larger-engined GSX-R and FZR rivals for mid-range torque, but delivered fierce, high-revving acceleration toward a top

Forkless Failures

In the early '90s, many people were convinced that telescopic forks were an inherent weakness in a motorcycle chassis. The previous decade's Elf project, backed by Honda, had been abandoned after failing to make a 'forkless' factory NSR500 GP racer competitive. But some engineers continued to experiment, notably Pierluigi Marconi of Bimota. Marconi had written a thesis on alternative suspension design as a student, and at Bimota he put it into production with the Tesi ('thesis' in Italian).

The Tesi 1D, released in 1991, featured a twin-sided front swingarm, working a single

shock unit. Its handlebars were linked by rods to the front wheel, which pivoted on a bearing inside its hub in order to steer. The Tesi was fast, thanks to its 904cc dohc V-twin Ducati engine, and the forkless front end gave outstanding stability under braking. But the complex system of rods reduced the rider's feedback from the front wheel, and was prone to bearing wear. Equally importantly, the Tesi's exotic construction resulted in a very high price. Few were sold, and the Tesi was a commercial disaster for Bimota.

Yamaha fared little better with its 1993 forkless sports-tourer, the GTS1000. The GTS

suspension system, designed a decade earlier by New Mexico-based engineer James Parker, featured a horizontal aluminum beam running from the wheel hub to a pivot on the frame. Steering was via a telescoping vertical strut linking the hub and handlebars. The system gave excellent stability but the GTS1000, powered by a four-cylinder FZR1000 engine detuned to 100bhp, had flaws including poor fuel range, excess weight, and a high price. The Yamaha's showroom failure ensured that most bikes would continue to use telescopic forks for years to come.

speed of 160mph (257km/h). Its light, racy chassis gave wonderful agility, plus an occasional flap of the handlebars to keep the rider's attention focused at all times. The Blade would lose a little of its raw excitement as chief engineer Tadao Baba refined it through the decade, but its emphasis on performance through light weight would have a lasting influence on super-sports design.

Above left: Bimota's forkless Tesi, more than a decade in development, was a costly failure that almost bankrupted the small Italian firm.

Top center: The sales failure of Yamaha's GTS1000 was blamed on its front suspension system, but the sports-tourer had other flaws.

Above: Soichiro Honda had long since retired, but his old firm backed research into alternative front suspension systems through its support for the Elf racer project.

Left: After getting into financial trouble with the Tesi, Bimota was once again saved by the success of a conventional bike – this time the stylish Ducati 900SS-engined DB2 of 1993.

Right: Guzzi's Daytona 1000, fashioned by American engineer 'Dr. John' Wittner, combined a new 95bhp, eight-valve V-twin engine with fresh styling and a chassis inspired by that of Wittner's racebikes.

Opposite top: Ducati's aggressively styled M900 Monster was such a hit following its launch in 1993 that it generated a new class of naked roadster, as well as prompting Ducati to create a family of Monsters in various capacities.

Opposite center right: Having once announced that its traditional flat twins would be dropped, BMW revived the boxer with the R1100RS, whose torquey eight-valve engine was matched by an innovative and fine-handling chassis.

Opposite below right: BMW's entry-level F650 was a bold step for the German marque, as the single was built in Italy around a motor from Rotax of Austria. The 'Funduro' performed well and earned BMW many new customers.

By contrast, Honda's other 1992 sports bike, the exotic, oval-pistoned NR750, occupied a technological cul-de-sac that no other manufacturer would have considered entering. The NR owed its existence to the NR500 four-stroke racebike with which Honda had attempted to take on the rival two-strokes on its return to grand prix racing in 1979. Limited to four cylinders, Honda had attempted to mimic a V8 by creating a V4 with pistons shaped like a running track, each with eight valves and two conrods.

Honda had never managed to make the NR500 competitive, and had abandoned the project in 1981 without a rostrum finish. But development of the engine continued, and the NR750 was launched 11 years later, incorporating high-tech features including a titanium-coated windshield, and twin mufflers set into a carbon-fiber reinforced tailpiece. The NR750 was a wonderfully stylish machine, as well as a hugely expensive one of which just 1000 units were planned.

Right: Ducati's Supermono racer combined sleek styling with brilliant engineering, as its 550cc 75bhp single-cylinder engine's dummy conrod dramatically reduced vibration. Sadly, hopes of a roadgoing version came to nothing.

Ducati M900 Monster (1993)	
Engine:	Air/oil-cooled sohc four-valve 90-degree V-twin
Capacity:	904cc (92 x 68mm)
Maximum power:	73bhp @ 7250rpm
Transmission:	Six-speed, chain final drive
Frame:	Tubular steel ladder
Suspension:	Telescopic front; single shock rear
Brakes:	Twin discs front; disc rear
Weight:	406lb (184kg)
Top speed:	130mph (209km/h)

The engine's maximum output of 125bhp at 14,000rpm made the NR the world's most powerful 750, and gave a top speed of almost 160mph (257km/h). But despite much use of lightweight materials, the NR weighed an excessive 488lb (221kg). Although its polished aluminum frame, single-sided swingarm, and high quality suspension gave good handling, the NR's flat power delivery meant it was not particularly exciting to ride, and no quicker than rival 750s costing a fraction of its price.

Bimota was not used to producing bikes in bigger numbers and for a lower price than a Honda, but that's what happened in 1993. Not with the long-awaited forkless Tesi, which had been a commercial flop on its release two years earlier, but with the more conventional DB2 that rescued the Italian firm's fortunes. Powered by the air/oil-cooled 904cc V-twin from Ducati's 900SS, the DB2 was a stylish, compact sportster that gained in agility what it lacked in straight-line speed. By Bimota standards the 140mph (225km/h) DB2 was inexpensive, and its sales success helped the firm recover from the disappointment of the Tesi.

Meanwhile Moto Guzzi had begun a fightback in 1992 with the Daytona 1000, a new generation V-twin with transverse, shaft-drive layout in the oldest Italian marque's own style. The American name was no coincidence, because the Daytona was inspired and created by 'Dr. John' Wittner, a Philadelphia dentist-turned-tuner whose rapid self-built Guzzis had been very successful in twins racing in the late '80s. Guzzi boss Alejandro de Tomaso brought Wittner to the factory to develop a roadgoing version, and the Daytona was the result.

The sleek, half-faired Daytona was powered by a 992cc air-cooled V-twin with a new 'high-cam' valve design and four valves per cylinder. Fuel-injection helped increase output to 95bhp. The Daytona's chassis was based on that of Wittner's racebikes. It combined a steel spine frame with Marzocchi forks, and a rear suspension layout that counteracted the drive-shaft's effect on handling. The Daytona rumbled toward its 150mph (241km/h) top speed with a typically long-legged feel. Stable handling, good brakes, and plenty of character contributed to an enjoyable bike that belatedly brought Moto Guzzi into the 1990s.

Ducati had also uprated its V-twin line-up in 1992, with the 900 Superlight, a sportier, single-seat version of the 900SS. The Bologna firm was fighting back under Cagiva control. Its eight-

Above: Reborn former East German marque MuZ's Skorpion Sport was a stylish and innovative machine. Its prototype used a Rotax engine, but production versions were powered by a 660cc five-valve single unit from Yamaha.

Above: After beating Honda to win the 250cc world title, Aprilia launched a fitting replica with the RS250. It combined the Italian firm's own bodywork and aluminum frame with a two-stroke V-twin engine from Suzuki's RG250.

Right: Cagiva's effort in the 500cc grand prix class was rewarded when Eddie Lawson won the firm's first victory in 1992. But despite further success in 1993, financial pressures forced boss Claudio Castiglioni to quit racing.

valve flagship the 851, uprated to 888cc in 1991, won three consecutive World Superbike championships, ridden by Frenchman Raymond Roche and America's Doug Polen. In 1993 Ducati unveiled the stunning Supermono 550 racer, designed by South African Pierre Terblanche, and powered by a dohc single-cylinder desmo engine, designed by chief engineer Massimo Bordi, that used a dummy conrod to reduce vibration. The Supermono was raced successfully but plans for a roadgoing model would repeatedly be postponed.

Ducati's success continued in 1993 with the M900 Monster, a naked all-rounder whose aggressive style would inspire a new generation of unfaired bikes. The Monster was created by Miguel Angel Galluzzi, Cagiva's Argentinean designer, who sketched a naked V-twin in his spare time, then persuaded factory bosses to put it into production. Its air-cooled sohc 904cc V-twin engine, from the 900SS, was housed in a frame from the super-sports 888, complete with rising-rate rear suspension.

The Monster's high-quality cycle parts gave excellent handling and braking by naked bike standards. The torquey V-twin engine and lack of weight ensured plenty of straight-line performance too, along with a liking for wheelies. This was a bike that was huge fun to ride at a slower pace, yet which had plenty of street cred. Despite a high price the Monster immediately generated so much demand that Ducati increased production to a quarter of the factory's 1993 total of 20,000 bikes. Soon the M900 was joined by M750 and M600 Monsters, and a naked-bike revolution was under way.

The other outstanding European twin of 1993 was BMW's R1100RS, a boxer whose appearance confirmed a remarkable change of heart. When BMW had introduced its new range of liquid-cooled fours and triples in the mid-'80s, word from Munich was that the traditional flat twins were heading for extinction. But public resistance was so strong that BMW not only introduced updated twins but developed a new boxer motor: a 1085cc fuel-injected air-/oil-cooled unit whose high-cam, four-valves-per-cylinder layout gave a maximum of 90bhp.

The R1100RS was equally notable for its chassis, which incorporated a clever new 'Telelever' front suspension system. This resembled telescopic forks, but the legs were hollow and joined to a horizontal arm that pivoted on the engine and operated a single shock unit. With stable handling allied to its flexible engine, reasonable wind protection, generous fuel range, and powerful anti-

Left: Ducati's 916 backed up its gorgeous looks with thundering performance from its eight-valve desmo V-twin engine, and superb handling from its tubular steel-framed chassis.

Ducati 916 (1994)	
Engine:	Liquid-cooled dohc eight-valve 90-degree V-twin
Capacity:	916cc (94 x 66mm)
Maximum power:	114bhp @ 9000rpm
Transmission:	Six-speed, chain final drive
Frame:	Tubular steel ladder
Suspension:	Telescopic front; single shock rear
Brakes:	Twin discs front; disc rear
Weight:	429lb (195kg) dry
Top speed:	160mph (257km/h)

lock brakes, the RS represented a fine comeback for the sports-touring boxer. Within two years it would be joined by a naked R1100R and R850R roadsters, plus an R1100RT tourer with bigger fairing and more upright riding position.

BMW's radical single

BMW had lacked an entry-level model since abandoning singles production in the late '60s. That changed in 1994 with the F650 Funduro. This was evidence of a radically different approach because it was built in Italy, by Aprilia, around a liquid-cooled 652cc single-cylinder engine from Austrian firm Rotax. The F650 was also the first chain-drive model in BMW's 70-year history. With striking looks, 100mph (161km/h) performance, and good handling, the Funduro was indeed fun to ride. It was competitively priced, and quickly became a success.

The F650 was not the year's only new German single. The former East German firm MZ, known for efficient but ugly commuter bikes, had been reborn after German reunification as MuZ. The firm's boss Petr-Karel Korous commissioned British consultants Seymour Powell to design a roadster around the 48bhp engine from Yamaha's XTZ660. The result was the striking Skorpion, available as a bikini-faired sportster and a naked roadster. With 100mph (161km/h) performance and agile handling from an innovative frame of large-diameter steel tube, it was a promising start for MuZ.

Meanwhile Aprilia was going from strength to strength. Ivano Beggio, who had begun motorcycle production in 1973 after taking over the family bicycle business, had found rapid success by assembling bikes using components sourced almost exclusively from outside, rather than manufactured in-house. Beggio had concentrated on small two-stroke sports machines and trail bikes, investing heavily in research and development via racing. In 1994 Aprilia produced 100,000 bikes, double the total of three years earlier, and beat mighty Honda to win both 250cc and 125cc world championships.

The following year the firm from Noale in north-eastern Italy celebrated rider Max Biaggi's 250cc title with a race-replica, the RS250. Its sleek bodywork echoed that of the factory racebike, and the RS featured a similar specification: liquid-cooled, two-stroke V-twin engine, strong

Below: Few small-capacity bikes have matched the style of Gilera's CX125, with its swoopy bodywork and mono-arm suspension at front and rear. But the two-stroke was not a success.

Above: Cagiva's Cucciolo, named after subsidiary Ducati's first ever bike, was one of scores of scooters from Italian manufacturers.

Below: Italjet's Formula 125 was very unusual for a scooter in having a twin-cylinder engine, but in most markets it was restricted to 12bhp.

aluminum twin-spar frame, and high-quality cycle parts. The 249cc motor, from Suzuki's RGV250, was modified with new cylinder heads that boosted power to 70bhp. The lightweight Aprilia screamed to 130mph (209km/h) and handled brilliantly. The final touch was a GP-style lap-timer in the cockpit, activated by a switch on the handlebars.

Cagiva had spent years battling against the Japanese factories in the even more competitive 500cc grand prix class, and had finally achieved notable success. Americans Eddie Lawson and John Kocinski won GPs on the Italian firm's V4 in 1992 and '93 respectively, and Kocinski briefly led the championship in the following season. Then Cagiva quit grand prix racing amid rumors of financial trouble.

Those problems would cause the delayed arrival of the bike that was the undoubted star of 1994. Ducati's 916 combined style, speed, and poise to stunning effect. Designed by former Bimota co-founder Massimo Tamburini and his small team at the Cagiva Research Center in San Marino, the 916 was a uniquely beautiful motorbike, from its sharp nose to the exhaust tailpipes poking from beneath its seat.

The 916cc eight-valve V-twin desmo engine was based on Ducati's previous 888cc unit, and used a revised fuel-injection system and new exhaust to produce 114bhp. Ducati had considered an aluminum frame before sticking with its traditional steel ladder, and added an aluminum single-sided swingarm that gave a dramatic look, in conjunction with a widest-yet 190-section rear tire. Details included adjustable steering geometry and a transverse-mounted hydraulic damper above the steering head.

With its compact dimensions, firm suspension, and aggressive riding position, the 916 was an uncompromising super-sports bike. Its powerful, smooth, and soulful motor sent the bike thundering to a top speed of well over 150mph (241km/h) and produced plenty of mid-range torque. Handling was a sublime blend of precision and absolute stability. A year later the 916 was joined by a smaller-engined model, the 748, which combined near-identical shape and chassis parts with a more rev-happy personality all of its own.

Right: Taiwanese firm PGO stirred up interest with this 1600cc prototype at the Cologne Show in 1992, but it did not reach production.

Left: *Wealthy Italian enthusiast Giancarlo Morbidelli's dream of producing an exotic 850cc V8 tourer was dashed when Pininfarina's styling work was so heavily criticized that the project was first delayed, then abandoned.*

Below: *Few bikes have captured the imagination like visionary Kiwi engineer John Britten's V-1000, pictured here on the Daytona start grid. The hand-built V-twin racer was fast, futuristic, and utterly beautiful.*

Gilera halts production

While Ducati celebrated the 916's success, another famous Italian name sunk to a new low. Gilera had made a big push in the early '90s, under Piaggio's control, with an unsuccessful 250cc grand prix racing team and several new roadsters including a retro-styled 500cc four-stroke single called the Saturno. More spectacular was the CX125, a racy single-cylinder two-stroke with single-arm suspension at both front and rear. But sales were disappointing, and in 1993 Piaggio closed the factory at Arcore, outside Milan, keeping the Gilera name only for use on sporty scooters.

The scooter market was booming, as convenient and inexpensive 'twist-and-go' machines were sold all over the world. European firms including Piaggio, Aprilia, and France's Peugeot benefited. So did firms in Asian countries including Taiwan and China, which produced a huge number of machines for sale in their own markets, and increasingly for export too. Few were interested in big-bike production, although China's Chiang Jiang produced flat twins based on the 1950s BMW R71. Taiwan's PGO displayed a promising 1600cc V-twin prototype sportster at the Cologne Show in 1992, but it did not reach production.

Another still-born project was the Morbidelli 850 V8, an exotic sports-tourer created by wealthy Italian businessman Giancarlo Morbidelli, whose racebikes had won several world titles in the 1970s. Morbidelli's 847cc liquid-cooled transverse V8 engine was a work of art. But the bike's styling, by famed car house Pininfarina, was a disappointment when unveiled in 1994. The bike was restyled, and tuned to increase peak output to 120bhp. But by the time the revised V8 was ready, the project had lost momentum, and Morbidelli abandoned plans for small-scale production after only a handful of bikes had been built.

Such disappointments were put into context by the death in 1995 from cancer of John Britten, the brilliant 44-year-old New Zealander whose V-twin racebikes had been universally admired. Few bikes have combined elegance and innovative engineering as successfully as the V-1000, a liquid-cooled, dohc V-twin that produced over 170bhp in an early 1108cc form. Britten and his small team made almost everything by hand, including the girder front forks and the rear

Above: Honda's 750cc RC45 did not match the impact of its V4 predecessor, the RC30, but it did eventually win the World Superbike title.

Above: Kawasaki's ZX-6R was a welcome addition to the 600cc super-sports battle, backing up its powerful 16-valve engine and excellent handling with plenty of character.

Right: Such was the sales success of Suzuki's quick, entertaining, and competitively priced Bandit 600 that rival manufacturers replied with unfaired middleweights of their own.

swingarm, both of which were fashioned from lightweight Kevlar and carbon-fiber. The Britten was hugely impressive in winning races at Daytona and elsewhere in the early '90s, when it was timed at over 180mph (290km/h). A handful of V-1000 racebikes were later built and sold. Britten's death robbed the motorcycle world of one of its greatest talents.

Britten had relished pitting his V-1000 against the dominant Ducatis, and in 1994 Honda had unveiled an exotic machine intended for the same job. The RC45, like its RC30 predecessor, was a 750cc V4 derived from Honda's factory racebikes. It produced 118bhp plus strong mid-range power, and its classy aluminum-framed chassis gave excellent handling. As a streetbike the costly RC45 had limited appeal. More seriously for Honda, the RC45 failed to beat the Ducatis in its first three World Superbike seasons. American John Kocinski would finally win the title in 1997, rewarding Honda's huge investment.

Kawasaki's sole World Superbike championship had been won by fellow American Scott Russell on a ZXR750 in 1993. The following year saw the firm further enhance its reputation for rapid straight fours with a new open-class charger, the ZX-9R. This was an 899cc 16-valve missile whose 139bhp peak output provided neck-wrenching acceleration toward a top speed of over 165mph (266km/h). The ZX-9R's styling was sharp, but this was a heavier and less extreme machine than its super-sport rivals. Its aluminum-framed chassis gave good handling, and the way the ZX-9R delivered performance in comfort made it a worthy successor to its illustrious forebear, the GPZ900R of ten years earlier.

Kawasaki suffered a blow in January 1995 when its home city of Kobe was hit by a devastating earthquake that left more than 5000 people dead and disrupted production. The year was also marked by the launch of the ZX-6R, a super-sports 599cc four designed to take on Honda's CBR600F, which had sold more than 100,000 units since its introduction eight years earlier. The ZX-6R's 16-valve engine, a higher-revving development of the ZZ-R unit, gave a top speed approaching 160mph (257km/h). The Kawasaki's rigid aluminum frame, taut suspension, and racy looks completed a fiercely competitive machine.

Naked fours streak in

Another outstanding middleweight was Suzuki's Bandit 600, a cheaper naked four offering lively performance. The Bandit was an instant hit, and was joined a year later by a more practical and only slightly more expensive half-faired model. Suzuki's success inspired other manufacturers. Over the next few years, quick and capable fours including Yamaha's Fazer 600 and Honda's Hornet would make the budget middleweight class one of motorcycling's most crowded.

The Japanese firms also produced a host of bigger naked fours. Suzuki's Bandit 1200 was the most popular, thanks to its blunt styling, flexible 16-valve engine, light weight, and competitive price. Honda's CB1000 was styled to resemble the CB1100R production racer of the early '80s, but lacked excitement until uprated to create the CB1300. Yamaha's XJR1200, powered by a detuned version of the FJ1200 sports-tourer's air-cooled engine, combined muscular looks with 140mph (225km/h) performance to match.

Triumph had confirmed its growing confidence in 1993 with a fully-faired four, the Daytona 1200, whose peak output of 145bhp defied the UK industry's self-imposed 125bhp limit. Although its tall, steel-framed modular chassis was dated, the 160mph (257km/h) Daytona was Triumph's fastest and best sportster yet. But most people preferred the more distinctive triples. Triumph's response in 1994 was the naked Speed Triple, which backed-up its 885cc engine's storming performance with low bars and plenty of attitude.

Although the Speed Triple owed its name to the 1930s Speed Twin, John Bloor had been keen to establish his firm as a modern manufacturer, so had avoided retro machines. By 1995, Bloor was ready to exploit Triumph's heritage with a classically styled model, the Thunderbird. This held a softly tuned, 69bhp version of the 885cc triple engine in Triumph's first non-modular frame. New bodywork incorporated details including a '50s-style Triumph 'mouth-organ' tank badge. The T-bird's blend of modern performance and traditional style went down well. It became Triumph's best-selling model, and led the firm's move into the US market, which proved difficult to crack due to its cruiser bias and the country's huge size.

Above: Like its predecessor the CB1000 'Big One,' Honda's CB1300 was styled to resemble the all-conquering CB1100R of the early '80s. Peak power output remained just under 100bhp, but the CB1300's liquid-cooled 16-valve engine had huge reserves of mid-range torque.

Left: Yamaha gave its retro-styled musclebike some extra grunt when the original XJR1200's air-cooled engine was enlarged to 1250cc to create the XJR1300. An uprated chassis incorporated Öhlins rear shocks.

Above: Triumph's Daytona 1200 four produced 145bhp, exceeding the unofficial UK limit.

Below: Harley introduced fuel-injection in 1995 on its Ultra Classic Electra Glide, which celebrated 30 years of the big touring V-twin.

Below right: Revitalized Triumph's first retro model was the Thunderbird triple, with 'mouth-organ' tank badge and 'peashooter' pipes.

Meanwhile, Harley-Davidson continued to make the most of its heritage. In 1995, Harley celebrated the 30th anniversary of its biggest and most famous model with the Ultra Classic Electra Glide, a US-market special edition of the giant tourer that was notable for introducing fuel-injection. The 1340cc V-twin engine was mechanically unchanged, but the injection gave sweeter low-rev running and improved fuel consumption. Even Harley didn't claim much in the way of improved performance from the Heritage Springer Softail that followed in 1997. But with its eye-catching springer front suspension system, allied to a hardtail-look rear, the new Softail was strikingly reminiscent of a 1940s Panhead.

The Japanese firms had tried to match Harley over the years with V-twin cruisers, with varying success. One of the better attempts had been Yamaha's neatly styled XV535 Virago, which had become especially popular with female riders due to its low seat. For 1997 it was joined by the Drag Star 650, with wide-spaced forks, forward-set pegs, and hardtail-look rear suspension to give some extra 'custom' style.

Honda's Shadow 1100 and Kawasaki's Vulcan 1500 had gained credibility with some potential buyers by being built at the firms' US factories. Honda showed even more determination to match Harley in 1995 with the Shadow ACE, short for American Classic Edition. Designed by American Honda, this had a revised version of the 1099cc liquid-cooled V-twin engine, with both conrods mounted on a single crankpin in Harley style, instead of spaced at 90 degrees. The result was a more 'American' feel and exhaust note. Harley's attempt to patent its 'potato-potato' exhaust sound would be abandoned years later, after much had been spent on legal fees.

Yamaha used its US base to create the XVZ1300 Royal Star, launched in 1996. Despite looking like an air-cooled V-twin, the Royal Star was a liquid-cooled V4. Its 1294cc dohc engine was a much detuned, 74bhp version of the V-Max's 140bhp unit. Performance was predictably modest, given the bike's 671lb (304kg) of weight. Despite disappointing sales Yamaha continued with plans to develop its Star line as a 'sub-brand' in the way that Lexus is an offshoot of Toyota, the car giant with which Yamaha had developed links.

The most improbable US success story was that of the Boss Hoss, the giant bike powered by a Chevrolet V8 car engine. Tennessee-based Monty Warne built his first V8 bike for fun, but so

Left: *Harley-Davidson's dedication to giving its modern bikes a traditional look reached a new level in 1997 with the Heritage Springer Softail, which featured old-style springer front forks, a hardtail-look rear, and 16-inch wire wheels with big fenders and white-wall tires.*

Below: *Yamaha's line-up of cruisers saw the Drag Star 1100 joined by a smaller V-twin, the Drag Star 650. While big cruisers were popular mainly in the US and a few European countries, notably Scandinavia, middleweights had wider appeal, especially for female riders.*

many people were interested that in 1991 he began selling chassis kits, then complete machines. A typical early-'90s Boss Hoss (the name was Boss Hog until Harley objected) featured a six-liter Chevy motor that produced 300bhp and gave a top speed of over 160mph (257km/h). Only the brave attempted it, given the scary handling that resulted from 1100lb (500kg) of weight and a square-section car back tire.

Warne refined the Hoss, adding an automatic gearbox (early models had just one gear: 'fast forward') and a round-section rear tire that improved handling. Before long he was selling several hundred per year, at $30,000 or more each. By 1997 Warne had built more than 1000 bikes, and had introduced a slightly lighter and cheaper 4.3-liter V6 model, the 'ladies' bike,' which produced a mere 200bhp.

Honda produced a unusual big bike in 1996: a 1520cc flat six that was called the Valkyrie in the US and the F6C in Europe. Its Gold Wing-derived engine delivered 100bhp, good for a top speed of 125mph (201km/h), plus so much low-rev torque that the rider required strong arms but rarely the gearbox. For a bike weighing almost 700lb (318kg) the six cornered and braked well too, thanks to a strong steel frame, firm suspension, and big triple discs. Honda billed the Valkyrie as the world's first 'performance cruiser,' and few who rode it disagreed.

The year's other big Honda was a performance machine of a more familiar variety. The CBR1100XX Super Blackbird, named after the US spy plane, was intended to recapture the unofficial world's fastest motorcycle title from Kawasaki's ZX-11. That it did, reaching a top speed of 180mph (290km/h) thanks to a powerful and refined 1137cc 16-valve engine, allied to bodywork that was aerodynamically efficient but which left the monotone Super Blackbird looking decidedly ordinary.

The key to the Honda's wind-cheating shape was its piggy-back headlamp, with twin lenses one above the other. This allowed a sharp, narrow fairing whose low screen was also ideal for maximum speed, if not for the Blackbird's intended sports-touring role. Despite that and its unexceptional low-rev power delivery, the CBR made a comfortable and entertaining long-distance blaster, and was popular in many European markets.

The once dominant 750cc class, which had lost importance over the years, was enlivened by the 1996 arrival of Suzuki's GSX-R750T. The racy four had been given a liquid-cooled engine four years earlier, in place of the original oil-cooled design. Now the 749cc unit was tuned and fitted with a ram-air system, and bolted into a twin-spar aluminum frame, in place of the taller traditional design. The resultant 126bhp, 394lb (179kg) Suzuki was a stunningly fast, focused, and fine-handling bike that stole the limelight from Kawasaki's stylish, but heavier and less powerful, new ZX-7R. A year later Suzuki produced an even more manic four, the GSX-R600, which combined similar looks and layout with an even revvier 104bhp engine, and screamed to a top speed of 155mph (249km/h).

Italian firms struggle

While the Japanese manufacturers were developing ever-faster sports bikes, several Italian firms were struggling. In 1993 Moto Guzzi, hindered by the ill-health of owner Alejandro de Tomaso, had built just 3000 bikes. The following year the firm was taken over by a Milan-based merchant bank, which by 1996 had doubled production, posted a modest profit and introduced a handful of new models. The 1100 Sport Injection and Daytona RS were revised versions of existing sporty V-twins. The new Centauro was a naked 992cc V-twin with curious styling and rather crude suspension, but at least Guzzi was showing signs of life.

Laverda had gone into receivership in 1987, and several attempts to relaunch it since then had ended in failure. In 1994, local entrepreneur Francesco Tognon took control, moved Laverda from its Breganze base to a new site at nearby Zané, and began production of a sporty parallel twin called simply the 650. This consisted of a 668cc 70bhp air/oil-cooled engine, derived from an old

Above: Honda's 1995-model Shadow ACE, short for American Classic Edition, was notable not for its typical Japanese cruiser styling, but for its 1100cc V-twin engine's use of a single crankpin, in order to replicate the offbeat exhaust note popularized by Harley-Davidson.

Right: The Royal Star was the first of what Yamaha intended would be a new family of cruisers, aimed mainly at the US market and based on the V-Max's liquid-cooled V4 engine.

'70s design, in a new twin-spar aluminum frame. The first 650 was an agile and torquey bike that was let down by inconsistent build quality. A string of new 668cc twins over the next few years led in 1997 to the 750S. This had a bigger 747cc liquid-cooled engine producing 82bhp. With sleek, fully-faired looks plus the traditional fine handling, it was Laverda's best twin yet.

Cagiva's financial problems came to a head in 1996, when production ground to a halt. In September of that year Claudio Castiglioni, Cagiva's President, sold a 51 percent controlling stake in Ducati to Texas Pacific, a US investment group that owned three airlines plus numerous other businesses. TPG's new management team, led by Federico Minoli, paid 700 suppliers more than

Above: The second Boss Hoss model, the V6, incorporated a new transmission, purpose-built forks, and improved brakes. Its 4.3-liter engine produced 200bhp, making this merely the world's second most powerful production bike.

Left: Honda's Valkyrie, known as the F6C in Europe, was a 'performance cruiser' powered by a slightly modified 1520cc flat six engine from the Gold Wing. It looked ungainly but handled and braked surprisingly well.

Honda CBR1100XX (1996)

Engine:	Liquid-cooled dohc 16-valve four
Capacity:	1037cc (79 x 58mm)
Maximum power:	162bhp @ 10,000rpm
Transmission:	Six-speed, chain final drive
Frame:	Aluminum twin spar
Suspension:	Telescopic front; single shock rear
Brakes:	Twin discs front; disc rear
Weight:	491lb (223kg) dry
Top speed:	180mph (290km/h)

Above right: Aerodynamics-led styling and dull paintwork ensured that the Super Blackbird was not particularly attractive, but its top speed of 180mph (290km/h) meant that it was the world's fastest production bike in 1996.

Below: Arguably the most important update in the life of Suzuki's GSX-R750 came in 1996 with the 750T, which featured a ram-air induction system, plus a twin-spar aluminum frame design that was more rigid than its predecessor.

Right: Moto Guzzi, apparently recovering under new ownership, unveiled a pair of updated V-twin sportsters, the 1100 Sport Injection (left) and the Daytona RS.

$50 million, restarted production, overhauled the Bologna factory to improve efficiency and quality control, and began a three-year program to invest a further $70 million in new equipment. An exciting new era had begun.

By 1997 production was up to a record 26,000, double the previous year's stoppage-hit figure, and Ducati had launched the sports-touring ST2 that had been under development for some time. Shaped as much for comfort and practicality as for style, the ST2 was powered by a 944cc 83bhp liquid-cooled version of the familiar sohc desmo V-twin. The ST2 was good for 140mph (225km/h), handled well, and its relatively upright riding position and long-travel suspension were welcome on long trips. Ducati had a way to go to match the build quality of Honda's VFR750F, but the ST2 was a promising start.

While Ducati was challenging Honda with a new sports-tourer, Honda and Suzuki were hitting back with V-twin sports bikes, both with 996cc, liquid-cooled, dohc eight-valve, 90-degree engines. Honda's VTR1000F Firestorm was a quick and capable machine that shared some of the VFR's practicality, thanks to a carbureted motor tuned for mid-range response rather than top-end

Left: The 750S was by far Laverda's best parallel twin so far, thanks largely to a new 747cc liquid-cooled engine that was smoother and more refined than its air/oil-cooled 668cc predecessors, as well as more powerful.

Below: Ducati's ST2 was important because it was the first of a new line of sports-tourers, but the 944cc V-twin's real significance was that it was the Bologna brand's first new bike since the take-over by US group Texas Pacific.

power. Despite that, the 110bhp twin was capable of almost 160mph (257km/h), and handled well thanks to an aluminum beam-framed chassis.

Suzuki's TL1000S had an exciting specification based on a fuel-injected V-twin motor that produced 123bhp – more than both the Firestorm and Ducati's 916. The aggressive, half-faired Suzuki's tubular aluminum frame incorporated a unique rear suspension system consisting of a single spring and separate rotary damper. The TL1000S was a star in almost every respect. Its motor was wonderfully torquey, with enough top-end power for a top speed of 160mph (257km/h), and its handling was light and precise.

But the TL's blend of acceleration and quick steering resulted in occasional instability, and bad publicity concerning crashes resulting from 'tank-slappers' prompted Suzuki to recall it for fitment of a steering damper. The TL1000S's sales never recovered. A year later it was joined by the TL1000R, with full fairing and more conventional beam frame. The R model was faster but heavier, and lacked the S model's mid-range punch.

The other outstanding sports bike of 1997 signified the second phase of Triumph's recovery. The T595 Daytona was a sleek, fully-faired triple that abandoned the British firm's modular concept, and was launched to confront the Japanese opposition head-on. The Daytona's 955cc engine, based on the original 885cc unit, was fuel-injected, and tuned with the help of Lotus Engineering to produce 128bhp. Its frame was an innovative design of twin oval-section aluminum tubes, which held an equally striking single-sided swingarm.

Triumph unveiled the Daytona at the 1996 Cologne Show to an enthusiastic response. The triple lived up to its promise, as its powerful and flexible motor sent the T595 surging toward a top speed of over 160mph (257km/h). Handling was excellent too, as the rigid frame and well-damped suspension gave unshakeable stability and neutral steering. The triple did not quite match the pure pace and agility of more focused Japanese super-sports bikes, but as a rapid roadster it was hugely impressive.

At the same time Triumph launched the T509 Speed Triple, an updated version of its naked streetfighter complete with bug-eyed twin headlamps, more powerful 885cc engine, and the Daytona's aluminum-framed chassis. The Triple's unique, stripped-down streetfighter style struck a chord, and the model became a big hit. The T595 and T509 names, taken from the factory code-

Above: Suzuki's TL1000S provided thrilling performance from its torquey eight-valve V-twin engine, but was criticized after its innovative chassis gave stability problems.

Below right: Triumph took a big step forward with its impressive new-generation three-cylinder machines, the super-sports T595 Daytona (left) and naked T509 Speed Triple.

Triumph T595 Daytona (1997)

Engine:	Liquid-cooled dohc 12-valve triple
Capacity:	955cc (79 x 65mm)
Maximum power:	128bhp @ 10,200rpm
Transmission:	Six-speed, chain final drive
Frame:	Tubular aluminum perimeter
Suspension:	Telescopic front; single shock rear
Brakes:	Twin discs front; disc rear
Weight:	436lb (198kg) dry
Top speed:	165mph (265km/h)

names in Triumph tradition, would later be dropped because many people found them confusing. But the new-generation triples confirmed Triumph's growing status.

BMW also unveiled two dramatic new bikes in 1997. With the R1200C, the firm's design chief David Robb – ironically, an American – proved that it was possible to create a stylish cruiser without copying Harley-Davidson. More than that, the R1200C flaunted its BMW heritage with a 1170cc boxer engine, and a Telelever front suspension with polished aluminum arm. The softly tuned 61bhp twin was flexible, handled well, and incorporated clever details including a pillion seat that hinged to become a backrest.

The more conventional K1200RS was another bold step for BMW because the four-cylinder sports-tourer's maximum output of 130bhp blew open the self-imposed 100bhp limit that had handicapped the German marque for years. The 1171cc 16-valve BMW shot smoothly to 150mph (241km/h) and was very stable, although at 573lb (260kg) it was also heavy. In 1998 BMW followed the four with a very different high-performance model, the R1100S flat twin. Its 98bhp 1085cc air-cooled motor was a tuned version of the R1100RS sports-tourer's unit. With distinctive styling, a flexible motor, 140mph (225km/h) top speed, and sound handling, the R1100S gave BMW its most competitive sportster since the R90S of two decades earlier.

Aprilia's superbike debut

The other outstanding twin-cylinder newcomer of 1998 was also eagerly anticipated. Aprilia's RSV Mille was powered by a 998cc dohc V-twin that produced 128bhp, and whose cylinders were arranged at 60 degrees, instead of the familiar 90 degrees, because this gave a more compact unit. Twin balancer shafts canceled the resultant vibration. Styling was shaped in Aprilia's wind tunnel; the strong aluminum twin-spar frame was designed in the firm's race department.

Predictably, Aprilia's first superbike proved to be superbly fast, stable, agile, and reliable. The RSV was rather tall, and despite some neat touches its styling lacked a little Italian glamor. But the V-twin thundered toward a top speed of 165mph (266km/h) in thrilling fashion, and delivered superb handling and roadholding. Thoughtful details included a high-tech instrument panel containing a lap timer and racer-style gearshift warning light. With one model, Aprilia had established itself as a major-league superbike manufacturer.

Left: The 1997-model K1200RS confirmed a significant change of heart at BMW. The big 16-valve sports-tourer's peak output of 130bhp far exceeded the self-imposed 100bhp limit that the German marque had observed in the past.

Below: BMW's R1200C cruiser was a distinctive and innovative bike that emphasized the marque's heritage. This R1200C Independent version added new paintwork, extra chrome, and a tinted screen to the basic format.

Even the RSV had to take second billing in 1998 to the bike whose vital statistics alone suggested that the superbike status quo had shifted again – and whose performance very much confirmed it. Yamaha's YZF-R1 produced 150bhp, weighed a mere 389lb (177kg), and had a wheelbase of just 54.9in (1395mm). That meant it was the most powerful, lightest, and shortest open-class sports bike yet. The R1's sharp, twin-headlamp fairing and bodywork helped give an aggressive look that perfectly matched its personality.

The new bike was a development of the 1996-model Thunderace, itself a fast and fine-handling 1002cc four. Yamaha's new 998cc 20-valve engine was more powerful and also more compact, thanks to a novel 'stacked' gearbox. The motor's extra stiffness meant it could form part of the chassis, allowing a lighter aluminum Deltabox II frame. The R1 backed up its 170mph (274km/h) top speed with a wonderfully broad power band, excellent brakes, and superb handling that let it scythe through bends with more poise than any 600cc sports bike.

A year later Yamaha broadened the YZF range with a similarly styled and focused 599cc model, the YZF-R6. The R6 used ram-air to reach a claimed peak output of 120bhp, and weighed

Left: More than two decades after the seminal R90S of the mid-'70s, BMW's fast and stylish R1100S proved that the air-cooled flat twin engine layout was still very viable as the basis for a high-performance superbike.

Aprilia RSV Mille (1998)

Engine:	Liquid-cooled dohc eight-valve 60-degree V-twin
Capacity:	998cc (97 x 67.5mm)
Maximum power:	128bhp @ 9250rpm
Transmission:	Six-speed, chain final drive
Frame:	Aluminum twin spar
Suspension:	Telescopic front; single shock rear
Brakes:	Twin discs front; disc rear
Weight:	416lb (189kg) dry
Top speed:	165mph (266km/h)

Above: The Aprilia RSV Mille was an instant hit.

Below right: Yamaha's R1: fast, light, and sharp.

Yamaha YZF-R1 (1998)

Engine:	Liquid-cooled dohc 20-valve four
Capacity:	998cc (74 x 58mm)
Maximum power:	150bhp @ 10,000rpm
Transmission:	Six-speed, chain final drive
Frame:	Aluminum twin spar
Suspension:	Telescopic front; single shock rear
Brakes:	Twin discs front; disc rear
Weight:	389lb (176kg) dry
Top speed:	170mph (274km/h)

a class-lowest 372lb (169kg). It quickly became established as the hardest and fastest of the 600cc race-replicas. But when the Supersport world championship for 600cc fours and 750cc twins began in 1999, the first winner was Frenchman Stephane Chambon, riding Suzuki's GSX-R600. Yamaha's exotic, limited-edition 750cc four, the YZF-R7, would also fail to make the hoped-for impact in World Superbikes.

In 1998 Honda celebrated its 50th anniversary by building its 100 millionth motorbike, and by giving its VFR sports-tourer a new 108bhp fuel-injected V4 engine to create the VFR800FI. A less happy anniversary was that of Norton, which reached its centenary in 1998. The firm's recovery had foundered in the mid-'90s. Several former directors were convicted of financial irregularities, and hundreds of enthusiast shareholders lost the money they had invested in the company. The marque's new Canadian owners put little money either into new models or into the dilapidated factory at Shenstone, which was left producing small quantities of spare parts.

In spring 1998 the Aquilini Group, Norton's latest owner, held a reception at the Dorchester Hotel in London's Park Lane to announce a stunning range of new models. The flagship, unveiled in prototype form, was a futuristic 1500cc V8 superbike called the Nemesis, which Norton claimed produced 280bhp and had a top speed of 225mph (362km/h), making it by far the world's fastest production motorcycle. The range would also include two large-capacity fours, a V8 cruiser and a 600cc single.

The Nemesis, which incorporated advanced features including active suspension, perimeter disc brakes, and a push-button gearchange and clutch, had been designed by Al Melling, head of Yorkshire based Melling Consultancy Design. Melling's claim that the radical, untried bike would be produced at Shenstone in six months' time was at best hopelessly optimistic, but many people accepted it. Positive media coverage would keep the Nemesis saga going for several years until the project's inevitable abandonment amid a flurry of solicitors' letters.

Ironically the only Norton produced in 1998 was the relatively humble C652SM, powered by the single-cylinder engine from BMW's F650. The single was devised by Joe Seifert, whose

Grands Prix versus Superbikes

The rise of the World Superbike championship during the '90s meant that motorcycling gained two rival series fighting for prestige and attention. The established grand prix championship offered the excitement and technical interest of pure-bred racing prototypes. The Superbike series for production-based machines put strict limits on which parts could be changed, resulting in close racing from bikes resembling standard showroom models.

Superbike's format made the series very relevant for manufacturers, encouraging much works team participation – plus

development of racy 'homologation special' roadsters such as Honda's RC45 and various limited-edition Ducatis. The organizers tried to ensure fairness by pitting 750cc fours against 1000cc twins, with varying additional weight penalties over the years. Despite this, Ducati's red V-twins dominated the decade by winning eight of the ten titles, including two for Texan Doug Polen and four for Englishman 'King Carl' Fogarty, whose hard-riding style and abrasive personality did much to make Superbikes popular.

The 500cc grand prix championship was ruled throughout the '90s by the two-stroke V4, although Yamaha's YZR500 differed from Honda's NSR500 and Suzuki's RGV500 by using twin contra-rotating crankshafts rather than one. By the end of the decade, peak power outputs had risen to almost 200bhp, and Honda's NSR500 had been timed at 200mph (322km/h). Californian Wayne Rainey won a hat-trick of titles for Yamaha before his career was ended by a 1993 crash that left him paralysed. Australian Michael Doohan

recovered from a serious leg injury to become grand prix racing's outstanding figure with five consecutive championships for Honda, before a crash ended his career in 1999.

While the Superbikes and 500cc grands prix battled for supremacy, and fans debated the merits of Doohan and 'Foggy,' the other racing classes were largely overshadowed. The 250cc grand prix twins, once almost as important as the 500s, declined in importance along with the 125cc singles. By the end of the decade the once popular but increasingly irrelevant sidecars had lost their world championship status, and were no longer part of the grand prix scene.

Above left: Ducati's eight-valve V-twin took Carl Fogarty to four World Superbike titles.

Above: Michael Doohan on Honda's NSR500 V4.

Left: The racy Yamaha YZF-R6 produced 120bhp.

Below: Honda's VFR800FI sports-tourer.

Above: Norton's stylish and futuristic Nemesis
prototype was unveiled at a London press
conference in 1998, making a claimed 280bhp from
its 1500cc V8 motor. Any intent the firm's owners
had to produce it came to nothing.

Above: The V92 was not the most stylish cruiser
on the block, but it was a creditable first attempt at
a big V-twin by Victory, the newly created
motorcycle division of US firm Polaris.

Right: Many enthusiasts were critical of reborn
Indian's use of Harley-based S&S engines, but
there was no denying that the Limited Edition
Chief was a stylish and imposing machine.

Norton Motors Deutschland firm owned rights to the name in most of Europe, and built by British specialist Tigcraft, who supplied its tubular steel frame. The agile single's straight-line performance was modest and only a few were sold, none of them in Britain because Seifert did not own Norton rights there.

The issue of marque ownership had generated bitter fighting in the US over the Indian name. In the early '90s Harley's revival prompted claims to Indian ownership by two individuals, both of whom seemed more keen to sell Indian-branded merchandise than to build bikes. Philip Zanghi ended up in prison for fraud; Wayne Baughman disappeared from the scene after extracting several million dollars from investors.

In 1996 the Indian issue was controversially settled in a Colorado court, when the receiver awarded rights to a Canadian-based consortium. The winning Indian Motorcycle Company paid the receiver almost $20 million, which was used to reimburse creditors, and took over the California Motorcycle Company, the leading maker of 'Harley clone' V-twins.

Return of the Chief

In 1999 Indian began production of its first bike, the Limited Edition Chief: a giant cruiser, powered by a 1442cc S&S V-twin engine, and with classic Indian features including huge fenders. Its price was high, quality was mixed, and many enthusiasts were unimpressed. But at least Indian was finally back in business. Kawasaki, which had recently launched a pair of Drifter models by revamping its VN800 and VN1500 V-twin cruisers with big fenders, was forced to pay the receiver $75,000 for hijacking Indian's trademarked feature.

Two other US firms had also launched high-profile V-twin cruisers. In 1998 Polaris, the snowmobile and watercraft giant, had begun production of the first bike from its new Victory motorcycle division. The V92C was not the most stylish of machines. But its 1508cc (92 cubic inches, hence the name) fuel-injected sohc V-twin produced a healthy 75bhp, and by cruiser standards the Victory handled and braked very well. It was also competitively priced.

The Super X from Excelsior-Henderson, launched in January 1999, was a heavier and more expensive machine, powered by a 1386cc dohc V-twin engine which, like the V92C, was air/oil-

Harley-Davidson FXDX Super Glide Sport (1999)	
Engine:	Air-cooled ohv pushrod four-valve 45-degree V-twin
Capacity:	1450cc (95.3 x 101.6mm)
Maximum power:	68bhp @ 5400rpm
Transmission:	Five-speed, belt final drive
Frame:	Steel twin cradle
Suspension:	Telescopic front; twin shocks rear
Brakes:	Twin discs front; disc rear
Weight:	661lb (300kg)
Top speed:	110mph (177km/h)

Left: Harley took a big step forward with its powerful and refined Twin Cam 88 engine, and the Dyna Super Glide Sport added to the appeal with very respectable chassis performance.

cooled and held its cylinders at a 50-degree angle. The old name had been revived by brothers Dave and Dan Hanlon, who had raised $90 million to develop the bike and create a purpose-built factory in Minnesota. The Super X produced plenty of low-rev power, and had a distinctive look from its leading-link front suspension.

Harley-Davidson responded to its new challengers with its first new engine in 15 years. The Twin Cam 88 got its name from its twin camshafts and capacity of 1450cc, or 88 cubic inches. Although most engine parts were new, the format of air-cooled, pushrod-operated, 45-degree V-twin remained. Peak output was increased from 50 to about 68bhp, cooling was uprated, and numerous parts were made more robust. The new motor gave notably more lively performance. It was especially impressive in the all-new Dyna Super Glide Sport, a lean and sweet-running roadster that combined effortless cruising ability with very respectable handling.

Harley was also keen to diversify, and in 1998 took control of Buell, having bought a 49 percent stake in the firm five years earlier. Under Erik Buell's control the company had produced some quick and cleverly engineered models, notably the 1996-model S1 Lightning with its mean, bikini-faired styling, tuned 91bhp Sportster 1200 V-twin engine and innovative, quick-steering chassis. With Harley's help Buell increased production, started exporting to several countries, and developed new models. The X1 Lightning, launched in 1999, kept Buells' quirky character, increased the V-twin motor's output yet again to 95bhp, and improved some cosmetic details including the notoriously large airbox. Buell still had some quality control issues to address, but with Harley's resources behind it the future looked promising.

Ducati was reaping the benefit of its new management and its run of World Superbike success. In 1999 the Bologna factory's production hit a record 33,000, with the company increasingly profitable. Ducati, by now fully owned by TPG, had taken control of some key importers,

Below: Seven Harley models were initially updated with the 1450cc Twin Cam 88 motor in 1999, including the laid-back Dyna Wide Glide (left) and more traditionally styled Road King.

established high-profile 'Ducati store' dealerships, and launched lucrative sidelines in tuning parts and accessories. New bikes in 1998 had included the ST4 sports-tourer, essentially the ST2 fitted with the 105bhp dohc eight-valve engine from the 916; and the restyled, fuel-injected 900SS sportster. In March 1999 Ducati, its recovery seemingly complete, was floated on the Italian and New York stock exchanges.

Moto Guzzi was less healthy, its lack of direction emphasized when the management arranged to move production from the traditional Mandello del Lario base to a new factory in Monza, outside Milan. The workers had other ideas, and Guzzi stayed put. But the firm was boosted in 1999 by the introduction of the V11 Sport, a neat naked roadster with a punchy 91bhp V-twin motor and plenty of retro style.

Bimota's two-stroke disaster

The situation was far worse at Bimota, after a promising few years. Between 1994 and '96 the firm had sold a record 1100 units of the Pierluigi Marconi-designed SB6, which wrapped Suzuki's GSX-R1100 engine in a sturdy aluminum frame that also enclosed the swingarm pivot. In 1997 Bimota hoped for even greater success with the revolutionary 500 V-due, with its 'clean-burning' direct-injection two-stroke V-twin engine. The stylish V-due was in huge demand but when deliveries began, it became clear that the direct-injection did not work reliably. Bikes were returned, payments refunded, and the factory was closed for much of 1998. Production eventually recommenced in 1999 under the control of former Laverda boss Francesco Tognon, but Bimota's situation remained precarious.

Cagiva had survived numerous financial scares during a decade spent developing its four-cylinder sports bike. But when, at the 1997 Milan Show, Claudio Castiglioni pulled the covers from the bike by then renamed the MV Agusta 750 F4, nobody doubted that the effort had been worthwhile. For the famous old marque's return, Massimo Tamburini had created a two-wheeled

Top: The S1 Lightning, Buell's first naked roadster, had a tuned 1200cc Harley motor.

Above: Ducati's ST4 sports-tourer used a 105bhp eight-valve V-twin engine from the 916.

MV Agusta 750 F4 Serie Oro (1999)	
Engine:	Liquid-cooled dohc 16-valve four
Capacity:	749cc (73.8 x 43.8mm)
Maximum power:	126bhp @ 12,500rpm
Transmission:	Six-speed, chain final drive
Frame:	Tubular steel and cast magnesium
Suspension:	Telescopic front; single shock rear
Brakes:	Twin discs front; disc rear
Weight:	406lb (184kg) dry
Top speed:	165mph (266km/h)

Right: The long-awaited F4 750 Serie Oro was a suitably stunning bike for MV Agusta's return.

sculpture to rank with his Ducati 916. The F4 was brilliantly engineered and utterly gorgeous, from the tiny twin headlamps in its fairing's nose, all the way to the four cigar-shaped tailpipes that emerged from beneath its tailpiece.

The F4's 749cc 126bhp liquid-cooled motor held 16 radial valves, and incorporated a grand prix-style removable cassette gearbox. An innovative chassis combined ladder-like steel tubes with cast pieces. On the limited-edition F4 Serie Oro (Gold Series) these and the single-sided swingarm were magnesium, instead of the standard bike's aluminum. In either specification, the F4 was magnificent. It raced smoothly to a top speed of over 160mph (257km/h), emitting a glorious induction howl, and delivered precise, agile handling and powerful braking. But even in its hour of triumph, MV suffered the familiar problem of production delays.

If MV's F4 was one of the most beautiful motorcycles of all time, then Suzuki's GSX-R1300R Hayabusa was arguably one of the least attractive, but there was a good reason for that. The Hayabusa, named after a fast-flying Japanese peregrine falcon, had been given its drooping fairing nose, large front fender and bulbous tailpiece to improve its aerodynamic efficiency. Suzuki's aim was to create the world's fastest bike, and the Hayabusa's 190mph (306km/h) top speed meant they had succeeded.

The Hayabusa's 1298cc motor was an enlarged and tuned version of the dohc 16-valve unit from the GSX-R1100. Fuel-injection and ram-air helped give 173bhp, a record for a production bike. The chassis, based on a twin-spar aluminum frame, was unexceptional. What was special was the Hayabusa's performance, which was not just mind-blowingly strong, but also remarkably well-controlled. Its power delivery was crisp and flexible; its handling neutral and stable. Its brakes, tires, and ground clearance were excellent.

So stunningly, addictively fast was the Hayabusa that its rider needed only a relatively short straight to see 200mph (322km/h) on its slightly optimistic speedometer. Whether that was entirely a good thing for a standard production streetbike in 1999 was another matter entirely.

Above: The V11 Sport used Guzzi's traditional 1064cc V-twin engine. Its lime green paintwork and red frame echoed the V7 Sport of the 1970s.

Above: Bimota's 500 V-due: brave but flawed.

Left: Suzuki's Hayabusa: ugly but seriously fast.

Suzuki GSX-R1300R Hayabusa (1999)

Engine:	Liquid-cooled dohc 16-valve four
Capacity:	1298cc (81 x 63mm)
Maximum power:	173bhp @ 9800rpm
Transmission:	Six-speed, chain final drive
Frame:	Aluminum twin spar
Suspension:	Telescopic front; single shock rear
Brakes:	Twin discs front; disc rear
Weight:	473lb (215kg) dry
Top speed:	190mph (306km/h)

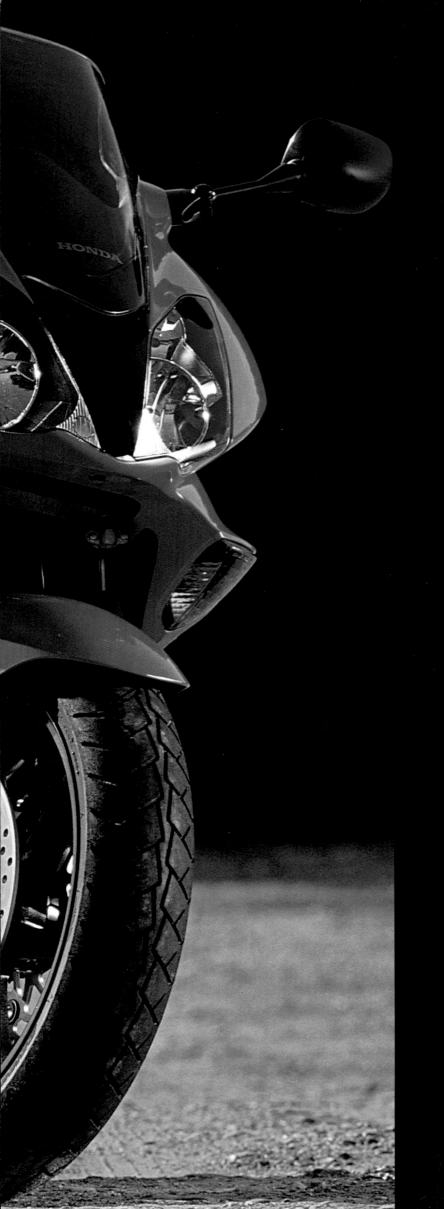

Toward the Limit
21st Century

Ducati MH900e (2000)

Engine:	Air/oil-cooled sohc four-valve 90-degree V-twin
Capacity:	904cc (92 x 68mm)
Maximum power:	75bhp @ 8000rpm
Transmission:	Six-speed, chain final drive
Frame:	Tubular steel ladder
Suspension:	Telescopic front; single shock rear
Brakes:	Twin discs front; disc rear
Weight:	409lb (186kg)
Top speed:	130mph (209km/h)

Above: Ducati's limited-edition MH900e combined retro style and modern engineering in unique fashion, and was great fun to ride.

Right: Harley's Fat Boy and the rest of the Softail range gained balancer-shaft equipped Twin Cam 88 engines for the 2000 model year.

Previous page: In 2002 the sharpened VFR800FI sports-tourer became the first motorcycle to use Honda's VTEC variable valve technology.

Motorcycling's new millennium began in suitably forward-looking fashion when, at one minute past midnight on January 1, 2000, Ducati's MH900e went on sale via the Italian firm's web site, becoming the first vehicle to be sold in this way. The initials stood for 'Mike Hailwood Evoluzione,' and the Ducati was an ideal bike to span the old and new eras, as it blended classical influences with modern features in unique fashion.

The MH900e also highlighted several key trends in motorcycle design. Its focus was on performance; it exploited a new marketing niche with limited-edition production; and it combined high technology with traditional engineering themes – in this case, Ducati's desmodromic V-twin engine and tubular steel ladder frame. Many other bikes had used some of those elements but few had combined them all so neatly.

Ducati's design chief Pierre Terblanche had begun planning the MH900e years earlier, inspired by Hailwood's Isle of Man TT win in 1978, when 38-year old 'Mike the Bike' had come out of retirement to ride a Ducati to a famous victory. Although it didn't look much like Hailwood's fully-faired racer, the MH900e had a '70s feel emphasized by its chrome-rimmed headlamp, period graphics, and the engine's large dummy sump. The prototype's rear-facing camera (instead of mirrors) did not make it into production, but the final bike included a stylish rev-counter and digital speedometer, and a single-sided swingarm made from tubular steel instead of the more familiar aluminum.

Public response was so positive that the planned 1000 bikes sold out in a few hours, and double that number would eventually be built. With a peak output of 75bhp from its 904cc air/oil-cooled V-twin engine the Ducati was not especially fast, but it rumbled to 130mph (209km/h), had plenty of character, and handled well. As a riding experience the MH900e was merely good; as a marketing exercise and a piece of design, it was brilliant.

Harley-Davidson, still the masters of retro styling, introduced a 2000 model range that looked almost unchanged but incorporated significant updates. Harley's six Softail models, including the ever-popular Fat Boy, were fitted with the 1450cc Twin Cam 88 engine, reworked to include twin balancer shafts to reduce the solidly-mounted V-twin's vibration. At the other end of the capacity scale, Harley's subsidiary Buell launched the Blast, a 492cc single-cylinder roadster aimed at converting new riders, especially women, to motorcycling.

Tough times ahead

Harley's continued success contrasted with the difficulties faced by many other manufacturers as major markets took a downturn in the new millennium, following faltering global economies. Italy, where recent legislation requiring riders to wear crash-helmets was an added factor, saw a dramatic drop in scooter sales, leaving manufacturers with a problem of over-supply. Piaggio was particularly badly affected, and so postponed plans to relaunch Gilera with 600cc four-cylinder and 850cc V-twin superbikes.

European scooter and small bike manufacturers were also facing increasing competition from countries including China, whose fast-growing industry was producing more than ten million machines per year, mainly for domestic sale but increasingly also for export. By contrast the biggest threat to large capacity bikes was from politicians, as governments' plans to reduce road casualties made superbikes, with their increasing power and speed, an easy target.

That situation came to a head in 2000 with the arrival of Kawasaki's ZX-12R, a high-tech 1199cc powerhouse which, with a top speed approaching 190mph (306km/h), was designed to challenge Suzuki's Hayabusa for the title of world's fastest motorcycle. Amid confusion surrounding the four-cylinder Kawasaki's precise power output came confirmation that it had become the first bike affected by a Japanese manufacturers' agreement to limit top speed to 186mph (300km/h), for fear of more severe government-imposed restrictions.

The Kawasaki's output was eventually confirmed at a ram-air assisted 176bhp. But its 16-valve fuel-injected engine was not the bike's outstanding feature. The ZX-12R was more notable for its innovative monocoque (one-piece) aluminum frame, inspired by that of Kawasaki's unsuccessful KR500 grand prix racer of the 1980s. The hollow frame incorporated the airbox; fuel lived under the seat. The lack of external frame spars allowed slim, aerodynamic bodywork that contributed to the Kawasaki's searing speed.

Despite being quite big and heavy, the sharply styled ZX-12R handled well, and made a capable sports-tourer thanks to a roomy riding position, reasonable wind protection, and powerful brakes. It restored Kawasaki's reputation for brutal four-cylinder performance but the firm still lacked a super-sports model to challenge Yamaha's revised YZF-R1 and Honda's FireBlade, which was redesigned for 2000.

Kawasaki ZX-12R (2000)	
Engine:	Liquid-cooled dohc 16-valve four
Capacity:	1199cc (83 x 55.4mm)
Maximum power:	176bhp @ 11,000rpm
Transmission:	Six-speed, chain final drive
Frame:	Aluminum monocoque
Suspension:	Telescopic front; single shock rear
Brakes:	Twin discs front; disc rear
Weight:	462lb (210kg) dry
Top speed:	186mph (300km/h)

Above: Kawasaki's ZX-12R looked relatively conventional, but was notable both for its electronically limited 186mph (300km/h) top speed and its monocoque aluminum frame.

Left: Honda's 2000-model FireBlade (right), called the CBR929RR in the US, echoed the original CBR900RR of 1992 with its highly competitive blend of power and light weight.

Following its sensational arrival in 1992, the CBR900RR had been updated every two years, remaining popular while losing a little of the original bike's raw excitement. That changed in 2000 with an all-new 'Blade, known as the CBR929RR in the US due to its increased engine capacity. The Honda's other figures were equally important because it produced 150bhp, equaling the R1's unchanged output, and at 375lb (170kg) was even lighter than the racy Yamaha. The revamped RR was just what Honda needed: a faster, lighter, more agile, better braked bike that was right back on the pace.

Another model Honda had needed urgently was one that could challenge Ducati's long-standing dominance of the World Superbike championship, and in 2000 the Japanese giant finally swallowed its pride and joined in with a big V-twin of its own. The SP-1, known as the RC51 in the US, was a fully-faired machine with a powerful 999cc dohc eight-valve motor and a high quality chassis, though it was closer to a normal production streetbike than a limited edition race replica like its V4 predecessor, the RC45.

Above: Honda's SP-1 was a rapid roadster, and the basis for a Superbike world title winner.

Below: Bimota created the cleverly engineered SB8K around Suzuki's TL1000 V-twin engine, before hitting more financial problems.

Below right: The new millennium's craziest bike was Louisiana firm MTT's Y2K, powered by a 286bhp gas turbine helicopter engine.

The racy SP-1 made a fast and uncompromising roadster, with plenty of character and performance from its fuel-injected, 136bhp engine. On smooth roads the firmly suspended, aluminum beam-framed V-twin handled superbly, too, despite being quite heavy at 431lb (196kg). Honda's effort was rewarded when Texan ace Colin Edwards rode the factory SP-1 to the World Superbike title in its debut season.

Even Honda's V-twin was almost ordinary in comparison with the year's most outrageous motorcycle: the gas turbine-engined Y2K produced by Louisiana firm Marine Turbine Technologies. With an output of 286bhp and a claimed top speed of 250mph (402km/h), Y2K was the most powerful and fastest bike ever to go into series production, albeit in very small numbers. The price of $150,000 meant it was also one of the most expensive.

MTT specialized in building boats and fire pumps using 'timed-out' aero engines; Y2K's Rolls-Royce Allison 250 turbine had previously powered a Bell Jet Ranger helicopter. For motorcycle use the turbine was heavy and impractical, but MTT's strong aluminum frame gave

Below: France gained its first superbike manufacturer with the arrival of Voxan, whose V-twin range was headed by the quick and charismatic Café Racer. After going bust in 2001, the firm was reborn two years later.

the long, fully-faired bike good stability to go with its awesome straight-line performance and unique, high-pitched sound.

Bimota, Italy's best known builder of exotic superbikes, received an unexpected boost when Australian star Anthony Gobert won a rain-affected World Superbike race on the firm's new SB8K, powered by the 996cc V-twin engine from Suzuki's TL1000S. But racing success proved short-lived, the firm's financial fortunes plummeted once again, and production in Rimini was abandoned for much of 2000. MV Agusta, too, was in trouble, with production suspended due to the collapse of merger talks with Piaggio, whose financial health had declined because of the scooter market crash.

Claudio Castiglioni had renamed his group MV Agusta, and had begun the year by launching the first Cagiva-branded superbikes, both of which also used the eight-valve TL1000S V-twin engine. The Raptor and V-Raptor were stylish roadsters designed by Miguel Galluzzi, the creator of Ducati's Monster. The sportier V-Raptor, in particular, was a striking bike with a sharp beak and dramatic fake air-scoops. With crisp acceleration, 150mph (241km/h) top speed and fine handling, the Raptors looked set for success. But no sooner had Cagiva unveiled smaller 650cc versions, powered by the V-twin engine from Suzuki's impressive new SV650, than the Varese production lines ground to a halt because of the company's financial difficulties.

Another firm with a range of V-twins was Voxan, an ambitious new manufacturer, based near Clermont-Ferrand in central France and run by industrialist Jacques Gardette. Voxan's modular three-bike range was based on a 996cc eight-valve engine with cylinders at 72 degrees. In 2000, the initial naked Roadster model, launched a year earlier, was joined by the half-faired Café Racer, featuring similar 100bhp output to comply with French law, and the same steel frame. The Voxans combined 140mph (225km/h) performance with good handling plus plenty of character, and sold well in France. But they were not profitable and, after a Scrambler dual-purpose model had been launched in 2001, the firm ceased production. It would return in 2003, under new ownership, with a smaller workforce and a revamped range of V-twins.

BMW had hoped that one face of motorcycling's future would be the C1, a curious egg-shaped commuter machine. Much more than simply a scooter with a roof, the innovative C1 incorporated a crash-resistant safety cell to protect the rider, who wore car-style seat belts, and in

Above: BMW earned top marks for imagination with the enclosed and crash-resistant C1, but drawbacks including high price and higher center of gravity ensured that sales were slow.

Suzuki GSX-R1000 (2001)

Engine:	Liquid-cooled dohc 16-valve four
Capacity:	998cc (73 x 59mm)
Maximum power:	161bhp @ 11,000rpm
Transmission:	Six-speed, chain final drive
Frame:	Aluminum twin spar
Suspension:	Telescopic front; single shock rear
Brakes:	Twin discs front; disc rear
Weight:	374lb (170kg) dry
Top speed:	180mph (290km/h)

Right: Suzuki moved the open-class super-sports fight to a new level in 2001 with the GSX-R1000, whose 161bhp engine and ultra-sharp chassis made an unbeatable combination.

most European countries required no crash-helmet. A 125cc 15bhp single-cylinder engine gave a top speed of 60mph (97km/h). BMW claimed the C1 was the world's safest bike. But it was also top-heavy and expensive, and few people bought one even when BMW offered a more powerful 200cc engine.

A more successful new style of commuter machine was the giant scooter. Most of the major manufacturers created variations on the theme. Suzuki's Burgman 400 was joined in 2001 by Piaggio's X9 500, whose 460cc single-cylinder engine sat on the swingarm in scooter style. Honda's Silver Wing and Yamaha's Tmax were more advanced twin-cylinder machines, of 582cc and 499cc capacity respectively. Their frame-mounted engines gave sharper handling to match their lively straight-line performance. The following year would see the appearance of Suzuki's Burgman 650 twin, whose gearbox offered both manual and automatic operation.

Suzuki also provided the high-performance highlight of 2001. The GSX-R1000 stormed onto the scene with a maximum output of 161bhp that gave it a 10bhp advantage over its super-sport rivals. The GSX-R1000 was heavily based on the GSX-R750, itself updated to good effect a year earlier. As well as looking almost identical, the new bike even shared most of its cylinder head with the smaller motor, and at 374lb (170kg) was only 9lb (4kg) heavier than the 750.

The GSX-R1000's savage performance was enough to send it straight to the front of the open-class superbike battle. Its 998cc 16-valve motor delivered massively strong mid-range response, and enough top-end power for a maximum speed of 180mph (290km/h). Handling and roadholding were outstanding, thanks to a rigid aluminum frame and high-quality suspension parts.

In typical GSX-R style the new bike was firm and uncompromising, but it made a thrilling street bike and an all-conquering racer. The Isle of Man TT was canceled in 2001, due to movement restrictions in the UK introduced as a response to foot-and-mouth disease. In 2002, Yorkshireman David Jefferies would lap the Isle of Man circuit at over 127mph (204km/h) in winning the Senior TT, and at over 124mph (199km/h) on a near-standard GSX-R as he raced to victory in the Production event.

New triples from Triumph

Triumph produced its best sports bike yet in 2001: the Daytona 955i. The comprehensively revamped, 147bhp triple was good for 170mph (274km/h) and handled superbly, though it had lost its predecessor's distinctive styling and single-sided swingarm. The British firm also used a detuned version of its new 955cc 12-valve engine to update the Sprint ST, an aluminum beam-framed sports-tourer that had been very competitive since its launch in 1999.

Triumph's most eagerly awaited model of 2001 was the firm's first twin, for which was reserved the most famous name of all: Bonneville. Unlike its illustrious predecessor, this Bonnie was not a high-performance bike but a gentle, retro-styled roadster designed to appeal to riders who remembered the old Triumph twins. It was styled to resemble the 650cc T120 Bonneville of the late '60s, and its 790cc dohc eight-valve air-cooled parallel twin motor was so softly tuned that its 61bhp output gave a top speed of 115mph (185km/h), similar to that of the old model.

The new Bonneville's performance was nothing special, but it looked good, was competitively priced, and sold well. Ironically the British bike found a rival in Kawasaki's W650, a 50bhp retro twin that had been launched in 1999, inspired by the Japanese firm's own W1 and W2 twins of the 1960s. Triumph would soon follow the standard twin with spin-off models, the Bonneville America and Speedmaster, whose cruiser look was aimed at the US market. But the firm's plans would be hit in April 2002 by a fire that destroyed most of the Hinckley factory and cost much of that year's production. Triumph, whose annual sales had risen above 30,000 units, took the opportunity to rebuild its production lines in a larger building on the same site, in anticipation of further growth.

Ducati was another firm to appreciate the value of cheap and softly tuned twins, as the Monster 600 had been its best-selling bike of recent years. By 2001 the Bologna firm had produced 100,000 Monsters, more than half of them the smallest V-twin, and marked the occasion with the Monster 620ie, featuring an enlarged 618cc engine, fuel-injection, more rigid frame, and twin front discs. The 60bhp motor gave a top speed of 115mph (185km/h), and the Ducati handled well, especially in M620Sie form, with uprated chassis and handlebar fairing.

Above left: Triumph's updated and renamed Daytona 955i was faster, lighter, and more competitive than its T595 predecessor, but had lost a little of the old triple's distinctive style.

Above: Yamaha's Tmax giant scooter had much in common with motorbikes, including a 39bhp dohc twin-cylinder engine that bolted to the frame, not to the swingam in scooter style.

Below: The 2001-model Triumph Bonneville looked like its namesake from 1968, and despite having a 790cc dohc engine its performance was similar to that of the old 650cc twin.

Above: Kawasaki beat Triumph to production of a retro parallel twin with the W650, which was a pleasant bike although few people had heard of the 1960s W1 and W2 twins that inspired it.

Below: Ducati's Monster 620Sie, the upmarket version of the revised naked middleweight, backed up its extra power with extras including a headlamp fairing and aluminum swingarm.

Meanwhile the big Monster was gaining muscles, by being fitted with the dohc eight-valve, liquid-cooled engine that had previously powered the mighty 916 sportster. The resultant Monster S4 was a wild 101bhp machine that snarled to 150mph (241km/h) and more than lived up to its name. Ducati's policy of using old super-sports engines for other models also produced a new sports-tourer, the ST4S, whose 996cc eight-valve engine produced 117bhp, and was matched by an uprated chassis with Öhlins rear suspension. The ST4S faced a capable new rival in Aprilia's first purpose-built sports-tourer. The Futura combined a 998cc V-twin engine, detuned slightly from RSV spec to give 113bhp, with distinctive, angular styling, and a single-sided swingarm.

Yamaha's long-running, air-cooled FJ1200 had been one of the outstanding long-distance bikes of the '90s, and in 2001 Yamaha introduced a worthy successor with the FJR1300. This had a similar look to the old FJ, but had a new liquid-cooled 1298cc 16-valve engine that produced 145bhp, and an aluminum beam frame that helped keep weight down to a reasonable 521lb (237kg). Unlike the old FJ, the FJR13000 was a purpose-built sports-tourer with shaft final drive. It was comfortable and fast, with generous low-rev torque and a top speed of 150mph (241km/h).

Yamaha also produced a versatile big four of a more basic variety with the FZS1000 Fazer, called the FZ1 in the US, which combined a YZF-R1-based motor with a tubular steel frame. Despite being detuned, the 998cc 20-valve engine produced 143bhp, enough for a top speed of 160mph (257km/h). A neat, twin-headlamp half-fairing, efficient steel-framed chassis, and excellent brakes helped make the big Fazer popular.

Left: Bolting the legendary 916's dohc eight-valve V-twin engine into the Monster chassis created the Monster S4, a snarling naked roadster with arm-wrenching performance.

Below: Aprilia broadened its V-twin line in 2001 with the Futura sports-tourer, featuring smooth and torquey 113bhp V-twin engine, aluminum frame, and distinctive, angular bodywork.

Honda caused some confusion by introducing two new versions of its long-time favorite, the CBR600F. Alongside the standard model was the CBR600F Sport, with identical 110bhp power output and very similar chassis, plus a few internal engine differences designed to facilitate race tuning. The CBR's versatility had long been an asset on the road, but a handicap in Supersport racing against more single-minded rivals such as Suzuki's GSX-R600. Ironically Australia's Andrew Pitt would win the 2001 world championship on Kawasaki's ZX-6R, which had been updated a year earlier but remained a practical all-rounder.

Honda also unveiled the GL1800, a revamped version of its long-distance legend, the Gold Wing. A biggest yet 1832cc version of the flat-six motor produced 117bhp and required valve adjustment only every 32,000 miles (51,000km). Other features included uprated fuel-injection, a twin-spar aluminum frame with single-sided swingarm, and a more aerodynamic fairing with a six-way adjustable screen. The Wing was still a huge motorbike, but it was faster, more refined, and more agile than ever before.

The most surprising arrival of 2001 was Harley-Davidson's V-Rod. The long, low, silver machine was a radical departure for Harley, both in its jaw-dropping styling and its 1130cc liquid-cooled 60-degree V-twin engine, whose 115bhp output was almost double that of previous Harley cruisers. The dohc eight-valve 'Revolution' motor was developed with the help of Porsche Engineering of Germany, and based on the V-twin unit of Harley's VR1000, which had been uncompetitive in US Superbike racing since its debut in 1994.

Above: Unlike the old FJ1100 model that it resembled, Yamaha's FJR1300 was a purpose-built sports-tourer whose four-cylinder engine delivered its 145bhp via shaft final drive.

Above: Yamaha's FZ1000 Fazer, known as the FZ1 in the States, was conceived as a steel-framed budget roadster but its 143bhp engine delivered plenty of speed and entertainment.

Below: Honda attempted to have the best of both worlds with its middleweight four in 2001, when this standard CBR600F was joined by a 600F Sport model with extra tuning potential.

Right: Kawasaki's fast and versatile ZX-6R was arguably the pick of the 600cc fours in 2000, and would gain an improbable edge two years later when its engine was enlarged to 636cc.

Style and performance

Visually the V-Rod was inspired, with its kicked-out forks, aluminum radiator shroud, slash-cut mufflers and solid disc wheels. Performance was thrilling, too. The Harley thundered away from the line, revving to its 9000rpm redline through the gears as it headed for a top speed of 140mph (225km/h). Its chassis was good by cruiser standards, especially the powerful twin-disc front brake. The V-Rod thrilled almost everyone who rode it, following its launch in mid-2001 as a 2002 model (in Harley tradition). But sales were disappointing, at least by Harley standards. Most Harley customers still preferred their bikes to come with a heavy dose of nostalgia.

Ducati's 999 was another distinctive V-twin that drew a mixed response from the public. By 2002, eight years had passed since the arrival of the iconic 916, during which time Ducati's eight-valve flagship had retained its look while evolving into the 998 via numerous capacity increases. Trying to improve on Massimo Tamburini's original design was comparable to repainting the Sistine Chapel ceiling, and Pierre Terblanche's 999 did not please every Ducati enthusiast. With its tiny, stacked headlights and single under-seat muffler, it looked different and suitably aggressive, while keeping many family features.

The 999 retained its predecessor's 998cc eight-valve desmo engine, known as the Testastretta ('narrow-head') due to its valve design, and weighed an almost identical 438lb (199kg). But the new bike was slimmer and much more refined, designed for added practicality as well as performance. It had a lower seat, adjustable ergonomics, sophisticated CAN line digital electronics, a longer swingarm for improved traction, and used 30 percent fewer components. Straight-line performance matched that of the 998, handling was slightly sharper, and the 999 was a more comfortable and rider-friendly machine. So too was the 749, which combined a 748cc Testastretta V-twin engine with near-identical chassis and bodywork.

Aprilia's Tuono, the other outstanding V-twin of 2002, was also long awaited. A naked Aprilia superbike had seemed inevitable ever since the RSV Mille's introduction in 1998. When the Tuono – *Thunder* in Italian – finally arrived, it combined its high bars and upright riding position

with a small fairing, complete with trademark triple headlights. Aprilia said this was necessary to ensure stability because the 998cc dohc V-twin RSV motor was not detuned, and its 130bhp output gave a top speed of over 150mph (241km/h).

That was doubtless true, and most who rode the Tuono were glad of its fairing because this was a wonderfully fast, charismatic, and entertaining machine. The big, flexible 60-degree V-twin engine was ideal for a high-barred bike, and the Tuono's chassis, based on the RSV's twin-spar aluminum frame, gave superb handling. Styling was suitably aggressive, and included round plastic crash-protectors for the frame. Few bikes came close to matching the Tuono for providing high-speed thrills with a reasonable level of comfort and practicality.

Aprilia followed a trend with the Tuono by first introducing a limited edition model, the Tuono R, shortly followed by the mass-produced standard machine, the Tuono Fighter, which had less exotic suspension parts. MV Agusta had pioneered this approach with its F4, initially hand built in ultra-limited Serie Oro ('Gold Series') form. The Varese firm did the same thing with its naked Brutale, which was again unveiled in standard Brutale S form, and as the Brutale Serie Oro with frame castings and swingarm in magnesium instead of the S model's aluminum.

In either form, Massimo Tamburini's latest creation was another remarkable motorbike, with its uniquely shaped headlight and a squat, pugnacious look for which the name Brutale was entirely appropriate. Its 749cc radial 16-valve engine was slightly detuned from 750 F4 specification but still produced 127bhp, along with a tuneful note from slash-cut mufflers. The MV's racy geometry, taut suspension, and weight of just 407lb (185kg) gave superb handling, too.

The Brutale was not a practical, sensible roadster, it was a hugely enjoyable naked sports bike that rarely failed to put a smile on its rider's face. But MV's financial problems, which followed the collapse of a proposed agreement with Piaggio, resulted in the debt-laden firm being placed in a state of 'controlled administration' to protect it from creditors. Full production would belatedly begin in 2003, ironically the centenary year of similarly troubled Husqvarna, part of Claudio Castiglioni's MV Agusta group.

Above: Honda's naked GL1000 Gold Wing of the '70s seemed a distant memory on the arrival of the GL1800, with its 1832cc flat six motor, aluminum beam frame, adjustable screen, built-in luggage compartments, and other luxury features.

Below left: Harley began a bold new era with the stunning V-Rod, which looked as though it had been hewn from a solid lump of aluminum, and delivered stunning performance from its 115bhp liquid-cooled V-twin engine.

Harley-Davidson VRSCA V-Rod (2002)

Engine:	Liquid-cooled dohc eight-valve 60-degree V-twin
Capacity:	1130cc (100 x 72mm)
Maximum power:	115bhp @ 8500rpm
Transmission:	Five-speed, belt final drive
Frame:	Tubular steel
Suspension:	Telescopic front; twin shocks rear
Brakes:	Twin discs front; disc rear
Weight:	594lb (270kg) dry
Top speed:	140mph (225km/h)

Ducati 999 (2002)	
Engine:	Liquid-cooled dohc eight-valve 90-degree V-twin
Capacity:	998cc (100 x 63.5mm)
Maximum power:	124bhp @ 9750rpm
Transmission:	Six-speed, chain final drive
Frame:	Tubular steel ladder
Suspension:	Telescopic front, monoshock rear
Brakes:	Twin discs front, disc rear
Weight:	438lb (199kg)
Top speed:	170mph (274km/h)

Right: *Ducati's 999 couldn't match the beauty of the 998, but was a better all-round motorbike.*

Above: *The 749S was at its best in fast corners.*

Below: *Aprilia's Tuono: naked V-twin thrills.*

Benelli's three-cylinder rebirth

Another glamorous Italian marque to start with a limited-edition model was Benelli, which had been reborn in the late '90s under the control of Andrea Merloni, a youthful bike enthusiast whose family controlled the huge Merloni group that owned white goods brands Indesit and Ariston. While gaining experience by producing scooters, Benelli had been developing a three-cylinder superbike, the Tornado. The 898cc 12-valve triple had bold styling, by British designer Adrian Morton, and an innovative chassis based on a frame of steel tubes and aluminum sections, held together using glue as well as bolts.

The Tornado's most unusual features were its under-seat radiator and pair of fans, set into the tailpiece. Benelli's relatively low-budget race team was not competitive in World Superbike. But the 143bhp Tornado roadster was a powerful and fine-handling replica of the factory racer, especially in initial Tornado Limited Edition form, with Öhlins suspension and other lightweight chassis parts. Those initial 150 hand-built bikes were quickly followed by the mass-produced Tornado Tre, also with 160mph (257km/h) top speed and excellent handling, while Benelli developed an equally distinctive naked triple, the TNT, for production in 2004.

While Benelli had been struggling to develop its own engine, Mondial, another famous old Italian name, was making a comeback with a sleek superbike called the Piega, powered by the 999cc V-twin engine from Honda's SP-1. The Piega was a stylish, fully-faired sportster that wrapped a Ducati-style tubular steel frame around the standard dohc, eight-valve SP-1 engine, whose output was raised slightly to 140bhp with new airbox, injection system, and exhaust. Mondial succeeded in selling small numbers of the Piega, despite its high price, and followed Benelli in developing a naked model, the Nuda, for launch in 2004.

Honda had also launched a naked version of its popular super-sports bike in 2002. But despite being essentially an unfaired version of the mighty FireBlade, the Hornet 900 lacked the imagination and attitude of the Italian machines. Rather than use its latest 954cc FireBlade motor, Honda detuned the 1998 model's 918cc unit to give just 108bhp. With styling similar to that of

The Movie Star's Accessory

Just as motorcycles have become popular in recent years by providing fun rather than essential transport, so their portrayal in the movies has followed suit. Bikes are frequently used in Hollywood productions, not as a central features of the film, as in *The Wild One* or *Easy Rider*, but generally as just one of a number of vehicles to be used, and often crashed, by the star.

Some bikes have made more of an impression, dating back to the '80s when Richard Gere rode a Triumph T140 Bonneville in *An Officer and a Gentleman*, and when Tom Cruise's Kawasaki GPZ900R proved almost as exciting as his F-14 Tomcat fighter in *Top Gun*. The theme continued into the '90s with a varied two-wheeled cast. Arnold Schwarzenegger's character rode a Harley Fat Boy in *Terminator II*. Pierce Brosnan, as James Bond, gave BMW's R1200C cruiser valuable publicity in the 1997 film *Tomorrow Never Dies*.

Triumph has frequently benefited from exposure in the movies. Pamela Anderson

rode a Thunderbird triple in the 1996 production *Barb Wire*. In 2001 Tom Cruise was back on two wheels aboard a Speed Triple, in *Mission Impossible 2*. More recently, *How to Lose a Guy in 10 Days* featured a Bonneville, and Colin Farrell rode Triumph's America twin in *Daredevil*.

Ducati made the most of its opportunity after its 996 sportster was used for a dramatic chase sequence in the 2003 release *The Matrix Reloaded*. At that year's Milan Show the Italian firm unveiled a limited edition 998 Matrix Reloaded replica V-twin, finished in the movie bike's dark green paintwork.

Above left: Tom Cruise gives Triumph's Speed Triple some valuable publicity in a fiery action scene from Mission Impossible 2.

Top right: The two-up chase sequence from The Matrix Reloaded *prompted Ducati to produce a special-edition V-twin in matching colors.*

Left: Massimo Tamburini takes a break from riding his latest creation, MV Agusta's Brutale Serie Oro. The influential Italian design genius co-founded Bimota before shaping bikes including the Ducati 916 and MV Agusta F4 750.

Above: Benelli re-entered the superbike market with the sleek Tornado Limited Edition, an innovative 898cc liquid-cooled triple based on the Pesaro firm's World Superbike racer.

Above right: Mondial, another famous old Italian marque, returned with the Piega, a glamorous sportster powered by the 999cc V-twin engine from Honda's SP-2.

the Hornet 600, the new bike had neither performance nor visual impact, but its rider-friendly nature and competitive price were some compensation.

The peak output of Honda's revamped VFR800 was also 108bhp, but the V4 sports-tourer was a very different bike. Its 782cc eight-valve engine was modified to incorporate VTEC variable-valve technology, as used by the firm's cars to give improved low-rev response. Sharper styling and a new high-level exhaust system added to the refined sports-tourer's appeal.

Yamaha also uprated an old favorite with the TDM900, a new version of the versatile parallel twin that had sold almost as many units in Europe as the VFR since its debut in 1991. Aggressive, bug-eyed styling was combined with a more powerful 897cc 86bhp engine, and a lighter, aluminum-framed chassis that made the TDM feel notably more lively.

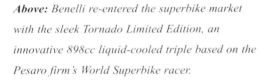

Right: Honda followed a popular format by using its FireBlade engine to power a naked roadster. The Hornet 900 was cheap but its severely detuned motor marred the fun.

Honda trumped Yamaha in the battle to create the biggest V-twin cruiser, with the arrival of the VTX, powered by a gigantic 1795cc 107bhp engine. The VTX out-cubed not only Yamaha's Drag Star 1100, but also the Wild Star, which was powered by a 1602cc air-cooled engine with pushrod valve operation. Meanwhile Kawasaki was taking a more aggressive approach with its Mean Streak, whose 1470cc V-twin motor was held in a sportier chassis incorporating upside-down forks and twin front disc brakes with four-piston calipers.

The emerging 'performance cruiser' category was enlivened by the arrival of Yamaha's Road Star Warrior. Powered by a Wild Star engine enlarged to 1670cc and tuned with hot cams and lighter internals, the Warrior delivered 80bhp with massive low-rev torque. Its chassis featured a tubular aluminum frame plus upside-down forks and twin discs borrowed from the racy YZF-R1. With its laid-back riding position and long wheelbase, the Warrior was much more of a cruiser than a sports bike. But it was a hard-accelerating, surprisingly sweet-handling machine, and good fun to ride.

While the Japanese giants were attacking the cruiser market with renewed enthusiasm, some of the US cruiser manufacturers were struggling. Excelsior-Henderson had been first to suffer, as slow sales of the Super X had forced the Minnesota firm to close its smart new factory by the end of 2001, having spent around $100 million. Reborn Indian's financial worries were temporarily eased in 2001 when a Boston-based investment group injected over $40 million. The following year Indian launched a new Chief, powered by a V-twin engine of the firm's own design, though the 1638cc 45-degree unit was still based on the old S&S powerplant. But in September 2003, Indian's revival stalled when its backers pulled out. The factory in Gilroy, California was closed with the loss of almost 400 jobs.

Victory had also failed to meet early sales targets, partly due to the V92C cruiser's bland looks. But parent company Polaris had the financial clout to continue. In 2003 Victory hit back with a much more stylish cruiser, designed in consultation with legendary custom builder Arlen Ness and his son Cory. The Vegas retained the V92C's 1507cc air-/oil-cooled V-twin engine, but almost everything else was new. A classical custom shape and a host of neat details made the Vegas an attractive bike, and stronger sales rewarded Victory's commitment.

Harley-Davidson's most important new models of 2002 were not cruisers but an innovative pair of new generation Buell sports bikes, the XB9R Firebolt and XB9S Lightning. The sportier

Above: Yamaha's 2002-model TDM900, a comprehensively reworked version of the firm's familiar parallel twin roadster, gained performance with a more powerful 897cc engine and lighter, aluminum-framed chassis.

Left: In an attempt to meet US market demand for 'performance cruisers,' Kawasaki created the Mean Streak by fitting its VN1500 V-twin with a sportier chassis featuring upside-down forks and six-piston brake calipers.

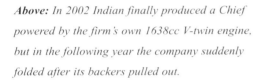

Above: In 2002 Indian finally produced a Chief powered by the firm's own 1638cc V-twin engine, but in the following year the company suddenly folded after its backers pulled out.

Above right: Yamaha's Warrior had laid-back cruiser looks but its 1670cc V-twin engine was held by a tubular aluminum frame, and its forks and front brake came from the YZF-R1.

Firebolt, in particular, was a dramatic machine, with an aggressive glare from its sharp twin-headlamp fairing. But the Buells' key feature was their innovative chassis. The frame's hollow aluminum spars doubled as the fuel tank, leaving the space between them for the airbox. The aluminum swingarm carried oil in similar fashion. And the front brake was the first perimeter disc seen on a production streetbike.

Buell's frame, which incorporated the familiar Uniplanar method of rubber mounting, was very compact, and combined with steep steering geometry to give light and precise handling. Although their new 984cc V-twin engine produced 92bhp, impressive for a unit based on Harley's humble air-cooled Sportster motor, the Buells were not particularly fast, with a top speed of about 135mph (217km/h). But they were stylish, agile, and distinctive enough to make an impact, and were joined in mid-2003 by visually similar XB12 models whose 1203cc engines produced notably more mid-range punch.

Right: Victory's Vegas, styled with the help of custom legend Arlen Ness, was a stylish bike that could be personalized by US customers via the firm's innovative custom paint program.

Buell XB9R Firebolt (2002)	
Engine:	Air/oil-cooled ohv pushrod four-valve 45-degree V-twin
Capacity:	984cc (88.9 x 79.8mm)
Maximum power:	92bhp @ 7200rpm
Transmission:	Six-speed, belt final drive
Frame:	Aluminum twin spar
Suspension:	Telescopic front; single shock rear
Brakes:	Single perimeter disc front; disc rear
Weight:	385lb (175kg) dry
Top speed:	135mph (217km/h)

Harley's happy birthday

Harley itself had no major new models in 2003, but the year was significant as it was the firm's centenary. Having struggled for many of the previous 100 years, Harley reached the landmark in remarkable health, with the year's production approaching 300,000, following 18 consecutive years of increased sales and profit. Not bad for a firm that had built just 32,000 bikes in 1986. The centenary was celebrated with a variety of events and parties, centered in August on a series of organized rides to Milwaukee from points across the US and beyond.

Shortly afterward Harley also introduced four new 2004 models in the one remaining family of bikes that had not recently been overhauled: the Sportsters. The new XL1200R Roadster and XL1200C Custom models had new, more powerful engines producing 70bhp, but the most important feature of those bikes, plus the two 883cc models, was the addition of rubber mounting, which made their performance far more usable.

While Harley had been growing fast, Kawasaki had been falling behind, and had announced an R&D agreement with Suzuki that suggested reduced investment in the future. But at the Munich Show in 2002, the firm's president Shinichi Morita made an unusually bold speech. 'We at Kawasaki are aware that over the past few years our machines have not fully met the expectations of our customers,' he admitted. 'We view this situation with great seriousness. Our stunning new 2003 models represent a re-confirmation of Kawasaki's reputation as a builder of high-performance, high-quality machines.'

Morita's words were backed up by two exciting bikes. The Z1000 was a striking musclebike with a twin-headlamp handlebar fairing, and a 953cc four-cylinder engine developed from the ZX-9R's 16-valve unit. Style was deemed as important as performance, so the Z1000 had an eye-catching four-muffler exhaust system even though it did not benefit the engine's 125bhp output. Even so, the Kawasaki was a lively, hard-charging bike with a top speed of 150mph (241km/h), good handling and plenty of streetfighter attitude.

More impressive still was the ZX-6R, a middleweight missile that put Kawasaki right in the thick of the super-sports action. The new ZX-6R shared its name and 636cc capacity with its predecessor, but this was a much more aggressive bike that produced 116bhp (123bhp with ram-

Above left: Buell's XBR9 Firebolt was an aggressively styled sportster whose innovative features included fuel-carrying aluminum frame spars and a perimeter front brake disc.

Below: The naked Buell XB12S Lightning produced a respectable 100bhp and had agile handling thanks to its compact and light chassis, racy steering geometry, and excellent suspension.

Right: Harley's new generation Sportster 1200 came in two versions: the XL1200C (left), with lower seat and wire wheels, and the XL1200R with retro-style paint and twin front discs.

Below: Kawasaki's Z1000 led the firm's fightback, living up to its famous name with suitably aggressive styling and storming performance from its 16-valve engine.

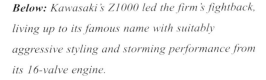

Opposite center right: Honda's CBR600RR was powered by a straight four rather than a V5, but its style and chassis design were closely based on the mighty RC211V MotoGP racer.

Opposite bottom right: Yamaha's 2003-model YZF-R6 was less dramatically updated than its rivals, but featured a more powerful 123bhp (with ram-air) engine and a more rigid frame.

air), weighed just 354lb (161kg), handled brilliantly and howled to a top speed of 165mph (266km/h). The ZX-6R also had lean, sharp looks, race-derived radial front brake calipers, and other neat details including an on-board lap-timer. It was arguably the year's outstanding bike, and confirmed Kawasaki's return to form.

Honda had the perfect response in the CBR600RR, a rapid 16-valve four that abandoned the CBR600's traditional versatility. Instead, the RR was a pure-bred super-sports charger that revved to 15,000rpm and produced 115bhp. Its chassis, inspired by that of Honda's all-conquering RC211V MotoGP racer, featured a high-level exhaust system and an aluminum frame that held fuel below the seat. The RR's speed and fine handling were not surprising, for Honda had reversed its normal design process for the first time, by firstly creating a racing prototype from which the roadster had been developed.

In an outstanding year for new middleweights, Yamaha's updated YZF-R6 featured fewer high-tech features, but was right up there with its 600cc super-sports rivals. And Triumph, which had found little success three years earlier with its TT600, handicapped by dull looks and poor fuel-injection, tried again with another in-line four, the Daytona 600. This British challenger was much more stylish, thanks to new, angular bodywork. Its 16-valve motor produced 110bhp, good for a top speed of about 160mph (257km/h), and its TT600-based, aluminum-framed chassis gave agile handling of the highest standard.

Among the most popular middleweights of recent years had been Suzuki's naked SV650 and half-faired SV650S V-twins. For 2003 Suzuki launched updated versions of both, and also introduced a pair of similarly styled SV1000 models, powered by a detuned 115bhp version of the 996cc V-twin engine from the discontinued TL1000S. The SVs couldn't match the TL's raw performance, but their more conventional aluminum frame design gave stable handling.

Arguably the best new V-twin of 2003 was Aprilia's RSV1000R. For all its pace and poise, the original RSV had not been the sleekest of superbikes, and the new model, although less distinctive, had a more streamlined look. Its 998cc 60-degree V-twin engine was tuned to give 139bhp, an increase of 9bhp, and the new, more compact chassis gave slightly lighter and more

Kawasaki ZX-6R (2003)	
Engine:	Liquid-cooled dohc 16-valve four
Capacity:	636cc (68 x 43.8mm)
Maximum power:	116bhp @ 13,000rpm
Transmission:	Six-speed, chain final drive
Frame:	Aluminum twin spar
Suspension:	Telescopic front; single shock rear
Brakes:	Twin discs front; disc rear
Weight:	354lb (161kg) dry
Top speed:	165mph (266km/h)

Left: Kawasaki's racy ZX-6R handled superbly.

precise handling. Alongside the standard RSV was a higher spec model, the RSV1000R Factory, featuring Öhlins suspension, radial brake calipers, and some carbon-fiber bodywork parts.

Moto Guzzi was showing increased vitality under Aprilia's control, having been bought by Ivano Beggio in September 2000. Beggio invested heavily in upgrading the old Mandello del Lario factory, increasing production to over 10,000 bikes, and in developing new models. The first of these was the Breva 750, a fairly simple roadster powered by a softly tuned 48bhp version of Guzzi's familiar air-cooled transverse V-twin engine.

The Breva's upright riding position, low seat, and shaft final drive made it a very practical bike. Its 105mph (169km/h) top speed and all-round performance were modest, but handling and braking were good, and the Breva made a useful entry-level machine. For 2004 the Breva would be joined by an 1100cc model, with 84bhp output and similar styling.

Guzzi was also working to develop the MGS-01, a handsome sports machine powered by a tuned 1225cc version of the Daytona model's eight-valve V-twin engine. The MGS-01 was developed as a prototype by Giuseppe Ghezzi of Ghezzi & Brian, a specialist firm with links to the factory. After the prototype was displayed to enthusiastic reaction at the Munich Show in 2002, Guzzi announced that the MGS-01 would be put into production, initially as a 125bhp limited-edition racebike, the Corsa, and with a roadgoing model to follow. A similarly striking naked roadster, the Griso, was also on the way.

Aprilia had also bought Laverda, another famous old Italian marque, and unveiled a new SFC1000 model for production in 2004. A long-term return to three-cylinder superbikes seemed likely but in the meantime the SFC was powered by a 998cc 141bhp Aprilia V-twin engine, to which it added a frame of tubular steel and aluminum, plus bodywork in Laverda's traditional orange. The Laverda would face a multi-cylinder Italian rival from MV Agusta, which unveiled its long-awaited F4 1000. Alongside the standard 998cc radial-valve four was the F4 1000 Tamburini, featuring innovative adjustable intake trumpets for a broader spread of power, and peak output increased to 173bhp. MV's financial future appeared to have been secured by an agreement with the Malaysian car firm Proton, backer of Kenny Roberts' MotoGP race team.

Right: Triumph's Daytona 600 was slightly down on power compared to its Japanese super-sports rivals, but the British marque's 16-valve four had the style and handling to become a success.

Above: The RSV1000R Factory was the upmarket version of Aprilia's revamped V-twin, and handled even better than the standard model thanks to Öhlins suspension front and rear.

Below: Laverda's comeback under Aprilia ownership began with the SFC1000, which was painted in the marque's traditional orange but used a V-twin motor from the parent company.

Right: Revitalized Moto Guzzi promised much with the MGS-01, which the Mandello firm planned to build in this Corsa racing form before production of a roadgoing version.

Meanwhile Ducati was broadening its range with the first of a new family of bikes, the Multistrada. Reputedly built to conquer the Futa Pass, a steep, twisty road of varying surface that runs through the Apennines between Bologna and Florence, the Multistrada combined a torquey air/oil-cooled 992cc V-twin motor with a steel-framed chassis that was typically Ducati, apart from its longer-travel suspension. The Multistrada's tall, un-aerodynamic styling was controversial, but most who rode the Ducati were impressed by its blend of flexible power delivery, easy handling, and long-legged comfort.

Austrian firm KTM had achieved an impressive rise during the '90s, based on its success with off-road competition bikes. A string of Paris-Dakar wins, backed up by motocross and enduro

Left: Ducati's Multistrada lacked the sleek style of the firm's sports bikes, but the 992cc V-twin's comfort, versatility, and agile handling impressed most people who rode it, boosting Ducati's plans for a family of similar bikes.

success, confirmed KTM's prowess, as did sales of over 65,000 bikes in 2002. The firm's ambitious plan to become Europe's biggest manufacturer was boosted the following year with the arrival of the Adventure 950, its first twin-cylinder model.

The dual-purpose V-twin was powered by a new 942cc dohc eight-valve engine with cylinders set at 75 degrees. The Adventure was quick, with lively acceleration to a top speed of 130mph (209km/h). Although it wasn't as smooth or comfortable as some big trail bikes, the KTM's excellent suspension and relatively light weight made it an outstanding off-road machine. Meanwhile, the Austrian firm was developing the V-twin motor to power a naked roadster, the Duke 990, plus a super-sports bike for eventual World Superbike racing.

With annual bike production having risen to almost 100,000, BMW was also enjoying its most successful period, and in 2004 introduced a new version of its best-selling model of all. The R1200 GS was the latest in the long line of dual-purpose boxers stretching back to the R80 G/S that had established the big trail bike class in 1980. The R1200 GS was a completely new bike whose 100bhp peak output was 15bhp up on its R1150 GS predecessor, and which was a substantial 66lb (30kg) lighter, at just 438lb (199kg) dry.

The air/oil-cooled, high-cam motor also gained a balancer shaft, which made the 135mph (217km/h) performance more usable. The GS was brilliantly versatile, as happy cruising at 100mph (161km/h) as negotiating a bumpy dirt track. It was also stylish, comfortable, and well equipped, with ABS brakes and adjustable ergonomics. With BMW also rumored to be developing a large-capacity, four-cylinder superbike with radical front suspension, the German firm's old reputation for dull touring bikes was now a distant memory.

Yamaha's trio of new dual-purpose bikes included the XT660X, the first purpose-built Japanese model inspired by the increasingly popular sport of supermoto. Essentially a cross between road-racing and motocross, supermoto had led to dirt bikes with stiffer suspension and fat, sticky tires being produced by European firms including Britain's CCM and Italian-based Husqvarna, which had built its first TD610E Super Motard several years earlier. When Yamaha

Below: Given KTM's background in off-road competition, it was no surprise when the Austrian firm's long-awaited Adventure 950 V-twin was much happier on the dirt than most of its rivals in the twin-cylinder trail bike class.

BMW R1200 GS (2004)

Engine:	Air/oil-cooled ohv eight-valve high cam flat twin
Capacity:	1170cc (101 x 73mm)
Maximum power:	100bhp @ 7000rpm
Transmission:	Six-speed, shaft final drive
Frame:	Tubular steel; engine as stressed member
Suspension:	Telelever front; single shock rear
Brakes:	Twin discs front; single disc rear with ABS
Weight:	438lb (199kg) dry
Top speed:	135mph (217km/h)

Below: BMW's brilliantly versatile R1200 GS, considerably lighter and more powerful than its predecessor the R1150 GS, was an outstanding performer both on- and off-road.

Right: Ducati tested market reaction to its 1970s-inspired SportClassic models by displaying the prototypes. The positive reaction convinced the factory to put all three into production.

launched a new single-cylinder trail bike, the XT660R, the firm also created the 660X by combining the same 48bhp liquid-cooled engine with stiffer suspension, roadgoing wheels and tires, and a bigger front brake.

Another 2004-model Yamaha was even more revolutionary. The WR450F 2-Trac was the first production bike to use two-wheel drive. Yamaha's system, developed with Swedish suspension specialist Öhlins (which it owned), used hydraulics to transfer some drive to the front wheel when the rear wheel broke traction. As well as being tested successfully in off-road competition, 2-Trac had also shown promising results in tests with large-capacity road bikes. Although the WR was initially destined for very limited production, two-wheel drive looked to have a promising future.

A more immediate trend in roadster development was toward sporty models with classical styling. Ducati followed the MH900e by unveiling three SportClassic prototypes, including a silver, half-faired bike inspired by Paul Smart's famous 1972 victory in the Imola 200 road race. Triumph introduced the Thruxton, a sportier version of the Bonneville parallel twin featuring an enlarged 865cc engine producing 69bhp, plus café-racer styling including low bars, rearset footrests, and humped seat.

Meanwhile, old rival Norton was set for another comeback, albeit in small numbers. The Commando 952 was a parallel twin in Norton tradition; a modern bike with much of the old models' familiar style. It was developed by Kenny Dreer, a leading Norton restorer and specials builder, based in Oregon, USA, who had raised several million dollars to buy the Norton name from its previous owners, both in Canada and Germany. With 85bhp from its 952cc air/oil-cooled engine, and a lightweight steel-framed chassis, the new Commando promised lively performance. Dreer reported strong interest at the projected $15,000 price, although the failure of Indian and Excelsior-Henderson gave warning that re-establishing Norton would not be easy.

While old British rivals Triumph and Norton prepared for a revival of hostilities, the first of the new breed of sporty parallel twins to reach the streets came from Germany, in the distinctively angular shape of MZ's 1000S. The tubular-steel-framed twin, initially intended to be boosted by a supercharger, had undergone lengthy development since being unveiled in 2000. With an output of 114bhp and dry weight of 462lb (210kg), the 1000S was not particularly powerful or light. But it handled well and confirmed the arrival of MZ, now under Malaysian ownership, in the large capacity market.

MotoGP's Four-stroke Takeover

Grand prix bike racing was transformed in 2002 when the 500cc class was replaced by MotoGP, which was open to four-strokes of up to 990cc. Although the 500cc two-strokes had provided memorably close racing in recent years, they had little in common with roadgoing bikes. By contrast the four-stroke MotoGP bikes would provide valuable development for production machines, and the class soon attracted interest from most major manufacturers.

Although the 990cc capacity limit was fixed, bikes with fewer cylinders were given a weight advantage, which encouraged a variety of different engine layouts. Honda considered a V6 before basing its RC211V on a 20-valve V5 with cylinders set at 75.5 degrees. Yamaha's YZR-M1 and Kawasaki's ZX-RR were transverse fours, Suzuki's GSV-R was a V4, and Aprilia's RS3 Cube was a transverse triple.

The racing was spectacular and loud, but the Honda was simply too fast for all the rest. Italian superstar Valentino Rossi, who had won the previous year's championship on

Honda's two-stroke NSR500, dominated the first two MotoGP seasons on the RC211V, whose engine revved to 14,000rpm, produced over 220bhp and gave the bike a top speed of over 200mph (322km/h). Only fellow Honda riders Alex Barros, in 2002, and Sete Gibernau, in 2003, put up a consistent challenge to the charismatic Rossi.

Predictably the lighter but less powerful 500cc two-strokes, several of which joined in during the first season, lacked the sheer horsepower needed to be competitive. Suzuki's and Kawasaki's four-strokes were also well off the pace. Even Yamaha managed only one rostrum place in 2003, though the firm's hopes were boosted by the signing of champion Rossi for 2004. By contrast Ducati's Loris Capirossi won a race in 2003, the debut year of the powerful Desmosedici ('Desmo 16-valve'), and was timed at a record 206.7mph (332.6km/h) on the thundering Italian V4 at the Italian GP at Mugello.

MotoGP's success was confirmed by the increasing number of factories considering involvement, and contrasted with the fortunes of the World Superbike championship. Ducati's British ace Neil Hodgson rode a works 999 to a convincing win in 2003. But controversial rule changes then resulted in most works teams abandoning the Superbike series, whose status was greatly diminished.

The future of real road racing was even more bleak. A succession of fatal accidents in Irish road racing was followed in July 2000 by the death of 26 times TT winner Joey Dunlop, the greatest road racer of all, at a minor meeting in Estonia. At the Isle of Man in 2003, multiple TT winner and lap record holder David Jefferies was killed when he crashed his Suzuki GSX-R1000 at high speed. Many riders still loved to pit themselves and their machines against the famous 37.73-mile (60.7km) Mountain Circuit and the roads of Northern Ireland's North West 200. But others were wondering how long these historic events could continue.

Foggy's new challenge

Malaysian oil giant Petronas had undertaken a high-profile project to produce and race a 989cc three-cylinder superbike, the FP-1, in conjunction with British former World Superbike champion Carl Fogarty. During the World Superbike 2003 season the Foggy Petronas team had struggled to make the hastily created racing version of the triple competitive against the dominant Ducatis. Development of the production FP-1 also took longer than planned, but Petronas appeared to have the financial resources to see the project to completion.

Above left: Valentino Rossi on Honda's RC211V.

Top center: Northern Ireland's North West 200 is one of the most spectacular real road races.

Above right: TT racing lost its brightest star when David Jefferies was killed in 2003.

Above: MZ's angular 1000S parallel twin finally entered production after years of development.

Right: The Thruxton 900 added performance and café-racer style to Triumph's parallel twin.

Above: The stylish, American-built Commando 952 gave hope of a genuine new Norton at last.

Below: Hyosung's Comet 650 owed much to Suzuki but was designed and built in Korea.

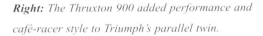

Another rising Asian force was South Korean firm Hyosung which, after beginning by producing small-capacity bikes in conjunction with Suzuki, was growing in size and confidence. While Daelim, another Korean firm, continued to build obsolete Honda models, Hyosung introduced 650 and 1000cc V-twins of its own design and construction. With increasing numbers of Comet roadsters and Aquila cruisers heading for export markets including Europe and the US, Hyosung looked set to emulate Korean car firm Hyundai by establishing a reputation for high-quality machines at competitive prices.

The outstanding new bikes of 2004, however, had more familiar origins. Kawasaki's impressive recovery gathered pace with the ZX-10R, an outrageously aggressive 998cc 16-valve super-sports four. The ZX-10R shared the lean, angular styling of the ZX-6R, had an even shorter wheelbase, and weighed just 374lb (170kg). Its peak output of 172bhp was increased to over 180bhp by the ram-air system, giving a power-to-weight ratio of well over one bhp per kilogram.

Those statistics suggested a stunningly fast, racy motorbike, and the ZX-10R did not disappoint. It screamed to over 100mph (161km/h) in first gear, lifted its front wheel under hard acceleration in thrilling fashion, and scorched to a top speed of over 180mph (290km/h). The Kawasaki also had handling so responsive that it verged on the nervous, plus superb braking thanks to radial front calipers and lightweight, wave-pattern discs.

Few bikes had ever come close to bringing such vicious, adrenaline-charged performance to the street, although one that had was Suzuki's GSX-R1000, which weighed just 370lb (168kg) following a 2003 update that also incorporated radial brake calipers. Yamaha joined in by comprehensively updating the YZF-R1 for 2004. Its revised 20-valve engine's 172bhp output matched that of the ZX-10R, and the Yamaha's new chassis incorporated a high-level exhaust system for the first time.

Honda faced the growing challenge with the fastest FireBlade yet. The CBR1000RR followed the CBR600RR by inheriting styling and chassis design from the RC211V racer. The 'Blade's new 998cc 16-valve engine produced 170bhp, and breathed out through a high-level exhaust system. At 394lb (179kg) the FireBlade was slightly heavier than its closest rivals, but it handled superbly thanks to its race-derived chassis, whose key feature was mass centralization. Ironically the FireBlade followed the RC211V in delivering its performance in relatively controlled, undramatic fashion, aided by a sophisticated steering damper. That arguably made it faster but less exciting to ride than some of its rivals.

Honda's most spectacular newcomer was the Valkyrie Rune, an innovative giant cruiser powered by the GL1800 Gold Wing's flat six engine. The Rune had begun as a concept machine designed by American Honda, and made it into limited production, with features including trailing-link front forks, enormous curved radiator, and a collection of striking bodywork shapes. Honda planned to build just 1200 units during 2004, all for US sale at over $25,000 each. The Rune's introduction sparked hopes that another futuristic American Honda prototype, the New American Sports, would one day lead to a production model too.

Even Triumph's Rocket III couldn't match the visual impact of the Rune, but the British firm's three-cylinder cruiser had an even larger capacity as well as much more performance. The gigantic 2294cc in-line triple produced 147bhp and delivered its maximum torque at just 2500rpm. Triumph claimed the Rocket III out-accelerated Suzuki's Hayabusa to 100mph (161km/h) – provided a pillion passenger was in place to help keep the enormous rear tire gripping the road.

Whatever the truth of that, the Rocket III showed the motorcycle world one new direction in which high-performance bikes might develop. With the latest crop of racy super-sports machines arriving just as motorcycling in some countries was under siege from rising accident rates, increased calls for legislation, record numbers of prosecutions for speeding, and even spiraling costs of track day insurance, any alternatives were welcome.

Kawasaki ZX-10R (2004)	
Engine:	Liquid-cooled dohc 16-valve four
Capacity:	998cc (76 x 55mm)
Maximum power:	172bhp @ 11,700rpm
Transmission:	Six-speed, chain final drive
Frame:	Aluminum twin spar
Suspension:	Telescopic front; single shock rear
Brakes:	Twin discs front; disc rear
Weight:	374lb (170kg) dry
Top speed:	185mph (298km/h)

Above: Kawasaki belatedly joined the open-class super-sports war with the ZX-10R, which boasted sharp styling, light weight, a rev-happy 172bhp engine, and neat details including wave-pattern front disc brakes.

Left: Yamaha overhauled its fearsome YZF-R1 to good effect for 2004. A more powerful 172bhp engine was angled forward in a slimmer and more rigid frame; and a new high-level exhaust system ended with an under-seat muffler.

Honda CBR1000RR FireBlade (2004)	
Engine:	Liquid-cooled dohc 16-valve four
Capacity:	998cc (75 x 56.5mm)
Maximum power:	170bhp @ 11,250rpm
Transmission:	Six-speed, chain final drive
Frame:	Aluminum twin spar
Suspension:	Telescopic front; single shock rear
Brakes:	Twin discs front; disc rear
Weight:	394lb (179kg) dry
Top speed:	185mph (298km/h)

Right: Honda's CBR1000RR FireBlade resembled the firm's RC211V MotoGP bike, and the roadster delivered suitably fierce performance.

Above: The huge and exotic Valkyrie Rune flat six was an American Honda project bike that somehow made it into very limited production.

Evolution continues

Back in 1993, the Guggenheim Museum's *Art of the Motorcycle* exhibition curator Thomas Krens had written of the bikes of the future: 'They cannot be built any bigger or faster without leaving the road, and space-age design certainly must have its own limitations. Logic and physics suggest the motorcycle has reached the end of its evolutionary potential, but somehow we know that cannot be completely true.'

It wasn't remotely true then, and more than a decade later the motorcycle's evolution was showing no signs of slowing. Motorbikes had come a long way since Einspur's first trip in 1885, bringing much pleasure and no little pain along the way. How they will develop in the future can only be imagined. But judging from the progress so far, it's sure to be an exciting ride.

Right: The instant demand for the Rocket III justified Triumph's decision to build the triple instead of a more conventional superbike.

MW00329150

The Prehistoric World of the
DINOSAUR

The Prehistoric World of the
DINOSAUR

Dr David Norman

GALLERY BOOKS
An imprint of W.H. Smith Publishers Inc.
112 Madison Avenue
New York, New York 10016

Published by Gallery Books
A Division of W H Smith Publishers Inc.
112 Madison Avenue
New York, New York 10016

Produced by
Brompton Books Corp.
15 Sherwood Place
Greenwich, CT 06830

Copyright © 1988 Brompton Books Corp.

All rights reserved. No part of this book may be reproduced or
transmitted in any form or by any means without written permission
from the copyright owner.

ISBN 0-8317-0852-2
Printed and bound in Spain by Gráficas Estella, S.A. Navarra.
Printed in Spain

10 9 8 7 6 5 4 3 2 1

Page 1 The first *Iguanodon* discoveries are mounted in Belgium.

Pages 2-3 A late-Jurassic scene showing a herd of *Diplodocus* being
overflown by the pterosaur *Rhamphorhynchus*.

Below A complete skeleton of *Styracosaurus* collected from the late
cretaceous rocks near the Red Deer River, Alberta, in the early part of
this century.

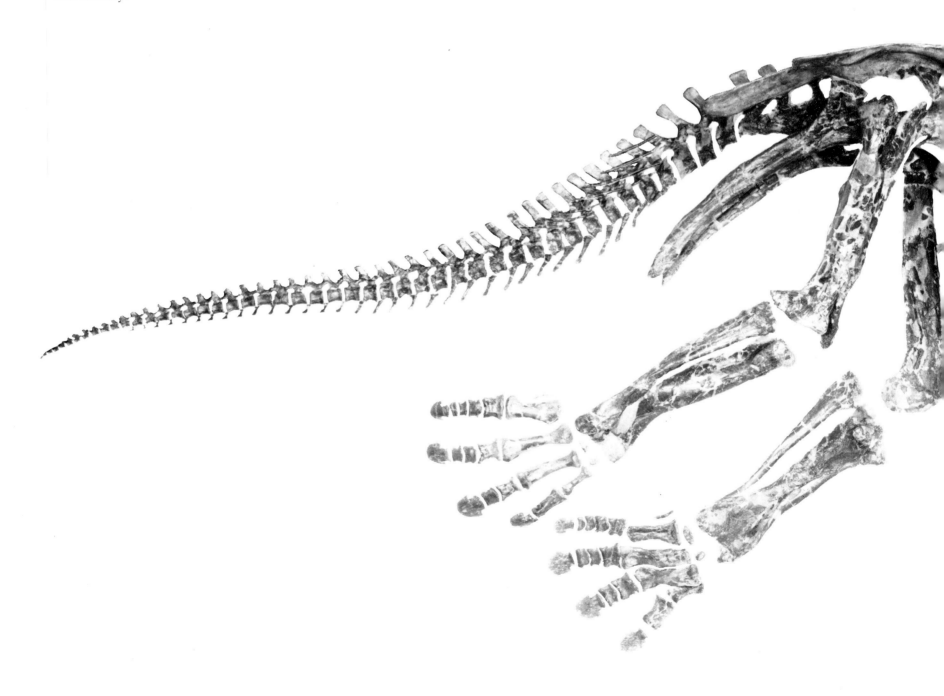

Contents

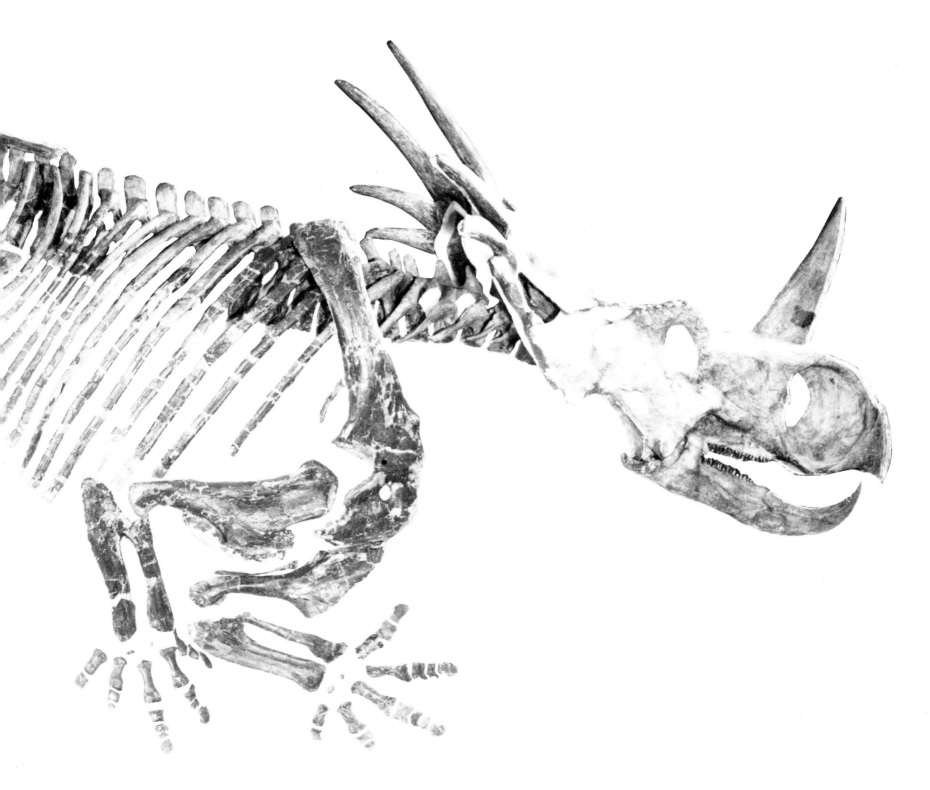

CHAPTER 1

Dinosaurs and their Environment

This book is primarily about dinosaurs, but before going any further it is most important to look at how geologists and paleontologists have been able to build up an understanding of the history of the Earth, estimating time geologically. The physical processes have in turn led to the deposition of rocks and the formation of fossils (the only real evidence of any prehistoric creatures), and the evolution of life, including the forms of life that came before and after the dinosaurs.

In this chapter I will provide a brief outline of these topics so that the historical position of dinosaurs can be more fully appreciated. I will also spend a little time explaining precisely what, scientifically, a dinosaur is understood to be. There is frequently some confusion about this.

Difficulties

Dinosaurs present a number of very difficult problems of interpretation, the most obvious being that they are all extinct. So when attempting to study their fossil remains, a paleontologist never has the opportunity to study a 'blue-print' of how they should look. Some living representatives would at least provide a certain amount of reassurance over the shape and arrangement of their bones, or add to interpretations of how they may have walked or run. Compare the work of a paleontologist working on a dinosaur with one working on the fossil remains of a prehistoric mammoth or a saber-toothed tiger. In the latter cases, there are still living examples of both elephants and large cats, close relatives of the mammoth and saber-toothed tiger. It is therefore much easier to form a picture of what such fossil animals may have looked like, and even how they may have moved and behaved. This is not to belittle the work of people working on these sorts of fossil, because there are many dangers which can arise from an over reliance on what related animals look like or do. However, it does emphasize the difficulty of the task faced by

some paleontologists, and perhaps more importantly highlights something which occurs frequently in this area of research. Namely there can be changes in views or opinions about dinosaurs, concerning either their appearance or way of life.

As an example of this, during the last 20 years there has been a profound change in opinion about the general way of life of dinosaurs. Until the mid-1960s dinosaurs were thought of as rather slow-moving (and by implication slow-witted) animals – destined for extinction. However views have changed quite dramatically following the discovery of a number of dinosaurs evidently designed for a very active lifestyle. In addition there has been a great deal of work devoted to building a picture of the physiology of dinosaurs. Researchers have been attempting to find out whether they were really like today's reptiles whose activities are governed by climatic conditions: the warmer it is, the more active

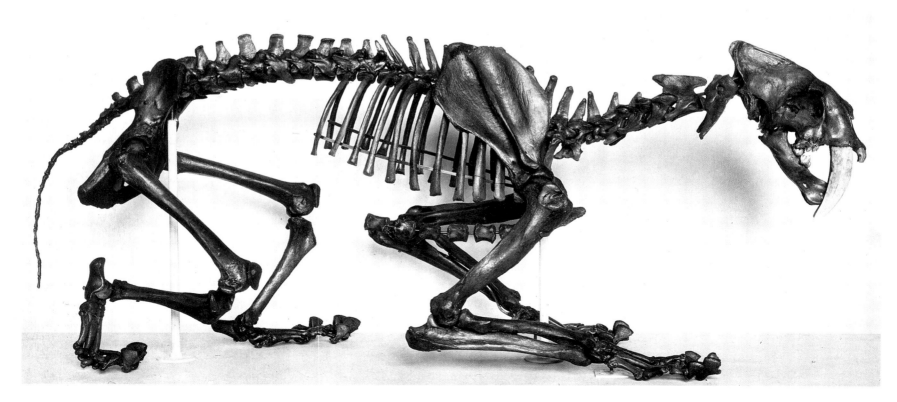

Left top Living elephants provide a good comparison for extinct mammoths.

Left bottom Saber-toothed cats are similar to lions and tigers.

Right The woolly mammoth has only recently become extinct and can be reconstructed accurately.

Below Skeletons of mammoths closely resemble elephants.

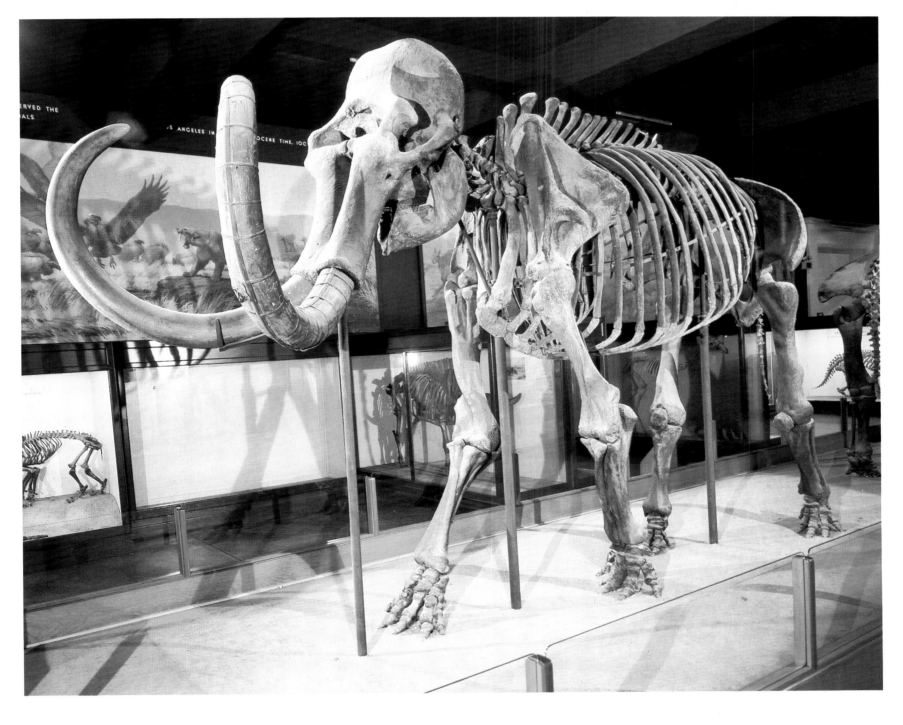

Left Extracting fossil bones from the rock is a lengthy job and the bare bones revealed are just the beginning of the story.

Below Dinosaur skin is not often preserved, but this is a fine example from *Euoplocephalus*, an armored dinosaur.

Above right and above far right Rhinoceroses are large and tend to be dull colored, lizards may be bright. Were dinosaurs dull?

Right *Iguanodon* bones tell us nothing about color, but may tell us much about how dinosaurs moved and lived.

they tend to be. Or were they like the more active, and hence climatically independent, birds and mammals? Although current opinion is somewhat divided, paleontologists tend to think that most dinosaurs were highly active creatures – much more like mammals and birds than like living reptiles. And this is certainly the impression that can be gained from looking at the pictures in this book.

Ultimately, the biggest problem with any interpretation of dinosaurs, by even the best of scientists, is the fact that we know so little about dinosaurs as living animals. All there is to go on are their fossilized bones – and usually incomplete skeletons at that. Skin impressions are very rarely preserved around the carcass; equally rare are those of fossilized stomach contents, droppings (coprolites), footprints, eggs or nests. Compared with a zoologist working on a living species the paleontologist has so little to go on that none of a dinosaur's life activities – walking, feeding, breathing – can be studied. Nor can its behavior or ecology be looked at and obviously little, if any, of the soft anatomy (muscles, organs, blood systems) can be studied directly.

Most of the work has to concentrate on the bony remains: the shape and arrangement of the bones, and the mechanics of the skeleton. This can then be used to build up an understanding of part of the muscle systems, especially in areas like the hip and shoulder, for here powerful muscles leave permanent scars on the surfaces of bones. In some cases bones (especially those in the skull) can indicate the positions of nerves and blood vessels, as well as the shape and size of the cavity for the brain. Bones can also be cut and polished as thin sections to be examined under the microscope. Such investigations reveal the way in which the bone grew which can sometimes reveal quite a lot about the lifestyle of the animal. Finally bones can be used to study the relationships of different species of animals because the more similar are the bones of different skeletons, the more likely are the animals to be close relatives.

Obviously, because of the constant need for reasoning and interpretation this is far from being an exact science. It is nevertheless challenging and requires a vast range of skills from the scientist in order to come as close as possible to a solution to the ultimate problem: what was any dinosaur like?

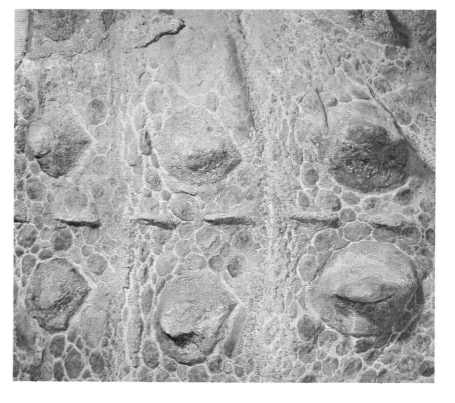

This book attempts to provide an impression of how dinosaurs, and a few other prehistoric animals, may have looked. Some are based on good skeletons and are therefore reasonably accurate as far as general shape and posture are concerned. However, whether they ever fed on the sorts of animal that they are pictured with, or the sort of plants that they are seen munching, is much more difficult to be precise about. It is even more difficult – in fact, almost impossible – to know what colors dinosaurs were. Generally I have advised the artist to use dull colors for very big animals since elephants, rhinoceroses and hippopotamuses are by our standards, big and dull colored. For the same reason, smaller and predatory forms are often given bright colors. Today's smaller predators after all tend to be so colored. Smaller herbivores are painted with a mixture of either camouflaged (*cryptic*, as in the case of the chameleon, or *disruptive*, as in the case of zebra), neutral or bright coloring.

Fossilization

To understand how fossils are formed, it is necessary to look briefly at the geological processes operating on Earth which create the conditions allowing fossils to form.

Sun, wind, rain, running water, ice, snow – all weather rocks. This erosion begins as large splintered pieces of rock and gradually the fragments break into ever smaller pieces. Eventually, when the rock has been weathered to sand-grain size, or smaller, it is washed down rivers into lakes, or into the sea, falling to the lake bottom or sea floor. In this state the particles of rock form sediment, which can either be coarse (as in the case of sands) or fine (as in the case of muds or silts).

Over thousands, or even millions of years, the continuous deposition of particles of rock in these areas leads to the formation of thick layers of sediment, and it is in these sediments that most fossils form.

Animals or plants living during a particular period have their remains trapped within the layers of sediment in the bottom of lakes or on the sea floor if a set sequence of events take place. First the organism must die (either naturally of old age, or as a result of predation). In the vast majority of cases a dead carcass does not survive for long, for its remains are comprehensively scavenged by a whole variety of organisms and it returns completely to the the ecosystem from which it came. However, in a few instances the organism either as a whole, or as a partly scavenged carcass, or even just a few remaining bones, may get washed into a river by rain or in a flash flood and carried to a lake or the sea. Here, as it decays it eventually sinks to the bottom, becoming covered in sediment.

As the layers of sediment thicken with the passing of time, the weight of the layers, just like some gigantic press, gradually squeezes the sediment particles together. In doing this the sediment is turned back into rock, trapping the remains of the organism permanently inside. With the passage of more millions of years water percolating through the sedimentary rock (as it is now called) carries minerals into the hard tissues and spaces, such as the bones, of the buried animal. Gradually the bones are turned into stone, a process known as petrification.

With the remains of the organism now safely preserved in rock, the last process required is the breaking open of the rock to reveal its fossils. This again requires other large geological processes to take place over very long periods of time. Movements of the surface of the Earth result in the periodic raising and lowering of parts of its surface. As a result, areas of land that are at times underwater may be raised up and become new land. In this way ancient sea floors or lake bottoms can be lifted up, sometimes even becoming high mountain ranges. Hence, the fossil sea shells found in rocks high up in the Andean mountains of South America.

Naturally, once rocks are lifted out on to land, they immediately start to erode once more. Eventually this leads to the exposure of the fossil remains which lay trapped within. If no one collects these remains, they will simply weather away and be ground down to form the sediment entombing future animals. So the process continues in a never ending cycle.

While most fossils form in this way, there are a few exceptions. On rare occasions animals are engulfed by wind blown sand. They are either buried in a sand dune, or after dying in a very arid area become covered in dust. The animal may dry out completely, becoming 'mummified.' A few dinosaurs have been fossilized in this way, and not only have well-preserved bones but also the skin texture has been preserved by an impression formed in the

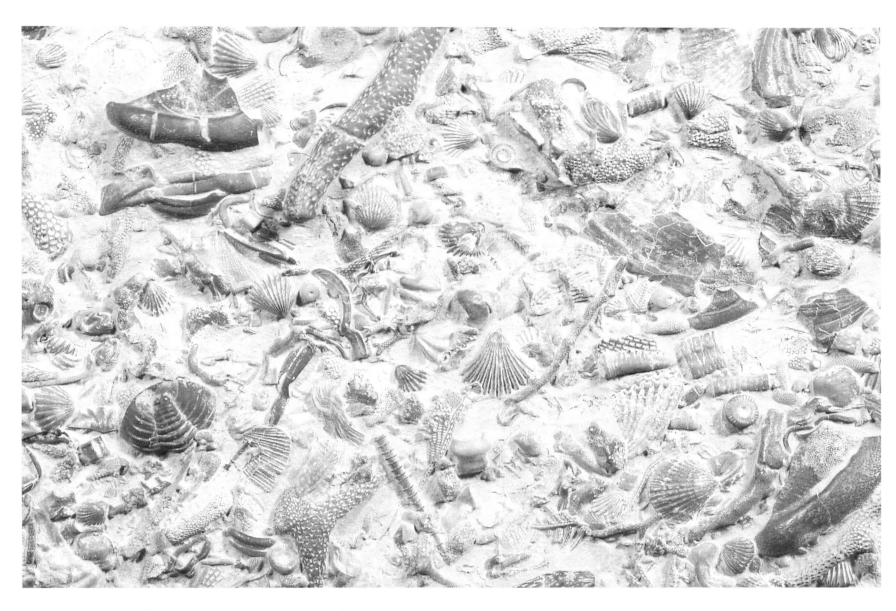

Above left Petrified forests usually consist of little more than broken stumps and part of the root system. These are exceptionally fine examples of tree trunks with their root systems intact, preserved by being buried by river sediments.

Top Sometimes remains are washed into particularly favored spots, such as in the eddy pools on the bends in a river; here they can form rich fossil bone beds such as this.

Right The beautifully preserved skeleton of this hadrosaurian dinosaur is seen here being excavated out of fine river silts in late Cretaceous rocks in southern Mongolia.

Left The badlands terrain of South Dakota is an ideal hunting ground for fossils (including those of dinosaurs). The soft sedimentary rocks are constantly being eroded away to reveal more fossils.

Right The carcass of the iguana would seem to be a candidate for fossilization, but on these volcanic islands the skeleton is more likely to be destroyed.

Below far left The rotting carcass of a sauropod dinosaur is washed down into a lake and sinks into the mud.

Below left The flesh decays away and the skeleton is buried by mud.

Below Further layers of mud bury the dinosaur and begin to compress the mud into rock.

Below far right Millions of years later earth movements have lifted the ancient lake bed up on to dry land. Erosion eventually begins to reveal the long buried dinosaur fossil.

Left Dinosaur eggs are a rarity in the fossil record and rarely can be associated with particular species; however these from Mongolia belonged to *Protoceratops*.

Below Footprints are also relatively rare. These are from a site near Winton in Australia and were probably made by a small carnivorous dinosaur.

Right The remains of this *Oryx* are about to become buried in wind-blown sand after having been scavenged, and the bones scattered and sun-bleached.

Bottom right Given the right conditions surprisingly complete skeletons may sometimes be preserved, as happened with this plesiosaur *Cryptoclidus*.

sand, subsequently hardened to sandstone. The skin is of course completely lost in the fossil but the sand keeps a remarkably clear image.

Other sorts of fossils provide indirect evidence of animals. Trace fossils such as coprolites (fossil droppings) and footprints can reveal a great deal about a creature's lifestyle. It is impossible to be sure which animal left the droppings or the footprints, which can be very frustrating. However, sometimes, if a certain animal's fossils are particularly common in an area which has either many coprolites or footprints then it is very suggestive that they may be linked.

Fossilized eggs or nests sometimes fall into the category of trace fossils as well, because again it is often impossible to tell which creature laid them. In one or two cases, however, it has been possible to discover which eggs belong to which dinosaur because nestlings or embryonic remains have been found either with the eggs' shells, or actually inside the eggs.

Geological time and the ages of the Earth

The oldest rocks so far discovered on Earth date back about 3600 million years. However, by dating meteorites from Earth's solar system, which probably formed at about the same time as Earth, geologists have estimated that Earth is, in fact, 4600 million years old. It seems that immediately after the Earth condensed from dust and vapor, it was made of hot molten rock. A long period would have been required before it had cooled sufficiently for a crust of hard rock, the future land, to form.

How have geologists managed to establish such dates for the formation of the Earth? One of two techniques are used to date rock or fossil samples. The most precise method is called Absolute dating, and is done by analyzing the proportions of radioactive isotopes of common elements within the Earth's crust. Radioactive isotopes are known to decay at an established rate, such that half of the isotope breaks down into a more stable element in a fixed time (the so-called half-life). Therefore, if it is known in what proportions the radioactive isotope and its stable version were formed and their proportions can be analyzed now, it can be calculated how old the rocks are. One of the best elements for this sort of calculation, because it has a very long half-life and is also very common in the Earth's crust, is Potassium 40. This decays to

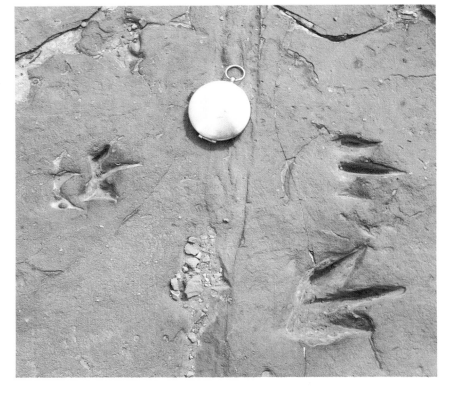

produce Argon 40 with a half-life of 1300 million years. The only drawback with this technique is that the ratio of Potassium to Argon can only be reliably measured in rocks of volcanic origin.

By looking in the rock record, geologists have been able to collect a series of absolute dates at intervals throughout the fossil record, providing a series of markers around which everything else can be dated by comparative methods.

Comparative dating, as the name implies, involves the making of comparisons. For example, fossil samples taken from rock formations in different areas can be compared. If they are very similar, then it would seem likely that they are from rocks of similar age. Such comparisons allow the degree of similarity of fossils, and therefore some measure of their comparative ages, to be assessed. This information can then be tied in with known rock sequences which have absolute datings to build up a geological timescale based on rocks and fossils from areas all over the world.

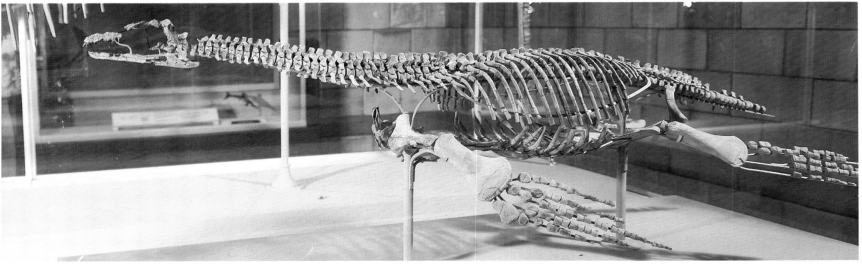

Eon	Era	Period		Epoch		Millions of Years ago

Phanerozoic Eon

The eon of obvious life. Phanerozoic sedimentary rocks may have plenty of fossils in them. Many animals that lived during this time had hard shells and bones that were easily fossilized.

Cainozoic Era

The era of modern life. With the extinction of the dinosaurs and other reptiles, the mammals and the birds took over. Climates became gradually cooler, largely because of the movement of continents, culminating in the Pleistocene Ice Age.

Quaternary Period The Ice Age and after.

Holocene (Recent) Epoch — 0.01
Pleistocene Epoch or Ice Age — 2
Pliocene — 5

Teritary Sub Era

Tertiary and Quaternary (third and fourth) are terms left over from a Victorian classification, in which the Mesozoic was called the Secondary, and the Paleozoic and Precambrian were called the Primary.

Neogene Period

The time of the grasslands and the modern mammals.

Miocene Epoch

The epoch in which the forests began to give way to grasslands. More modern mammals evolved.

Paleogene Period

Forests existed over much of the world, inhabited by primitive mammals.

Oligocene — 25 / 38

Eocene — 55 / 50

Paleocene

The epoch in which all kinds of new mammals evolved. — 65

Mesozoic Era

The era of middle life. The reptiles were the most important land animals, although the mammals evolved from the mammal-like reptiles at the very beginning, and the birds developed about halfway through.

Cretaceous Period

The climax of the age of dinosaurs. Dinosaurs, pterosaurs and sea reptiles became extinct at the end. Mammals and birds survived. Flowering plants evolved at the beginning. The continents were far enough apart for each to have its own distinctive dinosaur groups. — 100

Jurassic Period

Dinosaurs and other reptiles were widespread and varied. Birds evolved. Continents began to move apart. The supercontinent Pangea split up and shallow seas spread, bringing moist climates to most places. Forests replaced the deserts. — 144 / 150 / 200

Triassic Period

The first dinosaurs evolved as the mammal-like reptiles died out. — 213 / 248 / 250

Paleozoic Era

The era of ancient life. Abundant sea life at the beginning. Gradually plants and then animals spread to the land. All this time the continents were moving together, all meeting up to form the single supercontinent Pangea at the end of the era.

Permian Period

Deserts with many reptiles – particularly mammal-like reptiles. — 286 / 300

Carboniferous Period

Regarded in the US as two periods.

Pennsylvanian Period
coal swamps and amphibians. — 320 / 350

Mississippian Period
First reptiles; Spreading of shallow limey seas. — 360 / 400

Devonian Period
Earliest amphibians – the first land-living vertebrates. — 408 / 438 / 450

Silurian Period

Ordovician Period
Earliest fish and the first land plants. — 500 / 505

Cambrian Period
The time of the oldest abundant fossils. — 590

Proterozoic Eon

The eon of simple life. There are traces of life in some of the rocks dating from this time, but there are few good fossils. What living things there were had no hard shells.

Precambrian Period/Era

Anything before 590 million years ago is regarded as the Precambrian; this amounts to about 85 percent of the Earth's history. This is not reflected in the proportions of this chart, in which the time scale becomes larger towards the top – the more interesting end. The surface of the Earth is constantly moving and so Precambrian rocks tend to be old, broken and deformed – and difficult to interpret.

— 1000 / 1500 / 2000 / 2500

Archean Eon

The eon before life evolved. We are finding traces of life in older and older rocks, and the boundary is being pushed back continually.

— 3000 / 3500 / 4000

To make the immense period of time that is covered by the history of the Earth more easy to comprehend, geologists have split the timescale into manageable portions.

There is one main subdivision of the geological timescale, which is between the rocks containing obvious fossils and those with little or no obvious fossils – most fossil remains being microscopic bacteria and algae. This is a vast period of time known as the Cryptozoic, meaning 'hidden life.' The Cryptozoic runs from the formation of the Earth 4600 million years ago, until 600 million years ago. In rocks less than 600 million years old, fossils begin to be large and easily recognized. Continuing until today, the period is called the Phanerozoic Eon, meaning 'obvious life.'

The Phanerozoic Eon has also been divided up into large subdivisions of time, or Eras: the Paleozoic (ancient life), the Meso-zoic (middle life) and the Cainozoic or Cenozoic (recent life). Dinosaurs lived exclusively during the Mesozoic.

The Paleozoic Era (600-245 million years ago) marks the appearance of most of the major groups of animals and plants recognized today.

An enormous variety of fish and other marine creatures appeared in the seas, while many different invertebrate creatures colonized the land. Towards the end of this Era amphibians appeared, and from these first land-living vertebrates arose early reptiles. In general the reptiles were small, lizard-like creatures, but these soon gave rise to more sophisticated sorts of reptile. Some were rather like crocodiles, others were short-bodied and pig-like in proportion, a group eventually giving rise to the first mammals near the beginning of the next Era.

Left This chart summarizes the names given to the various spans of geological time which will be discussed in this book. The term Cryptozoic mentioned in the text refers to the two Eons: Proterozoic and Archean at the bottom of the left hand column.

Right The geological timescale shown here illustrates the time of appearance and survival of some of the major groups of backboned animals. The earliest backboned forms were simple, small fish-like creatures whose remains have been found in British Columbia in the mid-Cambrian (535 million years old).

Among the groups which will be receiving most of our attention are the dinosaurs which arose from archosaurs in the late Triassic. They were separated early on into two quite distinct groups: the ornithischian (bird-hipped) and saurischian (reptile-hipped) dinosaurs. Other important groups include the pterosaurs, which also evolved from late archosaurs and made their first appearance in late Triassic times. Mammals, too, arose from mammal-like reptiles in the very latest Triassic. Birds arose in mid-Jurassic times and probably evolved from small carnivorous saurischian dinosaurs.

Of these groups, it is notable that the birds and mammals survived the extinction at the end of the Cretaceous and the only true archosaur group to survive are the crocodiles.

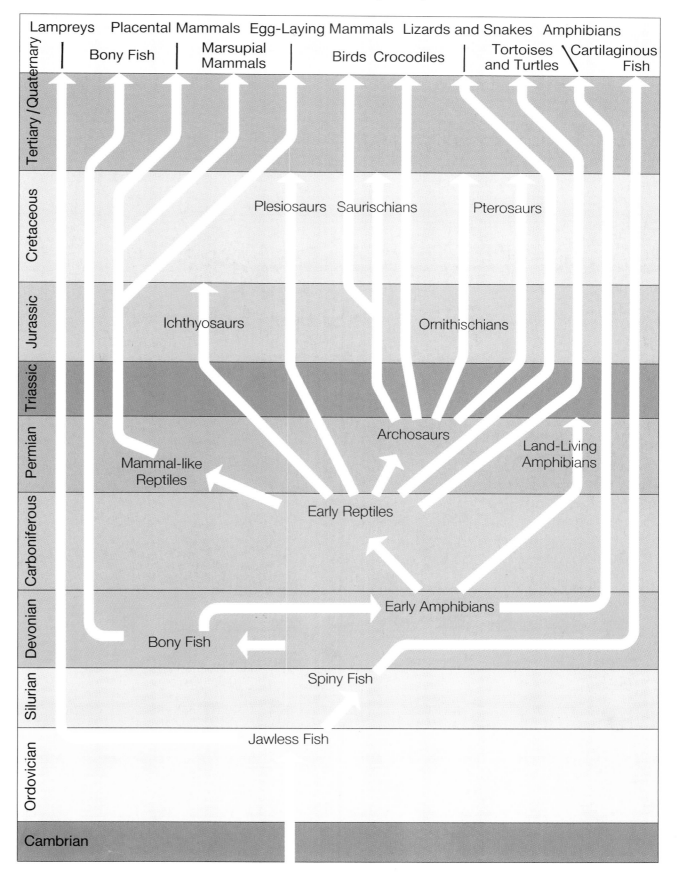

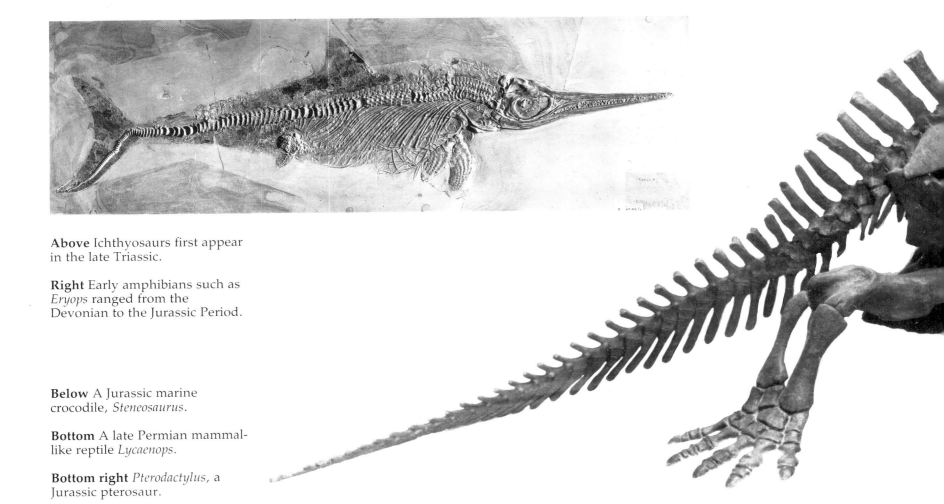

Above Ichthyosaurs first appear in the late Triassic.

Right Early amphibians such as *Eryops* ranged from the Devonian to the Jurassic Period.

Below A Jurassic marine crocodile, *Steneosaurus*.

Bottom A late Permian mammal-like reptile *Lycaenops*.

Bottom right *Pterodactylus*, a Jurassic pterosaur.

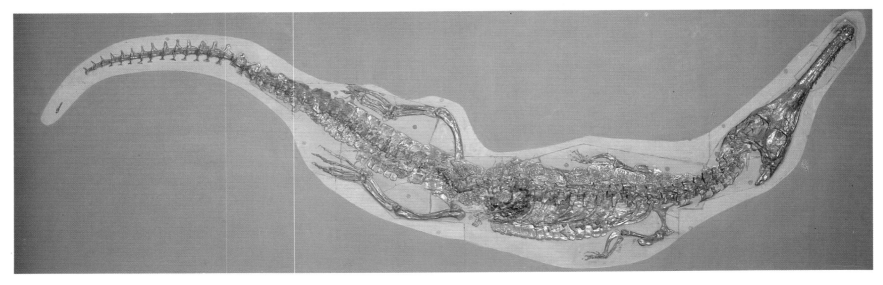

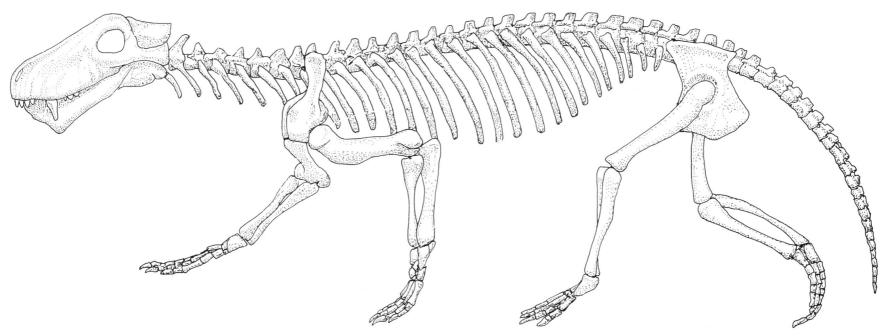

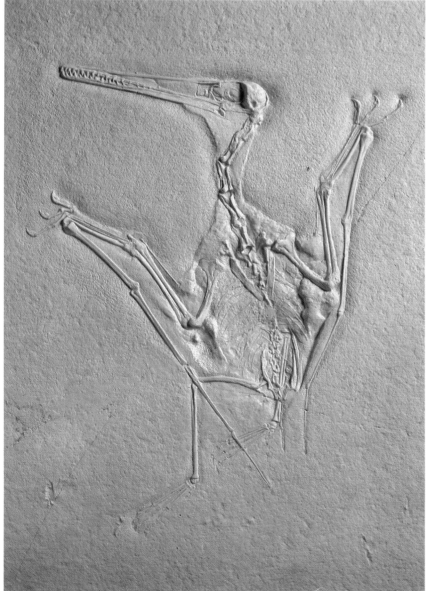

The Mesozoic Era (245-64 million years ago) saw the arrival of several modern groups of organisms, including mammals and birds. The first flowering plants and many of the modern groups of insect appeared too. Most important for this book, however, is the arrival of the dinosaurs, about 210 million years ago, and their rapid rise to dominate life on land right through to the end of the Mesozoic.

The Mesozoic Era is divided into a further three geological Periods: the Triassic (245-205 million years ago), the Jurassic (205-130 million years ago) and the Cretaceous Period (130-64 million years ago). At the start of the Triassic there were no dinosaurs. But there were a variety of slenderly built active reptiles, looking a little like short-bodied and long-legged crocodiles – if you can imagine such creatures. Alongside these animals were a very successful group of reptiles known as mammal-like reptiles. As their name suggests, they looked similar to mammals, and indeed are the ultimate ancestors of true mammals. These animals tended to have short barrel-like bodies, short tails and necks and well-developed heads equipped with complicated teeth for dealing with animal or plant tissues.

Near the end of the Triassic a relatively sudden change in the fortunes of these groups took place. The mammal-like reptiles became smaller, and less conspicuous, finally disappearing, leaving only their descendents (the mammals) as tiny shrew-sized creatures. By contrast the ancestors of the dinosaurs became more abundant. Even though they finally disappeared as well, they did give rise to the early dinosaurs which very rapidly became the largest and most numerous group of animals on land. At the same time other groups of reptile such as the plesiosaurs and ichthyosaurs (large swimming forms) appeared in the seas, while pterosaurs (quite close relatives of the dinosaurs) developed the ability to fly and became very abundant in the air.

A little later in the Mesozoic some other changes occurred. The most notable of these was the first appearance of birds in the late Jurassic Period and then of flowering plants in the early part of the Cretaceous Period.

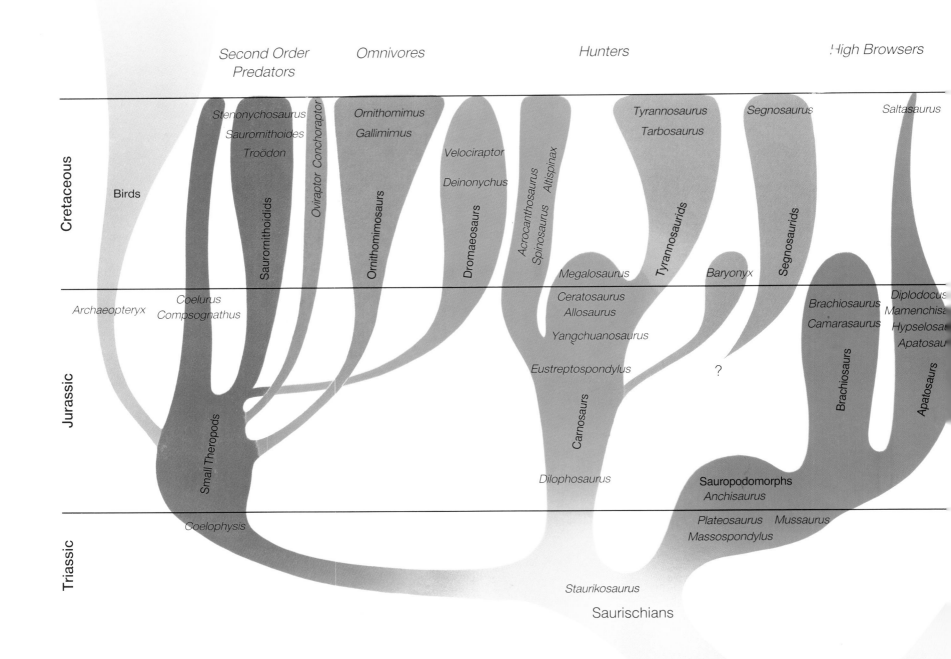

Second Order Predators   Omnivores   Hunters   High Browsers

Cretaceous

Stenonychosaurus
Saurornithoides
Troödon
Birds
Saurornithoidids
Oviraptor Conchoraptor
Ornithomimus
Gallimimus
Ornithomimosaurs
Velociraptor
Deinonychus
Dromaeosaurs
Acrocanthosaurus
Spinosaurus Altispinax
Tyrannosaurus
Tarbosaurus
Tyrannosaurids
Segnosaurus
Segnosaurids
Saltasaurus

Megalosaurus
Ceratosaurus
Allosaurus
Yangchuanosaurus
Baryonyx

Jurassic

Archaeopteryx
Coelurus
Compsognathus
Small Theropods
Eustreptospondylus
Carnosaurs
?
Brachiosaurus
Camarasaurus
Brachiosaurs
Diplodocus
Mamenchisa
Hypselosa
Apatosau
Apatosaurs

Dilophosaurus
Sauropodomorphs
Anchisaurus

Triassic

Coelophysis
Plateosaurus   Mussaurus
Massospondylus

Staurikosaurus

Saurischians

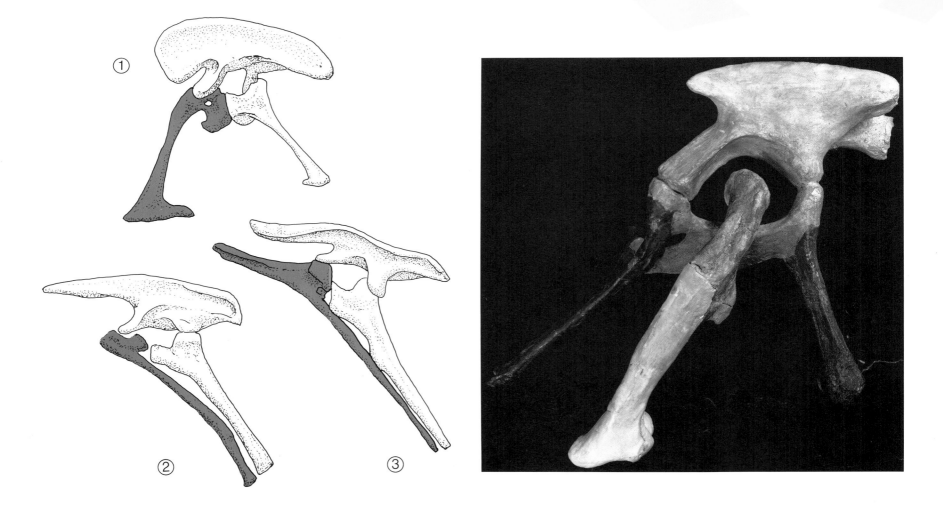

① ② ③

Classification

What precisely are dinosaurs? In very simple terms, they are essentially reptiles, possessing, as they do, tough, dry, scaly skin and they all appear to have laid eggs. However, they are distinguished from other reptiles in a number of ways, the most obvious being their upright posture. The legs of dinosaurs are pillar-like, holding the belly high above the ground, and the feet are close together. Other reptiles' legs tend to be short, and splayed outward, so that the belly is very close to, or even touching, the ground.

Pillar-like legs allow body weight to be supported very efficiently; consequently dinosaurs could grow very big. They are also very efficient at moving the animal at speed, so smaller, quicker moving dinosaurs also become a possibility. Differences in posture occurred with very important changes in the shape at the bones of the ankle, knee, thigh and hip.

So a dinosaur is simply a reptile that has developed the ability to walk using legs that are long and tucked beneath the body, rather than short and splayed to the side.

There are a large number of dinosaurs known, amounting to many hundreds of species, but they can be divided into two quite distinct groups: saurischians and ornithischians. These groups are based on differences in the structure of the hip bones.

Saurischian (reptile-hipped) dinosaurs had three bones in the hip on each side of the body meeting at the hip socket and radiating outward in different directions. The upper bone (ilium) connects with the backbone, while the lower ones point backward (ischium) and forward (pubis) for the attachment of leg muscles.

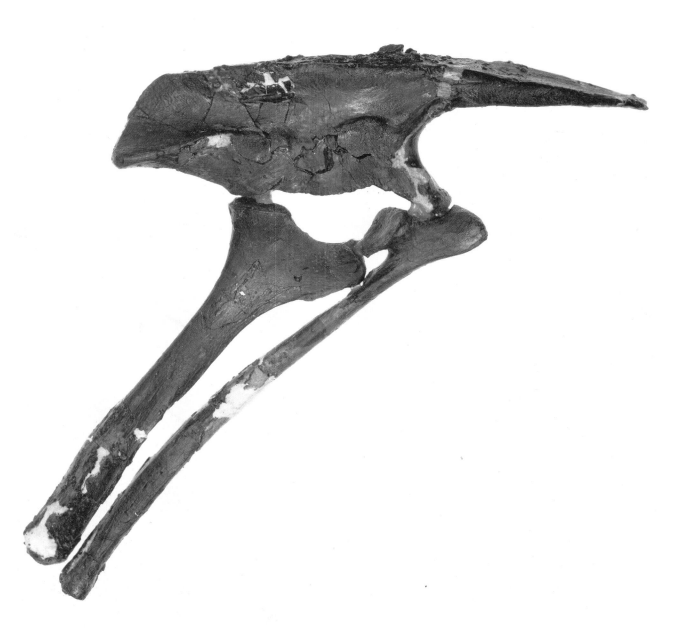

Low Browsers

Euoplocephalus
Ankylosaurus
anoplosaurus
Hadrosaurus Corythosaurus
Saurolophus
Parasaurolophus
Maiasaura
Stegoceras
Triceratops
Chasmosaurus
Styracosaurus
Protoceratops
Tenontosaurus
Pachycephalosaurs
Ceratopians
Hypsilophodon
Iguanodon
Ankylosaurids
Psittacosaurus
jiangosaurus
egosaurus
ntrosaurus
Camptosaurus
Psittacosaurs
Nodosaurids
Stegosaurs
Scelidosaurus
Ornithopods
Heterodontosaurus
Scutellosaurus
Lesothosaurus
Ornithischians

Above A diagram of a family tree of the various dinosaur groups within the Saurischia (reptile-hipped) and Ornithischia (bird-hipped).

Far left Dinosaur hips in left side views. 1, is a saurischian (pubis dark shading); 2, is an early ornithischian; and 3, is a later ornithischian.

Left The hip of *Massospondylus*, an early saurischian dinosaur.

Right The hip of an ornithischian dinosaur.

There are two main types of saurischian dinosaurs. First, there are the sauropodomorphs which include the large herbivorous dinosaurs such as *Diplodocus* and *Brachiosaurus*. Then there are the theropods which are largely carnivorous and include such dinosaurs as *Tyrannosaurus* and *Deinonychus*.

Ornithischian (bird-hipped) dinosaurs had quite a different arrangement of their hip bones. The pubis, instead of pointing forward and downward from the hip socket, points downward and backward and lies alongside the ischium. This is very similar to the arrangement of the hip bones in birds (hence the name), but despite this striking similarity there is no obvious close relationship between birds and ornithischians. In fact, birds appear to have had surprisingly close relations with saurischian theropods.

Ornithischians were all herbivores, and they all had a small horny beak at the tip of the jaw for plucking pieces of vegetation. Not so obvious unless you look at their skeletons in some detail, is the fact that ornithischians had long, thin, bony tendons lying along the spines on the backbone. Sometimes these tendons formed a large lattice-like array, but in many forms they were less regular and scattered along the sides of the spines. Ornithischians were much more varied than the saurischians, ranging from ornithopods such as *Hypsilophodon* and duckbilled dinosaurs, to ceratopians such as *Triceratops*, pachycephalosaurs such as *stegoceras*, stegosaurs such as *stegosaurus*, and ankylosaurs such as *Euoplocephalus*.

Left *Brachiosaurus* was one of the largest of the saurischian herbivores. The long, giraffe-like neck allowed these dinosaurs to pluck vegetation from high in the trees tops.

Right *Stegosaurus* is an ornithischian, remarkable for the fact that it has large plates down its back. It was a low browser.

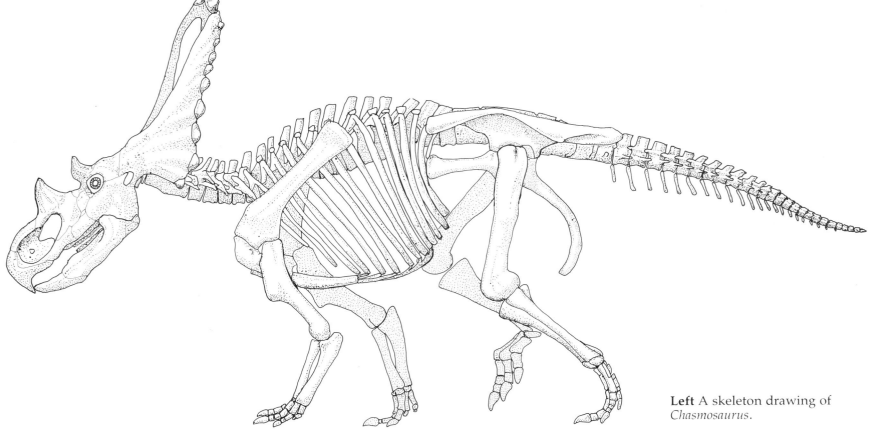

Left A skeleton drawing of *Chasmosaurus*.

Plate tectonics and evolution

The final section of this chapter concerns a somewhat surprising combination of subjects. Plate tectonics refers to geological processes occuring on the Earth, the result of which is the movement of the continents, albeit over enormously long periods of time. Evolution, on the other hand, is concerned with a study of the way in which organisms may change their appearance (again, in most cases over very long periods of time). So how are these two areas of study related to one another? Before I answer that question, though, a brief word to explain exactly what these two subjects are.

It is now well understood by geologists that the surface of our planet is divided into a series of huge areas or 'plates' of crust (the hard outer layer of the Earth), called tectonic plates. Tectonic plates are not fixed in position but seem to be constantly in motion. Mountainous ridges of rock form along the edges of some plates – there is a very large one running down the middle of the Atlantic Ocean – and these form the growing edges of plates. In other places there are found deep trenches where one plate is sliding beneath the other (the Marianas trench is one such, just off the coast of Japan). The best way to imagine the movement of tectonic plates is to consider them as gigantic conveyor belts which move crust slowly from the ridges, where new crust is forming, to trenches, where crust is disappearing. The continents, made of

Right *Camptosaurus* is an ornithischian ornithopod whose remains come from the late Jurassic of North America and have been more recently reported in Europe, indicating a land connection at this time. Stegosaurus, from the late Jurassic, is at the right.

Right *Ceratosaurus* is another species from the late Jurassic of North America. A small skull of similar age from England suggests that it may also be found in Europe.

Above Bony (ossified) tendons are clearly seen on the backbone of the ornithischian *Iguanodon*.

lighter rocks, literally float on these tectonic plates and are moved by them. So, for example, Europe and Africa are slowly moving away from North and South America at a rate of a few inches (cm) a year.

With the knowledge that continents are moving now, and that they must have done so in the past as well, it has been possible for geologists to reconstruct the positions of the continents at different times. It is quite surprising to see how far some continents have moved over many millions of years. India, which now sits snuggly up against the rest of Asia, used to be joined to Africa and Australia in the Jurassic Period, before floating off across the Indian Ocean to bump into Asia. Incidentally, it was the collision of India with Asia that crumpled the edge of the two continents where they met and formed the immense Himalayan mountain range.

It is now generally accepted that evolution occurs in nature: a process of change in organisms taking place through a mechanism, which Charles Darwin in 1859 called Natural Selection. Natural Selection relies on the fact that all organisms vary: apart from identical twins no two human beings are exactly alike. Given this variation within species it is likely that under difficult con-

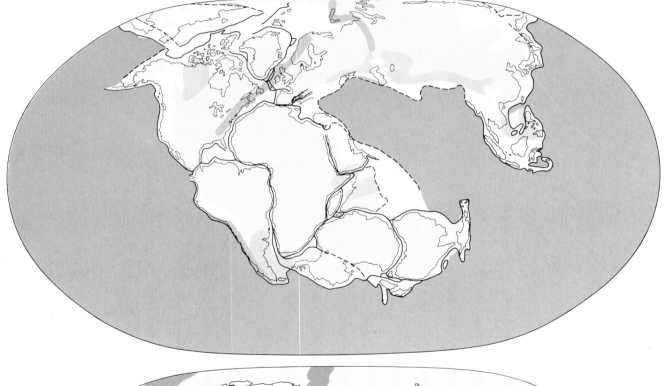

Above *Triceratops*, a ceratopian ornithischian, was one of the last dinosaurs to appear at the very end of the Cretaceous Period. Note the large, parrot-like beak.

Triassic Period
(240-200 m years ago)

Top left Continent positions in the Triassic show the existence of the supercontinent Pangea.

Present Day

Left Continental drift, made possible by tectonic plate movement, broke Pangea into the world we know today, and movement is continuing even now.

	Vegetation		Tundra & ice
	Mountain		Continental sea
	Desert		Deep ocean

ditions some individuals may be better able to survive. If such conditions persist for long enough the organisms which are better able to survive will inevitably produce more offspring, most of which may inherit the characteristics that favor survival. In this way a change in conditions of life can have the potential to alter the characteristics of species in a number of generations. Very rapid forms of evolution can be seen in the way that many insects have become resistant to pesticides: the resistance to such poisons has been a very strongly selected factor. A few individuals, by pure chance, inherited resistance to such poisons; these individuals have survived, and bred, and formed resistant strains within populations. This is obviously a very extreme example, but nevertheless points to the fact that Darwin's mechanism is essentially correct.

If this sort of process is applied to organisms living through the history of life on Earth, then during the hundreds of millions of years many dramatic changes can have taken place, given the right conditions.

If evolution is accepted as a way in which animals and plants may have changed during the history of life on Earth, then one among many factors that could have affected the course of evolution is plate tectonics.

The fact that continents have moved about on the surface of the Earth, sometimes meeting, sometimes being torn apart, moving across climatic zones and altering the patterns of the ocean currents, means that the environmental conditions on the continents must have changed dramatically with time. The effects of this would have been seen in the ways that animals evolved: in response to changes in climate, or as a result of a population being split up (by continental separation) or the merger of different populations (following the collision of continents).

The way in which the evolution of dinosaurs was affected by continental movement is dealt with later in the book. To highlight the point, small geographical maps of the time are included with the information on the dinosaurs and other animals which lived during the Mesozoic Era.

CHAPTER 2
The History of Dinosaur Studies and Collections

Professor Dong Zhiming, of the Institute of Vertebrate Paleontology and Paleoanthropology in Beijing has on record the fact that dinosaur remains were probably collected at least 1600 years before the birth of Christ. These were not collected as dinosaur remains, but rather as 'Dragon's Teeth,' which were widely believed to have great therapeutic value, when ground up and offered as medicine. Later, there are written reports of a collection of 'dragon bones' around AD 300, in areas of Sichuan Province (China), areas now known to be rich in dinosaur remains. During the last three centuries, there are other written, and sometimes illustrated, reports of large fossils in various parts of the world. In some cases they are reports of dinosaur remains, but the world was not ready to 'discover' dinosaurs until the early years of the nineteenth century.

The way toward the realization of dinosaurs was begun in earnest by Baron Georges Cuvier. Cuvier was a famous anatomist who lived and worked in Paris during the latter part of the eighteenth and early nineteenth centuries. He has rightly been called the father of modern paleontology, because many of the techniques for studying fossils, which he developed, are still in use today. However, Cuvier's greatest contribution in relation to the story of the origin of dinosaurs is his demonstration that fossils were the remains of extinct creatures. Until the time of Cuvier, religious beliefs were dominated by the concept of the *Plenum*, the supposition that God had created and populated the world with every conceivable organism. It seemed incomprehensible that such powers could ever have created organisms that had become extinct. Fossils that were dug up created a potential problem for this view of creation, but were dismissed as the carcasses of dead individuals of still living species.

A series of detailed studies by Cuvier of fossils from the area around Paris provided much solid evidence of extinct animals. However, one particular fossil provided a very important link to

Above Baron Georges Cuvier (1769-1832), the father of paleontology, established the fact of extinction and described the first giant fossil reptile, *Mosasaurus* (not a dinosaur).

Above right A Mosasaur is in the foreground of this display of marine reptiles.

Far left and left Gideon Algernon Mantell (1790-1852) described *Iguanodon* from bones and teeth discovered by himself and his wife Mary Ann Mantell. Gideon Mantell sent some teeth to Cuvier in the hope that he might be able to identify them.

dinosaurs: the giant mosasaur. The head of a gigantic reptile was discovered in a chalk mine at Maastricht in Holland in 1770, and after falling into the possession of a variety of people, eventually found its way to Paris (with the help of Napoleon's army) and Cuvier. Cuvier was able to prove that this was the skull of a giant, extinct, sea-living relative of the monitor lizard.

It seems probable that the publication of Cuvier's work on the giant lizard from Maastricht at the turn of the century, stimulated much interest among geologists throughout the developed world. Within the next two decades other gigantic reptiles began to be discovered – and among these were the first recognized dinosaurs.

Between 1816 and 1825 Gideon Algernon Mantell, who was a family doctor with a practice at Lewes, Sussex (England), spent much of his time collecting rock and fossil samples from the South Downs. Mantell was an extremely keen amateur geologist, who had even turned part of his house into a small museum. In 1822, or perhaps a little earlier, some large and unusual teeth came into his possession, collected by his wife. Mantell was able to trace the source of these teeth to a quarry near Cuckfield, which soon revealed fragments of large bones as well as more teeth.

Mantell was unable to identify the teeth directly, even though he described them in some detail in a book which he published on the geology of the South Downs in 1822. Several people, including Cuvier, were shown samples of these teeth, but to no avail. Cuvier was most interested in the find, although he suspected that the fossils might prove to be of a large fish (or a rhinoceros!), and actively encouraged Mantell to try to find more fossil material that would help to clarify these discoveries. Eventually Mantell found what he was looking for in the Museum of the Royal College of Surgeons in London: the pickled remains of an iguana lizard, at that time a fairly new discovery from South America. The teeth of this lizard, although much smaller, were quite similar to those that had been found at Cuckfield. As a result of this, Mantell published a description of the teeth in 1825, and gave them the name *Iguanodon* (iguana tooth) and supposed that they belonged to an extinct giant relative of the living iguana; in much the same way that the mosasaur, described by Cuvier, was an extinct giant relative of the living monitor lizard.

In 1833 Mantell discovered yet another interesting fossil in the same quarry. This time it was a partial skeleton of a large, partly armored reptile. He named this creature *Hylaeosaurus* ('forest reptile' – because the quarry lay in what was then known as Tilgate Forest).

Both *Iguanodon* and *Hylaeosaurus* were dinosaurs, though Mantell did not realize it at the time.

At the same time that Mantell was collecting fossils in Sussex, William Buckland, who was appointed a Reader in Geology at Oxford University, was shown large fossil bones which had been collected at a slate quarry in the village of Stonesfield in north Oxfordshire. Buckland finally published an article describing these large reptile remains in 1824, and called the animal *Megalosaurus* (big reptile).

Megalosaurus, *Iguanodon* and *Hylaeosaurus* continued to be the only giant land-living British reptiles to found during the 1820s and 1830s, despite vigorous exploration. *Megalosaurus* was a carnivore, with large serrated-edged teeth; *Iguanodon* a herbivore, with broad leaf-shaped teeth for chipping off pieces of vegetation; and *Hylaeosaurus* was a spiky-armored herbivore.

In the years leading up to 1841, Professor Richard Owen, who was regarded by the British as their equivalent of Baron Cuvier, was given the task of reviewing all the fossil reptiles discovered in Britain up to that date. During this review, Owen noted that the three newly discovered species: *Megalosaurus*, *Iguanodon* and *Hylaeosaurus*, were clearly different from almost all other types. They were large, land-living types of reptile but, more importantly, he was able to show that they had an anatomical construction reminiscent of large living mammals such as the elephant, hippopotamus or rhinoceros. Even though the remains of

all three animals were very poor and fragmentary, there were enough bones to show that these three animals had long, pillar-like legs carried beneath the body. All reptiles typically have short legs which are held out at an oblique angle from the body, so that the belly is close to the ground when they walk.

The unique difference with the three reptiles noted by Owen was their ability to walk and run in a much more efficient way. Long pillar-like legs are much better able to support a heavy body than short, bent legs; they are also able to swing through a greater arc of stride and therefore have the potential to move an animal much more quickly. Owen's conclusion was that these three reptiles represented the apex of reptilian organization: they were the Mesozoic equivalent of the large mammals of today, literally scaly equivalents of the elephant, rhinoceros and hippopotamus. To recognize the uniqueness of these fossils he proposed that they be given a new title: the Dinosauria. The name derives from the Greek words *deinos* meaning 'fearfully great' and *sauros* meaning 'crawling creature', or in this case, 'reptile.'

Owen announced the findings at the eleventh meeting of the British Association for the Advancement of Science which was held at Plymouth in 1841, and his report was published in 1842. So for the scientific world, dinosaurs came into existence then. The announcement promoted a great deal of interest in these types of

reptile particularly in Britain and the United States of America. Despite vigorous attempts to find more and better preserved material in Britain, none was forthcoming for many years. However, interest was so great in these ancient animals that Owen was asked to supervize the construction of several life-sized dinosaur models in the grounds of the Great Exhibition when it was moved from the site on Hyde Park, to a new and permanent site at Sydenham in south-east London and opened in 1854. The dinosaurs were reconstructed as giant scaly creatures a little like modern mammals. *Iguanodon* looks for all the world like a giant scaly rhinoceros – complete with horn on the nose. *Megalosaurus*

looks a little like a long-nosed lion. The models can still be seen today, even though the Crystal Palace building, which housed the Great Exhibition, burnt down in the 1930s.

Even though we know these reconstructions to be inaccurate today, they represent an interesting and important phase in the study and understanding of dinosaurs. At the time of Cuvier, Mantell and Buckland, dinosaurs did not exist. Rather, the remains they had collected and described were thought to be those of exceptionally large lizards (which was absolutely correct in the case of Cuvier's mosasaur only).

Owen provided a completely new interpretation of dinosaurs,

Above far left Dean William Buckland (1784-1856) described the remains of the first dinosaur ever discovered, *Megalosaurus*, in 1824.

Above left Richard Owen (1804-1892) was the first to recognize dinosaurs as a separate group.

Left Right hindlimb of the dinosaur *Megalosaurus*.

Above Upper tooth of *Iguanodon*.

Right The original workshop in which Waterhouse Hawkins constructed the models placed in the grounds of the Great Exhibition.

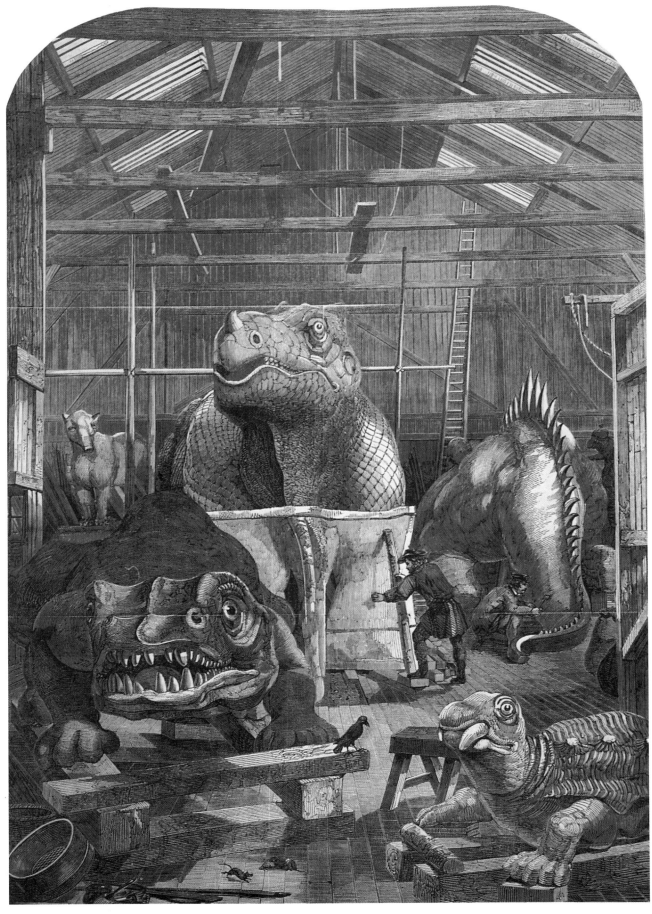

based on the best material that was available to him at the time. His conclusions were bold, far sighted and show a fine knowledge of reptile anatomy. Even though his reconstructions have subsequently proved to be inaccurate, his work on the arrangement of their legs is still the basis upon which dinosaurs are recognized today.

Soon after Owen's dinosaur reconstructions had been shown in London, discoveries of dinosaurs began to be made in the USA. A great deal of work was being done to survey the rocks of North

Above Many *Iguanodon* skeletons were found in Belgium in the 1870s; here technicians mount the first discoveries.

Right A flesh restoration of *Iguanodon*, 33 feet (10m) long.

Land reptiles

Left A skeleton of *Allosaurus*, a fairly close relative of *Megalosaurus*. It is one of several which have been sent around the world from Utah, where Jim Madsen and colleagues have collected vast numbers of bones of this dinosaur in late Jurassic rocks.

America, and while this was being done, fossils were being collected. In 1855 in Montana, scattered teeth were found which seemed to resemble those of *Iguanodon* and *Megalosaurus* from Britain. Joseph Leidy named these teeth *Trachodon* and *Deinodon* respectively. In 1858 Leidy obtained more material, this time of a partial skeleton from Haddonfield, New Jersey. The skeleton included teeth, similar to those of *Trachodon*, and both front and back legs. The new skeleton was named *Hadrosaurus*, and Leidy was able to show that this animal had a kangaroo-like posture, rather than an elephantine posture.

In a stroke Leidy had brought dinosaurs far closer to an accurate picture than over 30 years of work by Cuvier, Mantell, Buckland and Owen, but he had the advantage of an at least partial skeleton to go on. An exhibition of dinosaurs and other prehistoric animals was prepared for New York's Central Park between 1868 and 1871 by Benjamin Waterhouse Hawkins. Unfortunately this project was vandalized and never completed, though there are photographs and drawings recording the form of some of the early skeleton casts which were to be the basis of the reconstructions.

All of these activities indicate that from their very outset dinosaurs seem to have gripped the public imagination. In the 1870s this interest was to be given added spice through the virtually simultaneous discovery of bigger and better dinosaurs both in Europe and the American Mid-West.

In April 1878 miners working in coal seams 348 yards (322m) below ground at the village of Bernissart in southwest Belgium discovered a fissure of clay. The clay turned out to be packed with skeletons of the dinosaur *Iguanodon*. Excavations carried on at Bernissart for four years, under the supervision of a team from the Royal Museum of Natural History from Brussels, and nearly 40

skeletons were removed, some almost complete. The skeletons were studied by Professor Louis Dollo in Brussels and he was for the first time able to provide an accurate reconstruction of one of Owen's three original dinosaurs.

It confirmed the work of Leidy, rather than Owen, and showed an animal with kangaroo-like posture. The 'horn' which Owen had at first placed on the nose of this animal, and given Owen problems in later years (placing it on the foot, and later as a spur on the wrist) turned out to be a highly modified thumb bone.

Today most of the dinosaurs recovered from Bernissart are on display at the Royal Institute of Natural Sciences, Brussels, where they can be seen protected behind enormous glass screens.

In America in 1877, just before the discoveries at Bernissart, rich deposits of dinosaurs were found in Colorado. Curiously, discoveries were made independently by two collectors, both of whom were school teachers. Arthur Lakes found fossils at Morrison, Colorado, and sent them to Othniel Charles Marsh at Yale College while O W Lucas found fossils at Canyon City, Colorado, and sent his fossils to Edward Drinker Cope in New Jersey.

It just so happened that both of the scientists were active paleontologists and keenly competitive. The rivalry between Cope and Marsh is now legendary; each scientist trying to beat the other to the description of newer and better material, and employing rival gangs of collectors to find new material at all costs. Between 1877 and the late 1890s Cope and Marsh between them had named and described 130 new species of dinosaur. Many of these are now to be found in the galleries of the large state, university and national museums in the United States of America. The death of Cope in 1897 and Marsh in 1899 saw the end of the bitter feud and the start of a more co-ordinated approach to the collection of dinosaurs.

Left Mongolian expeditions led by the American Museum, New York, recovered precious dinosaur eggs for the first time.

Below The skeleton of *Saurolophus*, a large hadrosaur, being excavated in Mongolia (1971).

Right Chinese discoveries are becoming increasingly important. This is a fine skeleton of the dinosaur *Yangchuanosaurus*, from Sichuan Province.

Bottom right Base camp in the Nemegt Basin, Mongolia, for the Polish-Mongolian expeditions to this area of the early 1970s.

Further collections took place at the turn of the century in Wyoming, at a locality called Bone Cabin Quarry, where dinosaur bones were strewn so thickly on the ground that a shepherd, not knowing what they were, used some to make a small cabin as a shelter for himself. A little later new discoveries were also made in Utah, near Vernal. This site was excavated until the 1920s by the Carnegie Museum at Pittsburgh and yielded many fine skeletons. In fact the site has been so productive that it became by Presidential decree, the 'Dinosaur National Monument' in 1915 and today forms a permanent working museum and exhibition center. The steeply tilted amd richly fossiliferous rocks form a 'mural' upon which preparators work to reveal more fossils under the watchful gaze of visitors and scientists alike.

While dramatic finds were being made in the USA, equally fine material was being discovered in Alberta, Canada, in the badland terrain where rivers have cut down into the prairie. During the last 20 years of the nineteenth century much survey work had revealed dinosaur bones near the Red Deer River in southern Alberta. However it was not until the arrival of Barnum Brown, a prodigious fossil collector who worked for the American Museum of Natural History in New York, that really important discoveries were made. Brown launched a broad barge (scow) on the Red Deer River, fully equipped with sleeping quarters and expedition equipment. Stopping at intervals along the river to both explore and collect systematically, he amassed a tremendous collection of fine dinosaur skeletons, which are now on display in New York.

The success of Brown's expedition of 1910 was soon followed by Canadians from 1912 to 1917. These were equally successful and many skeletons are to be found in museums both in Canada and many other parts of the world.

Although the early dinosaur discoveries were made in Europe and America, they have subsequently been found in all continents except Antarctica. Even here they are likely to be found once the main problem, the difficulty of access to rocks of the correct type and age, has been overcome.

Africa has yielded a rich crop of dinosaurs. The first were discovered at Tendaguru by a team of German scientists who were carrying out survey work in what was then known as German East Africa, now Tanzania. Several skeletons were excavated using local African labor, the most remarkable of which was the skeleton of *Brachiosaurus*. This is now on display in the Museum

of Natural History in East Berlin and is the biggest mounted skeleton of a dinosaur in the world. Since the time of the German expeditions, several other areas of Africa have been investigated, such as Niger, Mali, Morocco and Kenya, all of which have yielded dinosaurs in various degrees of completeness.

Asia, too, has revealed a storehouse of fossils. The first inkling that dinosaurs were to be found in any numbers in this part of the world came after an expedition to look for fossil Man in Mongolia. The expedition, which ran for several years in the 1920s, was organized by the American Museum of Natural History in New York, and a remarkable number of dinosaurs were collected. Among the finds was the first well-documented evidence of dinosaur eggs and nest sites. Since then a variety of expeditions have gone to Mongolia and Northern China in search of dinosaurs and have met with considerable success. China has done a great deal of work over the last few years to explore its many dinosaur-bearing rock formations, also with spectacular results. Many completely new dinosaurs have been discovered in areas ranging from Xinjiang in the northwest to Sichuan in south central China and Heilongjiang in the extreme northeast. Almost every year some new and exciting results are being published, and the excitement generated over these new discoveries must be very

Left Dinosaur footprints are seen here in this sandy mudstone which was probably a dried out river bed when this dinosaur walked here in late Jurassic times (about 135 million years ago).

Below Dinosaur National Monument, USA. The incredible richness of the fossil deposits at this site near Vernal in Utah led to it being declared a National Monument. It is now a working museum, with technicians constantly at work excavating new specimens with enormous care, under the watchful gaze of visitors.

much like that which surrounded the discoveries of Marsh and Cope at the end of the last century.

In recent years dinosaurs have also begun to be discovered in Australia, although to date no really dramatic and well-preserved skeletons have been discovered. However, it would seem only to be a matter of time before some really interesting and important discoveries are made.

India has yielded a number of fossil forms this century, many of which are unfortunately not well preserved. The best example, though, is the sauropod *Barapasaurus* from central India. Finally, South America has a long history of dinosaur discovery, particularly Argentina. Over the last decade many interesting and new discoveries have been made, largely through the work of Professor Jose Bonaparte and colleagues in Buenos Aires. The very latest discovery, early in 1989, is that of dinosaur remains in Antarctica by the British Antarctic Society.

It is interesting to chart the way in which scientists have portrayed dinosaurs over the years since they were first described by Mantell and Buckland. It very vividly demonstrates the ways that ideas have changed – and sometimes gone full circle.

The years 1820-40 saw the earliest discoveries of dinosaurs, indeed, at that time the fossils collected were not called dinosaurs at all. Following the work of Baron Cuvier on the big marine reptile *Mosasaurus*, all large reptile fossils were assumed to be just larger versions of their living cousins the lizards. The only known illustration from this period, is a sketch by Gideon Mantell of his *Iguanodon*. There is no mistaking the fact that this is modelled on a lizard (even though Mantell estimated that this lizard may be upwards of 100 feet [30m] in length). Although the sketch is undated, by looking carefully at the bones which he illustrates in the skeleton, it seems likely that this was drawn sometime after 1834. At this date he was presented with a fine, though somewhat broken, partial skeleton which had been blasted from a quarry near Maidstone in Kent.

The subsequent 20 years (1840-60), was the time of the first naming of dinosaurs by Owen and the building, under Owen's supervision, of the models at Sydenham. In Owen's original report published in 1842, he clearly outlined what he thought of dinosaurs compared with other known reptiles:

The *Megalosaurs* and the *Iguanodons*, rejoicing in these undeniably most perfect modifications of the Reptilian type, attained the greatest bulk, and must have played the most conspicuous parts, in their respective characters as devourers of animals and feeders upon vegetables, that this Earth has ever witnessed in oviparous and cold-blooded creatures. Owen 1842:200.

It is clear from what Owen says that he regarded dinosaurs as the most advanced of all reptiles, in that they came as near anatomically as they could have to mammals. The reconstructions super-

Above Powerful hand-held hammer tools are used to cut channels around the fossils so that they can be removed.

Above right Winches lift the heavy block containing fossils safely away from the face.

Right The first remains of *Brachiosaurus* to be found included gigantic arm bones such as this specimen shown here. This is a humerus or upper arm bone.

Left Skeletal restoration of the giraffe-like *Brachiosaurus*.

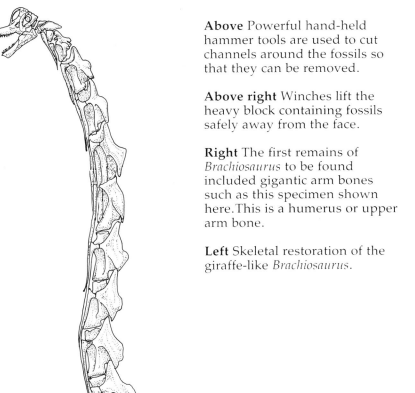

vised by Owen reflect his views, and although they have the appearance of rather ponderous beasts, nevertheless these images were a far cry from the giant lizards of the time before Owen. And the implications from Owen's writing were that dinosaurs had a far more active style of life than is common for reptiles living today.

From 1860 to the 1940s is a period during which vast amounts of information about dinosaurs began to accumulate as a result of the discoveries which were being made in Europe and North America, and then spread worldwide. Much of the time of scientists seems to have been given over to the fairly mundane tasks of describing the dinosaurs, rather than thinking too much about the details of how they may have looked and behaved.

One influential thinker of the 1860s was Thomas Huxley, a biologist and philosopher in London. He noted that the legs and hips of many dinosaurs showed a close similarity to those of living birds. This led him to suggest that birds and dinosaurs were more closely related than was believed up to that date. This sort of information was used in two ways by paleontologists of the time: first it was used to guide reconstructions of dinosaurs (some becoming notably bird-like in their posture) and secondly the association of dinosaurs with birds gave them the possibility of higher degrees of activity.

Reconstructions reflecting these attitudes can be seen both in scientific illustrations and in the models of dinosaurs made at the time. These ideas were further reinforced by the work of Harry Govier Seeley, another geologist from London, who noted that while some dinosaurs had rather bird-like hips, others did not. He decided that it was possible to distinguish between these two groups, which he named: *Ornithischia* (bird-hipped) and *Saurischia* (reptile-hipped), names which have continued to be used through to the present day.

The years 1940-65 appear to be a period when the interest in, and amount of work done upon, dinosaurs started to wane. Dinosaurs continued to be collected in some numbers, but views about their biology and way of life do not appear to have been the subject of a great deal of debate. It could be summarized by saying

that dinosaurs were by this time a reasonably well-known group of fossils, represented by some fine skeletons in museums. They still posed some awkward questions, such as the perennial 'so why did they become extinct?', but other than that they did not stimulate much discussion. It became accepted that dinosaurs were big, wallowed in swamps, had very little intelligence and were destined for extinction. In short they were nothing more than biological absurdities.

Above Indian dinosaurs are not so well known as they might be, but this is the site of excavation of *Barapasaurus*. This is a large saurischian sauropod herbivore related to forms such as *Diplodocus* and *Apatosaurus* from the Jurassic.

Left These are the majority of the teeth which were first described by Mantell and given the name *Iguanodon* in 1825. They were identified by the author and are in the collections of the Natural History Museum, London.

Top right The first pencil sketch by Mantell of *Iguanodon* as a giant lizard. Note the thumb spike perched on the nose. Mantell thought that this giant lizard was over 100 feet (33m) long.

Right Robert Bakker's very dynamic image of *Deinonychus*.

Finally, 1965 to the present could be termed the dinosaur renaissance. In the mid-1960s a startling new discovery in Montana, and the work of a then young paleontologist, Robert Bakker, who fortunately also happened to be a skilled artist, prompted a revival of interest in dinosaurs. This occurred not only among paleontologists, but also among scientists in other scientific disciplines who became drawn into some of the controversies.

The important discovery was of a new dinosaur, which was named *Deinonychus* (terrible claw). *Deinonychus* was described by Professor John Ostrom of Yale University and proved to be a remarkably sophisticated little carnivorous dinosaur. First, careful examination of the fossil showed that it was a very fast runner; it had leg proportions which could only be developed for speed. Second, it had a large head and forwardly pointing eyes to clearly see its prey, and long grasping clawed hands to hold the prey with. Third, the feature which gave this dinosaur its name was a large, sickle-shaped claw on the inside of its hind foot. Fourth, the dinosaur had a peculiarly stiffened tail. How were all these characteristics explained?

Professor Ostrom demonstrated that this dinosaur was a fast-running predatory type which was capable of running down its prey, holding it firmly by the front claws and balancing on one one leg (using the tail like a tightrope walker's balancing rod) while disemboweling the prey with vicious kicks from the claw on the hind foot. It may also well have been able to jump and kick with both feet at larger prey.

The simple question that can be posed by this assortment of capabilities is this: does this range of capabilities fit most closely with what we know that modern reptiles can do? The answer must be a resounding no! The implications from Ostrom's work are that *Deinonychus* was a highly intelligent, or at the very least very well co-ordinated, and highly active predator; no present-day reptiles come anywhere near this degree of sophistication. This in turn suggests that dinosaurs like *Deinonychus* had high levels of activity, which in the present day are normally associated with the likes of mammals and birds.

In some ways we have almost gone full circle in argument, from the earliest musings of Richard Owen, who came very close to saying that dinosaurs may have been capable of activity levels comparable to mammals, through a long time when dinosaurs were simply regarded as rather large, but otherwise pretty unexceptional reptiles, back to the more Owen-like views of the present day.

Robert Bakker, one of Professor Ostrom's students, has been at

IGUANODON

the forefront of a campaign to review the status and lifestyle of dinosaurs generally. Bakker has taken the observations which Ostrom made about the sophisticated nature of *Deinonychus*, and added to these a variety of arguments based on observations and intuitive notions about dinosaurs which he feels make an overwhelming case for considering dinosaurs as physiologically equivalent to mammals and birds. These arguments will be considered in greater detail in chapter 9. Although many of Bakker's arguments are now seen to be flawed, the persistence of his views, and the graphic way in which he has been able to illustrate his views through his own natural artistic talents, have had a pervasive effect upon a broad range of scientists involved in the whole field of dinosaur studies. Many of Bakker's views are vigorously denied, but the main thrust of his argument – dinosaurs were in all probability highly active creatures, quite unlike the reptiles with which we are so familiar today – is agreed with by most dinosaur research workers.

Robert Bakker has also influenced a whole generation of illustrators of dinosaurs, of which there are now many, particularly in the United States. The first life-like restoration of *Deinonychus* was done by Bakker, and through his style very clearly indicated the grace and potential of the animal. This was followed by further drawings of dinosaurs both in scientific literature, as an accompaniment to scientific descriptions, and in the more popular literature. The grace and dynamism of these illustrations has been emulated by a variety of illustrators, all of whom have done much to revive the interest in and appreciation of dinosaurs and many other prehistoric animals.

Bakker '69

CHAPTER 3

Dinosaur Origins

The Triassic Period, which lasted from 245 to 205 million years ago, was a time during which many groups of reptile evolved and spread widely across the world. It saw the flourishing of a particular group of land reptiles – the mammal-like reptiles which had begun to become numerous in the Permian. However, successful though the mammal-like reptiles were in the short term, by the end of the Triassic Period the dinosaurs had arrived and were beginning to dominate all the land faunas. The events that led up to the change from faunas dominated by mammal-like reptiles to dinosaurs in the Triassic Period are interesting, and still present paleontologists with many outstanding problems.

With careful research it is possible to learn something about the world prior to the dinosaurs: the types of animals that came before them and the sorts of environments which they lived in. Ultimately this may perhaps tell us about the dinosaurs themselves – what was special about them, giving them the qualities for survival at this particular time in history. We can see from fossils that dinosaurs replaced the majority of Triassic reptiles at the end of the Period. Why did this happen? Did the dinosaurs do something special that gave them a competitive 'edge' over the earlier reptiles? Were the dinosaurs just lucky to be around at a time when lots of old reptile groups were becoming extinct? Before beginning to answer these questions it is necessary to look at the state of Earth during the Triassic Period.

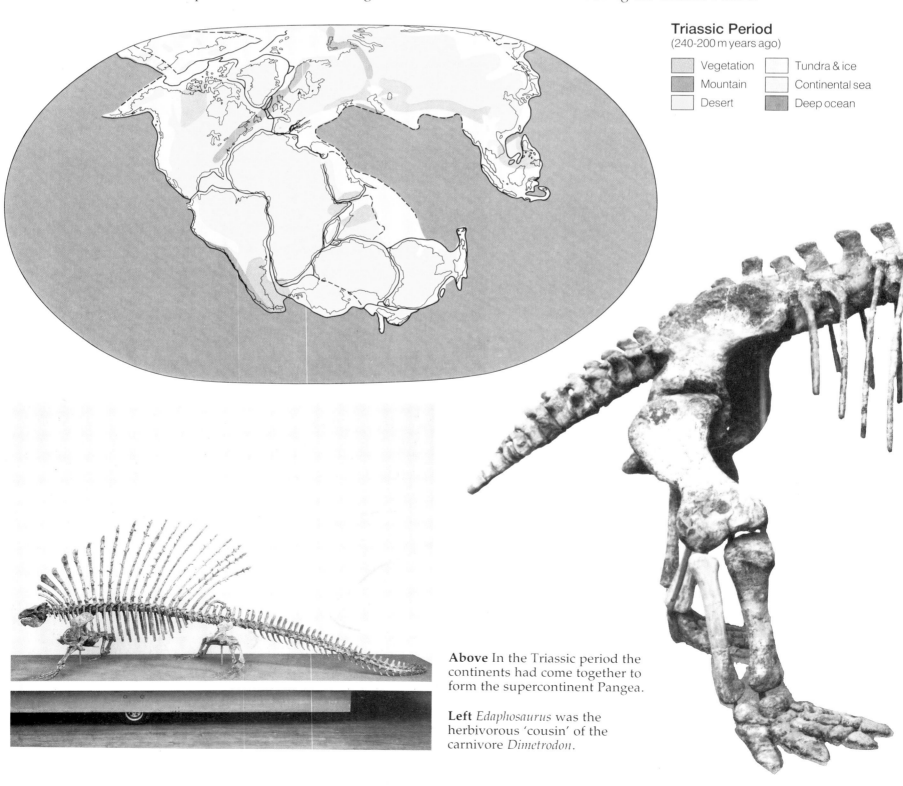

Triassic Period
(240-200 m years ago)

- Vegetation
- Mountain
- Desert
- Tundra & ice
- Continental sea
- Deep ocean

Above In the Triassic period the continents had come together to form the supercontinent Pangea.

Left *Edaphosaurus* was the herbivorous 'cousin' of the carnivore *Dimetrodon*.

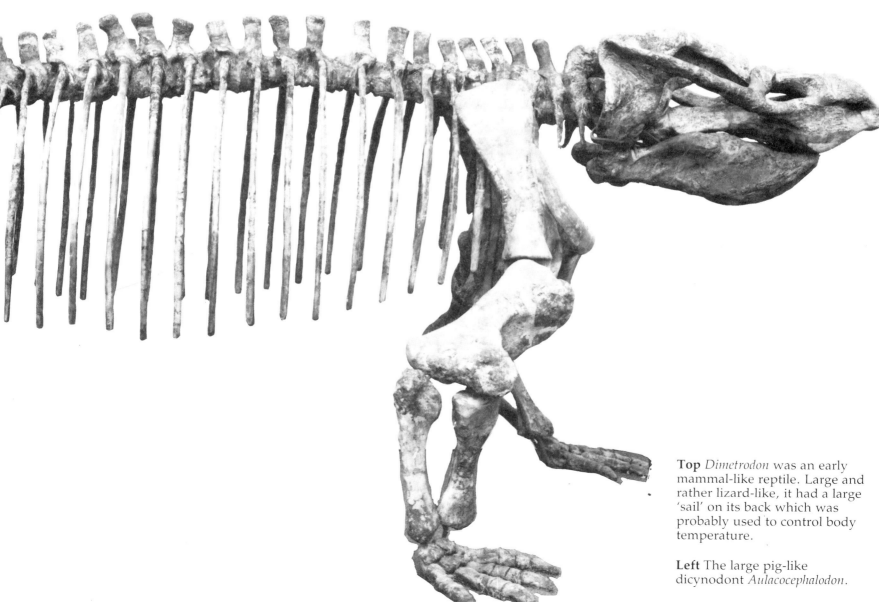

Top *Dimetrodon* was an early mammal-like reptile. Large and rather lizard-like, it had a large 'sail' on its back which was probably used to control body temperature.

Left The large pig-like dicynodont *Aulacocephalodon*.

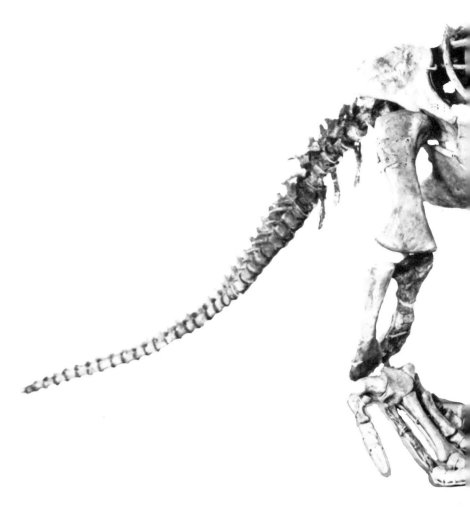

Reconstructions of the positions of the continents during the Period show the remarkable fact that the continents of the world were all joined together to form a supercontinent, which is called Pangea. We know this for two reasons: first of all there is the geological evidence. Analysis of the magnetic polarity of rocks of Carboniferous, Permian and Triassic age, in continents which are clearly separate today, have shown that the only way that the direction of magnetization in rock can be explained, is if the continents are packed together as shown. This arrangement is confirmed because when the fossil animals that lived on the land at these times, but now found on separate continents, are compared they are found to be remarkably similar. For example fossils of a mammal-like reptile named *Lystrosaurus* have been found in Antarctica, South Africa and North America. This suggests that there was relatively free movement of species across large geographical areas. If the species had existed on separate continents, they would tend to be very different in appearance, because animal and plant groups when left to evolve in isolation tend to become quite distinctive. A good example of this situation can be seen in Australia. This continent has evolved its own unique fauna as a result of almost 100 million years of isolation from other continents.

The Triassic world was thus very different to today. The question is how different, and what did this mean to the sorts of animals that we know to have lived during these times?

Early Triassic animals

The earliest Triassic was a time during which the mammal-like reptiles were particularly abundant. One of the most abundant groups was that known as dicynodonts. There was an enormous variety of these animals, all of which were rather stockily built herbivores. These sorts of reptiles were already showing many indications of changes which anticipate the body form of later true mammals. The legs, although rather short, tended to be very mobile and could be tucked under the body, so that they could move quite efficiently when they needed to. Indeed it was almost as though they had two 'gears': one 'low' for slow ambling, with the legs flexed and held somewhat obliquely out from the sides of the body, the other 'fast' with the legs tucked up and straighter so that their stride was longer and more efficient. The torso was barrel-shaped, to accommodate the large gut which all herbivores re-

quire in order to deal with a diet of plants, and the tail was very short and not very powerful. This latter point is very important because the large muscles which moved the hind legs were no longer in the tail, but originated mostly on the hip bones instead, as they do in modern mammals.

The most important part of the dicynodont was its head. The name dicynodont means 'two dog tooth' and the name refers to the fact that, quite literally, most of these animals only had two teeth. These teeth, the canines, were long and curved, pointing downward from the front edge of the upper jaw. The remainder

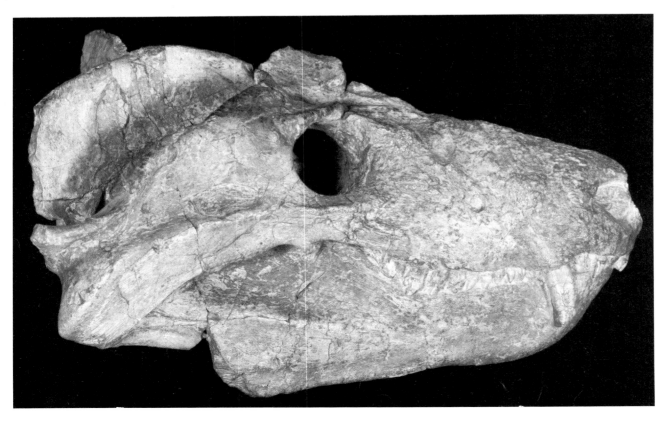

Left *Cynognathus*. This Triassic cynodont has a singularly dog-like face. Note the long snout and the large stabbing canine teeth.

Above A rhynchosaur from the late Triassic of South America. Note the hooked beak, long tail and high body carriage.

Right Rhynchosaurs were quite abundant for a short period at the very end of the Triassic Period.

of the jaw consisted of sharp-edged bone, sometimes ornamented by a few additional ridges. The shape of the jaw bones is very similar to those of turtle jaws, and it seems certain that in life these animals had sharp horny beaks. A further peculiarity of many dicynodonts is that they had remarkably flexible jaw joints, combined with very powerful jaw muscles. This meant that the lower jaw could slide around both backwards and forwards and side to side in elaborate chewing movements, controlled by large jaw muscles draped around the side of the head behind the eyes.

In the early Triassic, dicynodonts were a very specialized type of herbivore. Their sharp, ever growing beaks allowed them to bite and chew up all manner of plant material, which could be fermented in the stomach so that all the nourishing nutrients could be extracted. They were evidently very successful animals, because their remains are found in huge numbers in Permian and Triassic rocks in some parts of the world, most notably in South Africa. They were also quite varied, ranging from small forms which may have burrowed for roots and tubers in the soil, through middle-sized types, to large, almost cow-sized ones, which would have browsed on a wide range of foliage.

Successful though the dicynodonts were in the Permian and early part of the Triassic, it is evident from the number and variety

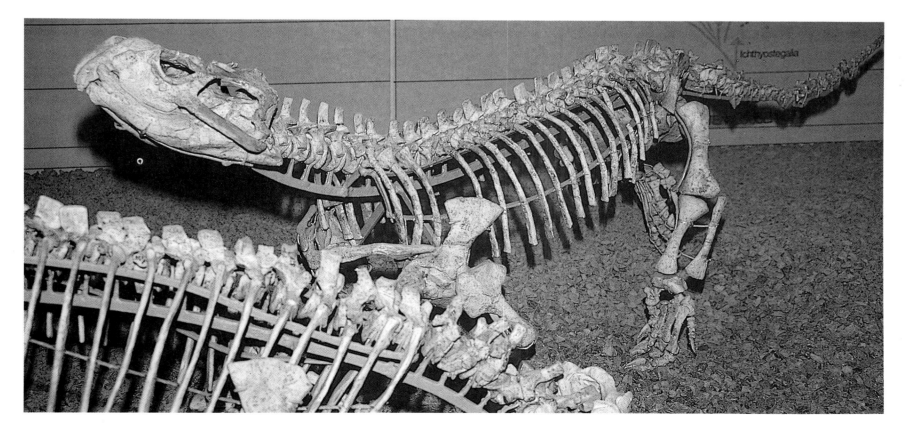

of fossils preserved that during the middle and later part of the Triassic Period, the dicynodonts became less and less abundant. The group as a whole appears to have died out just before the end of the Triassic, about 215 million years ago.

Other groups of mammal-like reptiles were also important during the Triassic such as the cynodonts (dog tooth). Although their body proportions were quite similar to dicynodonts, they were not specialized as herbivores in the same way for they had a full set of teeth, and no sharp horny beak. Instead many cynodonts were dog-like carnivores somewhat like *Cynognathus*. Like the dicynodonts, they were capable of running quite effectively using the two gear system, and most likely preyed upon a variety of dicynodonts. Cynodonts had long-snouted faces, with short nipping incisor teeth at the front, followed by large stabbing canine teeth, and a variety of more complicated cheek teeth which they used for shredding or slicing flesh.

Living alongside these 'typical' or cynognathoid cynodonts, were another group which are called diademodontoid cynodonts. These latter types were herbivorous, and although they looked very like the carnivorous cynodonts, can be distinguished by their cheek teeth which are broader and more suited for crushing up plant material. The herbivorous cynodonts seemed to evolve at the expense of the dicynodonts in middle and late Triassic times.

Despite the fact that both the dicynodonts and the cynodonts were clearly very complex and sophisticated animals, especially when compared to the typical model of a reptile such as a lizard, they were destined for only a brief evolutionary success during the Triassic, and did not survive the extinctions at the end of this Period.

Yet another group with a similar fate was the rhynchosaurs (beaked reptiles). Again, we are dealing with a group of rather squat, short-bodied animals, not unlike dicynodonts in external appearance. However, the tails were not quite as short as those of the dicynodonts (or mammal-like reptiles generally), and the legs carried the body quite high off the ground so that they could work more efficiently when necessary.

The most distinctive part of a rhynchosaur's anatomy was the head, which was short and deep, and very heavily boned. At the tip of the snout the bones of the upper jaw (premaxillae) were developed into a pair of large, downwardly directed spikes, lodging between the tips of the lower jaw. Behind these spikes the jaws bore long plates with dozens of small, spiky teeth arranged in rows along the length of the jaws. The jaws seem to have been operated by massive jaw muscles attached to the inside of the heavy skull bones.

Although some fairly bizarre diets have been suggested in the past – such as molluscs – these very curious beasts were evidently herbivores judging by the way the teeth were arranged as sharp crushing and cutting edges for slicing plant fibers. It also seems probable that the extraordinary hooked beak may have been used to help while digging, or grubbing around for roots.

Rhynchosaurs first appeared in the early Triassic, and although they never became particularly diverse, they have been found quite widely across Pangea: South America, South Africa, India, Europe and North America throughout the rest of the Triassic. As was the case with the cynodonts, the rise of the rhynchosaurs mirrors the decline of the dicynodonts through the Triassic. But they were also destined for extinction at the close of the Triassic.

During the Permian and Triassic Periods there was another group of reptiles which became increasingly important in the ecosystems of the time, both in number and variety. These were

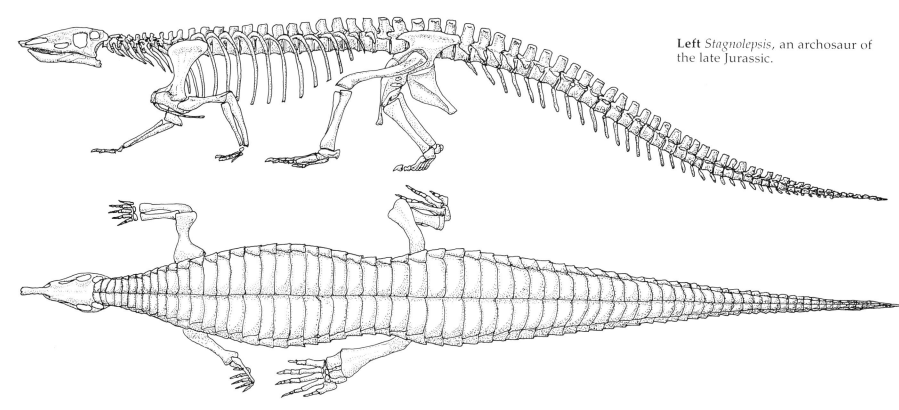

Left *Stagnolepis*, an archosaur of the late Jurassic.

known as archosaurs (ruling reptiles) and, unlike the previous groups mentioned – at least in their earliest forms – were much more similar to modern reptiles. Modern crocodiles are direct descendents of the archosaurs of the Triassic. Archosaurs are distinguished from other reptiles in a number of ways: they have a distinctive pattern of openings in the skull and lower jaw, associated with the attachment of jaw muscles; they have teeth embedded in sockets in the bone of the jaw; and most have bony plates, arranged in rows and embedded in the skin of the back.

Euparkeria is a good example of an early archosaur. The remains of one discovery come from the early Triassic of southern Africa and reveal an animal about 32-40 inches (80-100cm) in length. Although rather lizard-like at first sight there are many subtle differences. The head is rather large, as are the teeth, which are deeply rooted and have serrated edges – it was clearly a carnivore. In addition, along the length of the backbone can be seen a paired row of bony plates.

Most importantly for the origin of dinosaurs, some subtle changes were taking place in the hips and hind leg bones. These changes were to do with the way in which the hind leg was able to move. In particular the thigh bone (femur) is distinctively curved, and the hip socket into which the femur fitted is socketed in such

a way that the leg can be either held out from the side of the body at an oblique angle, as is the case of modern reptiles, or it can be held partly beneath the body. These changes are very similar to the ones already described for the other groups, and seem to represent a common evolutionary trend among terrestrial groups at this time. However, this trend does not seem to be associated with a shortening of the tail and the movement of the leg moving muscles as was the case with the mammal-like reptiles.

Archosaurs such as *Euparkeria* were apparently quite fast moving predatory types, and as such seem to have been very successful, presumably preying on mammal-like reptiles of various types. A wide range of these archosaurs appeared during the Triassic, some of which were very large (13 feet [4m] or more in length) and formidable creatures.

Toward the end of the Triassic, as the other reptile groups were becoming extinct, the archosaurs suffered no such decline. If anything, they took advantage of the disappearance of the other groups and continued to improve on the anatomical changes that had been set in forms such as *Euparkeria*. By the late Triassic, archosaurs ranged enormously in size. At one extreme there were the large, heavily built, four-footed predators such as *Saurosuchus* (creeping crocodile). The changes that had allowed smaller types

Left *Lagosuchus* from the late Triassic of South America was a light and slender archosaur, very close to some early dinosaurs in appearance.

Far left Rhynchosaurs were low browsers; they fed on seed ferns and possibly grubbed for roots with their hooked beaks.

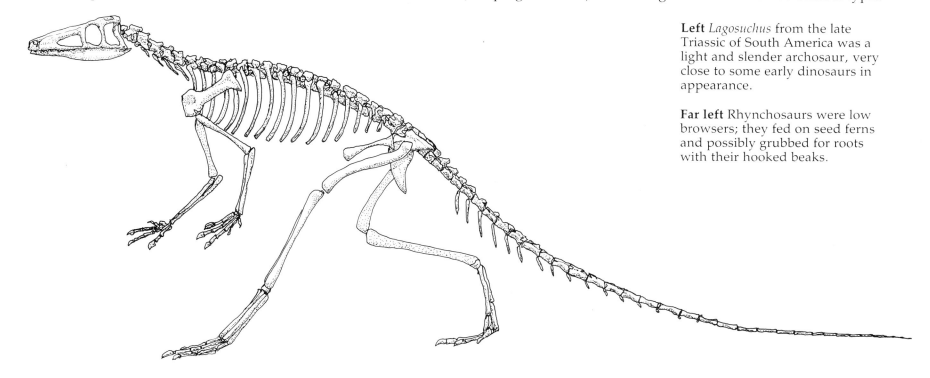

such as *Euparkeria* to tuck their legs beneath their bodies and scamper around at speed, were instead used to allow the legs to act as weight-supporting pillars to carry a heavy body. At the other extreme there were types which had developed their lightness and fleetness of foot as far as possible. *Lagosuchus* (rabbit crocodile) is one such example from the late Triassic of Argentina. The legs had become extremely long, and the feet slender, as befits a runner, the arms (forelimbs) were shorter, and clearly little used for walking upon; the tail, which was long and slender, could be used as a counterbalance to allow this animal to walk and run on its hindlegs. Another very similar type is *Scleromochlus* from the late Triassic of Scotland, which is characterized by extremely long and slender limbs. Also from Scotland is *Ornithosuchus* (bird crocodile) a much larger (11⅓ feet [3.5m] long), but still bipedal, carnivorous archosaur.

These archosaurs, which had developed bipedal habits, were very close in form to the earliest dinosaurs, and there has been much confusion over the exact position of some of these species.

Above *Ornithosuchus* from northeast Scotland was a heavily armored archosaur. It was one of a variety of late archosaur carnivores.

Left By contrast to *Lagosuchus*, *Saurosuchus* is one of the large and aggressive late Triassic archosaurs.

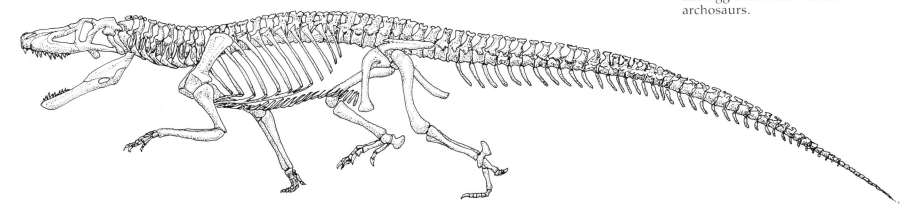

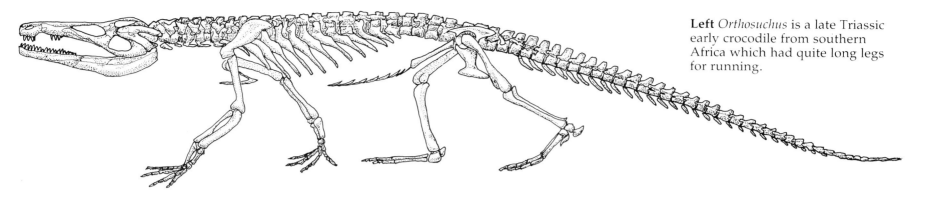

Left *Orthosuchus* is a late Triassic early crocodile from southern Africa which had quite long legs for running.

The earliest dinosaurs

The very earliest dinosaurs are unfortunately very poorly known at the moment. This fact has lead to a great deal of speculation about the nature of the origins of dinosaurs, and the precise type of the earliest ones.

Staurikosaurus is one of the earliest known of all dinosaurs, having been found in rocks of the late Carnian age of the Santa Maria Formation in Brazil. At the moment this dinosaur is known from much of its backbone, the hips and the hind leg bones, and a lower jaw. From this evidence it is clear that the dinosaur was a small (6½ feet [2m] long) lightly built, swift moving predator. Generally, the dinosaur is little different from advanced archosaurs such as *Lagosuchus*. This early dinosaur probably fed upon smaller mammal-like reptiles and lizards, which it could have caught with relative ease.

Two other early dinosaurs come from South America: *Herrerasaurus* and *Ischisaurus*. *Herrerasaurus* comes from the Ischigualasto Formation of Argentina, which is dated at late Carnian/early Norian, and therefore slightly younger than the formation from which *Staurikosaurus* has been collected. It is evidently known from good material, because photographs of apparently complete skeletons are known. At present however we do not have a detailed description of this animal, although it seems likely that new collection work done on this material by a team of paleontologists from Buenos Aires and Chicago may soon produce new information.

Herrerasaurus is slightly larger and appears to be more heavily built than *Staurikosaurus*, reaching lengths of about 8 to 10 feet (2.5 to 3m). The skull is much larger and more robust than would appear to be the case in *Staurikosaurus* (at least judging from the shape of the lower jaw). This was clearly a powerful predatory dinosaur, but it may not have been as fleet footed or as agile as *Staurikosaurus*.

Ischisaurus also comes from the Ischigualasto Formation of Argentina, and is currently only known from very fragmentary pieces of skeleton, but would appear to be another, medium- to small-sized predatory dinosaur.

Finally from South America, there are the partial remains of another, but rather different dinosaur named *Pisanosaurus*. Again small and evidently agile, it does not appear to have been a predator, but an herbivore, judging by the closely packed, chisel-like teeth which can be seen in its jaws.

Elsewhere in the world, a variety of slightly younger forms of dinosaur are known. These include the extremely poorly-known *Saltopus*, a few scrappy bone impressions from Scotland; *Azendohsaurus* which is represented by a quite large collection of broken jaw fragments with teeth from Morocco, and many other isolated fragments which have yet to be described. There are, however, two other dinosaurs which are well preserved.

First, the remains of *Coelophysis*, which were first discovered in the early 1880s in northern New Mexico. Even though these remains were very scrappy, it was clear that this was a lightly built early dinosaur. Further collecting from this area was undertaken just after the Second World War by a team from the American Museum of Natural History. The return visit brought handsome rewards with the discovery of a veritable 'graveyard' of *Coelophysis*, where literally dozens of skeletons were preserved in a very small area, all jumbled together. Even today it is not certain quite what caused this mass accumulation of these dinosaurs. However one likely cause may have been a local catastrophe, such as a flash flood, which may have caught and buried a herd of these animals in a wave of mud.

One remarkable feature of this discovery is the fact that animals of all ages have been recovered, and this is very useful because it allows us to understand the method of growth during the life of the species. This can be particularly useful when it comes to studying other species, or in comparing the remains of *Coelophysis* with other dinosaur remains from the same area. Quite often, if a

Left *Ornithosuchus*, another of the late Triassic archosaurs. This is a large predatory form from Scotland. Unlike *Saurosuchus* (opposite) this type was bipedal.

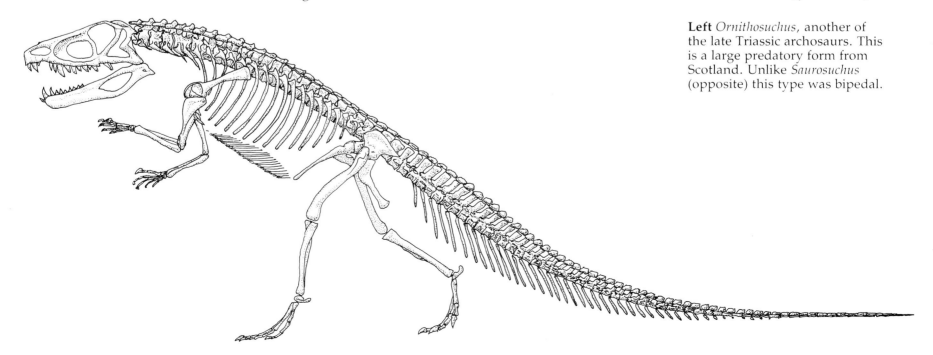

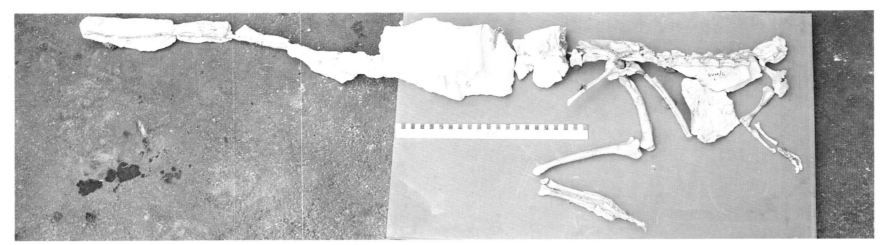

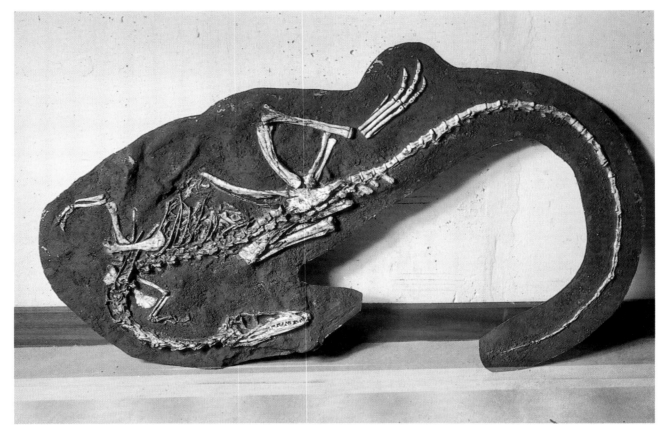

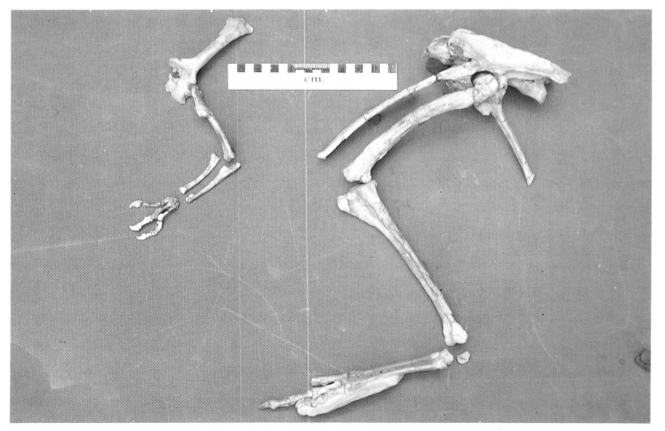

Above The left hand of *Syntarsus*, a similar creature to *Coelophysis*.

Top A *Syntarsus* skeleton, partially prepared in the laboratory.

Center left *Coelophysis* is another well-preserved early dinosaur from the late Triassic of New Mexico and Arizona. Closely related types are also known from southern Africa.

Left *Syntarsus* fore- and hindlimbs.

Left A skull of *Plateosaurus* prepared so that the individual bones can be studied at will. Note the relatively small, slender, leaf-shaped teeth, clearly those of an herbivore.

Below Full skeletal restoration of a *Plateosaurus* in several views, to show the body proportions. This animal appears to have had the option of walking quadrupedally or bipedally.

dinosaur is poorly known, and more material is found in rocks of a similar age, it can be impossible to prove whether the remains are of a new dinosaur, or merely more pieces of a younger or older version of the same dinosaur.

Coelophysis was clearly a slenderly built, fast-moving predatory dinosaur, which grew to a length of about 10 feet (3m). The skull was light, pointed and slender, and the jaws were lined with sharp, curved teeth with serrated edges for slicing through flesh. Their prey may well have included small lizards, and perhaps the young of contemporary dinosaurs. In fact, their diet was probably quite varied.

One rather macabre insight into the diet of *Coelophysis* has come to light through a study of the skeletons from New Mexico. One or two have been discovered to have piles of small *Coelophysis* bones in the chest area. Although it is always possible that these were the remains of baby dinosaurs within the body of female *Coelophysis*, the most likely explanation seems to be that these are cases of cannibalism: the adults having made a meal of some of their young.

Other remains of *Coelophysis* have been recovered from simi-larly aged rocks in Arizona and a similar dinosaur, named *Syntarsus*, has been described from the latest Triassic/early Jurassic of Zimbabwe. *Syntarsus* and *Coelophysis* are so similar that some paleontologists have tried to give both of the dinosaurs the same name: referring to the species from New Mexico as *Coelophysis bauri* and the one from Zimbabwe as *Coelophysis rhodesiensis*.

The similarity between these dinosaurs reflects the fact that even though the continents are well separated today, in the late Triassic, southern Africa and North America were relatively close together.

The other extremely well-known late Triassic dinosaur, whose remains have been recovered from a variety of quarries in East and West Germany, as well as southern France and Switzerland, is *Plateosaurus*. The first remains were recovered in the 1830s, but it was not until the early years of this century that the first well-preserved remains were collected at Trossingen. Rather like the case of *Coelophysis* above, the remains of *Plateosaurus* were found in large numbers in fairly small areas within the quarry sites. This leads to the suspicion that these dinosaurs were the victims of some natural disaster, such as a flash flood.

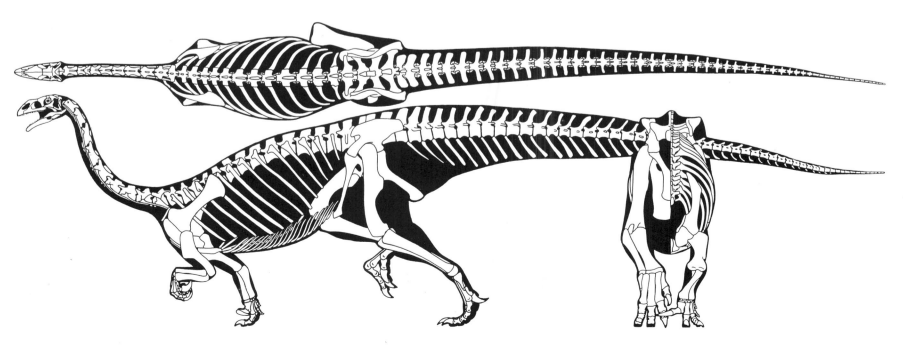

Plateosaurus was quite a large creature, larger by far than any of the other early dinosaurs, reaching maximum lengths of 26 feet (8m). The large tail counterbalanced the front part of the body, so that the animals could walk on their hind legs at times, or could pitch forward to walk on all fours. The trunk was barrel-shaped, to accommodate a large gut, and the belly area was reinforced by bony rods known as gastralia, while the back bone was heavily built to provide support in this area. The neck was quite long and flexible, providing a wide range of movement and long reach for the head. The head in turn was quite small, in comparison with the bulk of the body. The snout is deep and long, rather than pointed as in the case of the majority of predatory species, and although the jaws were lined with large numbers of teeth, these were small and leaf-shaped, rather than curved and sharp edged as we have seen in the majority of cases.

The arms and legs of *Plateosaurus* were powerfully built, and clearly intended for different purposes. The legs were long and strong and designed to support the bulk of the body, whereas the the forelimbs were shorter, although very powerful, and had hands with long, spreading and sharply clawed fingers. It seems likely that the hands were used for walking on, because the fingers could be bent backwards to make a weight-supporting platform. However, the hand was also clearly designed to be used

as a grasping organ. The digits were long and slender and had sharp claws for holding with, and the thumb was large and twisted inwards. Not only a powerful grasping tool, the hand could also have been used as a slashing weapon of defense.

What sort of animals were plateosaurs? The small, leaf-shaped teeth and small head point to the fact that they were herbivores. They could rear up on their hind limbs and, in combination with the long neck, would have been able to reach up into the branches

Far left A beautifully preserved skull and neck of *Coelophysis*, which has been collected in Arizona.

Left *Syntarsus (=Coelophysis)* from southern Africa is extremely similar to the dinosaur from Arizona and New Mexico and some research workers have proposed that they be given the same generic name.

Below This late Triassic scene shows a pack of *Syntarsus (=Coelophysis)* feeding upon lizards, and in the background the medium-sized, plant-eating sauropodomorph *Massospondylus*.

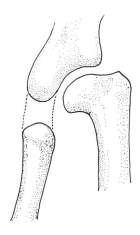

Above Front view of the hip socket of a dinosaur showing the femur fitting against the supra-acetabular crest and the open back of the hip socket (dotted).

Left Mounted skeletons of *Plateosaurus* on display at the Paleontology and Geology Institute, Tübingen.

Below left The hand of a *Plateosaurus*. Note the large inner claws.

Right The beautifully preserved skeleton of the early pterosaur *Eudimorphodon*.

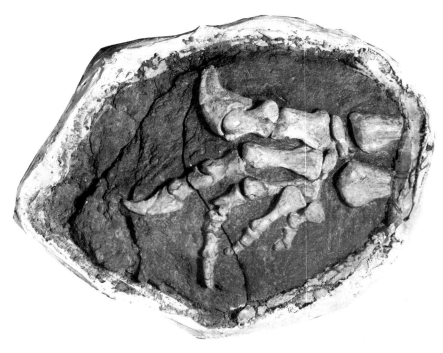

of trees for their food (leaves and conifer needles) with ease. The large bulk of these animals was necessary to accommodate a large gut, which would have allowed the huge quantities of vegetable matter to ferment and be broken down before digestion could proceed.

In fact, plateosaurs were the first high browsers to evolve. Up until the late Triassic all land vertebrates had been quite low-slung animals, feeding (if they were herbivores) on low ground cover vegetation, and at the very best being able to lean against the trunks of trees, or climb into trees to feed on high browse. Pla-

teosaurs, then, represent a new and very important group of animals because they were the first ones to develop for a life as high browsers. As such, they represent the first in an evolution-ary line leading to some of the biggest and most spectacular of all dinosaurs which appeared during the latter half of the Jurassic Period.

Recognizing and classifying the earliest dinosaurs

We clearly recognize the animals mentioned above as being dino-saurs, yet when looking at some of the late Triassic archosaurs, such as *Lagosuchus*, it is difficult to see any significant difference. In essence, the differences are all to do with the way in which these advanced archosaurs (such as *Lagosuchus*) and early true dinosaurs move their legs.

As we have seen earlier, Richard Owen recognized that dino-saurs were able to walk as mammals and birds do today, with legs held vertically beneath the body, and the feet very close to the midline. In order to do this several important changes have to take place in the structure of the bones of the hips (which make up the hip socket), as well as the thigh bone (femur), knee, lower leg, ankle and foot. These changes can be seen quite clearly in fossils, provided, of course, that the all-important pieces of the skeleton are preserved.

Some of the most obvious features are found in the hip region. The hip socket (or acetabulum) is a deep cup-shaped socket (in-stead of a shallow depression) and has an opening on its inner surface (known as a 'fenestra' – window). Above the socket there is also a prominent ridge, the supra-acetabular crest. The femur is specially modified to fit against the acetabulum so that the upper end of the femur (or head) is developed into a large, rounded joint surface, which is bent inwards to fit into the hip socket. It is held in position by the supra-acetabular crest. The femur is also modified by the presence of special bony projections near the head, and another known as the 4th trochanter on the shaft, for the attachment of special leg moving muscles. The knee joint allows the knee only to bend in the parasaggital plane (parallel to the midline of the body), as does the ankle, which has its bones rearranged to allow only this type of motion. Finally the toes of the foot are roughly symmetrical, with the middle toe the longest and the outer toes (1st and 5th) much reduced or absent in later dinosaurs. These changes in the foot are all associated with moving the foot beneath the body and only placing the toes on the ground when they walked (*i.e.* digitigrade), rather than the whole length of the foot (*i.e.* plantigrade – as we are, when we walk).

The four earliest dinosaurs are well enough preserved to show at least some of these characteristics but not necessarily all of them because they are poorly preserved or described. They are therefore clearly dinosaurs, but they do not fit neatly into any of the well-known groups of dinosaurs that we know from later periods. For this reason it is probably best to regard these forms as 'Protodinosaurs,' a special grouping to recognize their very early position in the evolution of the group as a whole.

Staurikosaurus, *Herrerasaurus* and *Ischisaurus* resemble theropods in general details (they are bipedal and carnivorous) but they cannot be assigned to any of the theropod saurischian subgroups. Equally, although *Pisanosaurus* appears to have the jaw shape and biped locomotion of an ornithopod ornithischian, it cannot be clearly referred to the group for lack of evidence.

The closest relatives of the early protodinosaurs seem to be the lightly built and agile archosaurs such as *Lagosuchus*, which are light, fast-moving creatures. In many details of their anatomy, apart from the crucial ones relating to the posture of the legs, they are very much like the earliest dinosaurs.

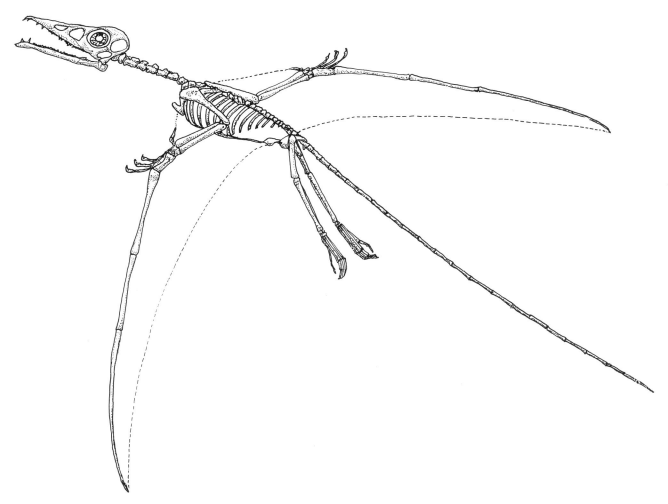

Left A reconstruction of the skeleton of *Eudimorphodon* based on the skeleton on the previous page.

Below right Chart showing the first and last appearances of dinosaurs (blue) and other groups of reptiles which lived around the late Triassic/early Jurassic time zone (here broken down into stages Scythian-Bajocian). The steady decrease and disappearance of several groups of non-dinosaur reptile is obvious, as is their replacement, primarily by dinosaurs. Clearly the figures do not show a precise cut-off of one group and their replacement by another and this leaves the question of the reason for the change an open one.

Pterosaurs – flying reptiles

The pterosaurs are another group which should be mentioned at this point. They are also archosaurs, first appearing in the Triassic, and although they did not have any great influence upon terrestrial life during the Mesozoic, they were quite close relatives of the dinosaurs.

The group as a whole had a checkered history to start with. Their remains were first discovered toward the end of the eighteenth century in southern Germany. At first they were thought to be some form of sea creature, while others argued for their bird-like flying abilities. It was finally settled in the middle of the nineteenth century, when it was pointed out that the bones of pterosaurs were very thin and had air spaces running through them, which could be only explained if they were light, flying creatures.

With the study and discovery of better material it became clear that pterosaurs were large-brained, highly sophisticated flying reptiles, totally unlike the modern conception of a reptile. Some pterosaurs have been preserved with what appears to be a 'pelage' or furry covering surrounding the body. If this was real, as it appears to be, rather than an artefact of preservation, then it doubly emphasizes how little like modern reptiles pterosaurs were. The implication of a large brain, complex flight control and a furry covering to such an animal, is that it may have been endothermic (warm blooded) and therefore physiologically much more like today's mammals and birds than like any reptiles.

Eudimorphodon comes from the late Triassic of Italy and was a very early pterosaur. Discoveries show that the skull was like that of some of the later archosaurs, in that it was long and tapering and had many spiky teeth lining the jaws. The diet would appear to have been fish, which they swooped down upon and caught at the water's surface. The neck was long and flexible, though short, and the trunk was also short and strong, anchoring the bones and muscles of the wings. The tail was long, though, and appears to have been quite stiff, and probably assisted in flight control, acting as some sort of aileron.

The forelimbs were typical of all pterosaurs, with short, stout upper and lower arm bones, attached to a powerful shoulder girdle. The hand was grossly modified to support a wing membrane. The first three fingers of the hand were normal, ending in typical reptilian claws but the fourth finger was enormously elongated. Comprising four thin rods, they were jointed together on their ends to support the wing membrane. The pelvis and hindlimbs were comparatively normal, looking rather like the hindlimbs of protodinosaurs.

It has been argued that pterosaurs are close relatives of the early dinosaurs, and it is certainly clear that many aspects of their anatomy (skull and hindlimb in particular) are similar. But the specializations associated with flight in the forelimbs and backbone make a very close relationship difficult to prove. The most dinosaur-like reconstruction of a pterosaur can be seen in the next chapter (*Dimorphodon*) where there is further discussion of the relationship between pterosaurs and dinosaurs.

Mammals

The final group which should be mentioned in this chapter are the mammals. This is an important group – not the least because they include our own ancestors. They were completely dominated during the time of the dinosaurs and only rose to prominence after the demise of the dinosaurs at the close of the Cretaceous Period, some 150 million years later.

The ancestors of the mammals were to be found among the cynodont mammal-like reptiles. The first mammals appeared at the very end of the Triassic, during the Rhaetian, and therefore about 10 million years after the first dinosaurs had appeared. Their remains have been found in Europe, China, South Africa and North America and they were at their beginning a very widely spread group. However, they were all small, probably nocturnal creatures which fed on insects, much like modern-day shrews and hedgehogs. They appear to have scurried around at night, away from the attentions of the dinosaurs.

It could almost be said that the mammals were simply waiting in the 'wings' for the dinosaurs to disappear and give the mammals their chance to evolve and diversify.

The late Triassic puzzle

From our vantage point in the present, we can look at the animals living today, and compare them with those that lived in the past in order to try to understand how and why animals of the past lived in the way that they did. If we do that now, though, we are confronted by a clear problem: today mammals dominate as large animals on land, while reptiles are relatively poorly represented (the only exceptions appear to be in some isolated tropical communities, such as the islands of Aldabra and Galapagos). However, in the late Triassic the situation was completely reversed: the dinosaurian reptiles were the dominant land animals while the mammals were confined to relative insignificance. This situation lasted for over 150 million years, and seems only to have changed with the extinction of the dinosaurs at the end of the Cretaceous Period. There have been a number of attempts to explain why this should have happened, all which have tried in one way or another to explain the apparent change in fortunes of the two principal groups, the mammals and the reptiles.

First, there is the link between dinosaur success and posture. This argument relies on a belief that the efficiency with which dinosaurs were able to walk and run in late Triassic times was a key to their success.

As already noted, dinosaurs developed an ability to hold their legs in an erect position through modifications to their hip joint and legs. These changes resulted in an ability to both carry the weight of the body much more efficiently (enabling dinosaurs to grow to large sizes); and also to move much more quickly, because the legs were able to swing vertically beneath the body and provide a much longer stride. Dinosaurs, and particularly the early ones, became very efficient hunters of the Carnian stage of the Late Triassic. Their light build and high speed gave them natural advantages over their prey, particularly mammal-like reptiles and rhynchosaurs which were by comparison quite short legged and slower moving forms. These dinosaurs also had the advantage over their predatory competitors, which were mainly the cynodont mammal-like reptiles and some of the advanced – and very dinosaur-like – archosaurs. As a result of this superiority in ability, it is argued, the early predatory dinosaurs were able to out-compete other predators, thus causing their extinction and driving their prey to extinction as well. This left the dinosaurs free to exploit the late Triassic world. The disappearance of the herbivorous mammal-like reptiles and rhynchosaurs provided an opportunity for the dinosaurs to evolve herbivorous forms – protodinosaurs such as *Pisanosaurus* perhaps, or plateosaurs and early ornithischians in the latest Triassic and the early Jurassic.

The observation that dinosaurs gained an efficient locomotor system is fully agreed upon. However, whether the development led to the evolutionary scenario outlined above is a matter of personal preference and the subject of some dispute. It would seem rather unlikely that one group of predatory animals would cause the extinction of all their prey, because that would ultimately lead to the extinction of the predator as well. Nature invariably acts in such a way as to balance the numbers of predator and prey wherever possible, so as to maintain a sort of uneasy equilibrium. Also the notion that 'competition,' of the sort being suggested here, taking place between large related groups of animals (*i.e.* archosaurs, dinosaurs, mammal-like reptiles, rhynchosaurs) rather than between individuals or species is considered by some to be extremely improbable.

However, despite these various misgivings, this is still one of the most widely quoted explanations for the success of dinosaurs over mammals in the Triassic.

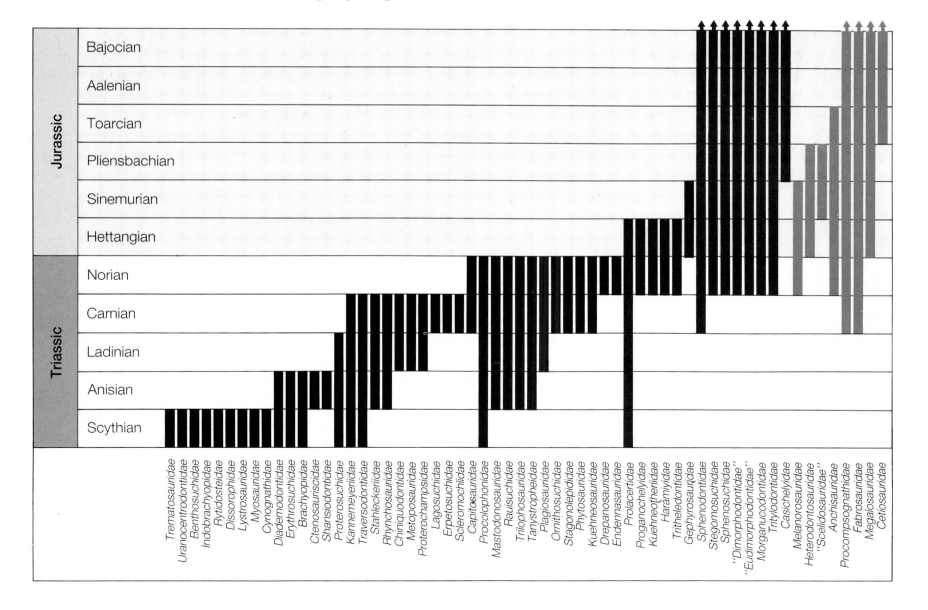

Another argument for their success is based on the theory that dinosaurs were endothermic. This explanation is one of powerful simplicity and comes from a direct comparison of the biology of animals today and in the Triassic.

Mammals today are dominant and very successful animals. One of the reasons for their success is considered to be their possession of an endothermic physiology, by which we mean that mammals are able to regulate their internal body temperature to a very fine degree. They are able to do this by generating body heat internally (which is the literal meaning of endothermy – endo [internal], thermy [heat]), and controlling the loss of body heat to the air by means of hair on the skin or fat layers beneath the skin (or a combination of both). Excess heat can be dissipated by evaporative cooling (perspiration). By this means, mammals are able to remain active when the weather is cool, which reptiles cannot do, and perhaps more importantly are able to live extremely active lives: they have much greater endurance than similarly sized reptiles.

Reptiles are by comparison ectothermic which means that they rely upon ecto (external) sources of heat (ultimately the sun) to power their body processes. For this reason reptiles are far more active in warm climatic zones (tropical and subtropical regions) and can maintain quite high activity levels for much of the day by constantly monitoring their body temperature and shuttling between heat and cold. By doing this, reptiles can keep an even internal temperature, so that their bodily chemical processes can take place most efficiently. This style of life is clearly quite efficient in that reptiles do not need to eat vast amounts of food in order to generate internal body heat. But the drawback of this system is that it has limited their ability to exploit a variety of cooler environments. And even in the tropics there can be cool or overcast days, during which reptiles are unable to reach their normal operating temperatures and remain very sluggish.

Comparing mammals and reptiles of today with those of the Triassic, we are presented with an interesting paradox. Whereas today's mammals are the successful group, in Triassic times dinosaurian reptiles were the most successful, and appear to have confined the mammals to the role of small nocturnal insectivores on land. How could this be so if dinosaurs were comparable to present-day ectothermic reptiles?

The answer that has been put forward by some paleontologists is that dinosaurs must have been endothermic as well. This would appear to be the only explanation if we are to assume that the mammalian success seen today is explicable through their development of endothermy. It should also perhaps be added that another major group of vertebrates – the birds – are also extremely successful today and are also notable for their possession of endothermy.

Again this appears to be a very persuasive argument. Indeed, it has been greatly elaborated by other observations, such as the one above about posture and the success of dinosaurs. It is claimed that dinosaurs were able to attain an upright posture only *because* they had developed an endothermic physiology.

However, again as a word of warning, it might be observed that being endothermic may not always be advantageous. For example there are certain costs associated with being warm blooded, which can be easily overlooked, particularly by people living in cool or cold climates. The first is food. Endotherms have very large appetites because 80 percent or more of their food intake is simply burned to provide body heat. As a result much time must be devoted to finding and consuming food, and food needs to be relatively plentiful. Water is also in constant demand since it

Left Lizards spend much of their time basking on rocks.

Right Tortoises such as these provide the classic example of the 'reptile': slow-moving animals with an ectothermic physiology. Appearances, however, can be deceptive; large green turtles are capable of maintaining a high internal body temperature when they swim in cool seas!

Toad (undivided heart)   **Reptile** (semi-divided heart)   **Endotherm** (fully divided heart)

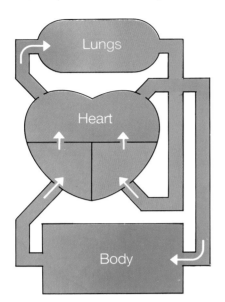
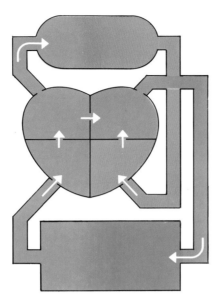
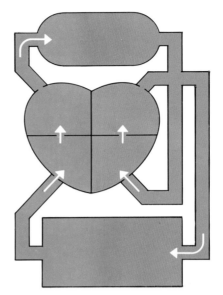

Left Heart circulation. Amphibians (left) completely mix blood from the lungs and the body in the main heart chamber (ventricle). Modern reptiles (middle) have a valve which partly separates blood from the lungs and the rest of the body. Mammals, birds and – possibly – dinosaurs (right) have completely separate circulation – the most efficient arrangement.

■ Oxygenated blood
■ Deoxygenated blood
■ Mixed blood

is lost during evaporative cooling (perspiration) and breathing. By comparison a reptile employing an ectothermic physiology is much more economical in the sense that food requirements are considerably less than for mammals, and water requirements are less because most reptiles do not have a permeable skin. This leads us to a third line of reasoning which has been used to explain the success of reptiles in the Triassic.

It has been argued that the reason for the apparent success of the reptiles in Triassic times was that they were better able to cope with the climate and general environmental conditions than others such as mammals.

According to this argument later Triassic climates worldwide were warm and dry, with extensive desert or arid conditions. Under these conditions, it is conceivable that reptiles, with their ectothermic physiology may have prospered at the expense of the mammals. As was discussed above, reptiles are essentially very economical creatures, in that they have modest food requirements, low water requirements, and because of their reliance

upon external temperatures for their activities, are very tolerant of a wide range of body temperatures.

If the world of the late Triassic was indeed very warm and dry, with extensive arid areas, then this may have suited reptiles very well. High temperatures ensure constant high levels of activity, aridity means that food is a limiting factor – but reptiles have low food requirements. Water is also going to be of limited availability, and reptiles conserve water very well and lose it very slowly. By contrast, endothermic mammals are not suited to hot arid conditions because of their constant need for food, their requirement for copious supplies of water, especially for cooling, and the fact that high environmental temperatures are very stressful to endotherms. Endotherms seem generally far better at retaining heat through feathers, subcutaneous fat and hair, than at losing it, and it could be argued that they are adapted to cope with variable/cool climatic conditions rather than warm/hot ones.

The argument then, hinges on the idea that certain animals are suited to differing environmental conditions, and that world-

wide changes in climate may influence the success, or otherwise, of different groups of organisms. The burden of proof for this scenario lies with the geologists and their ability to demonstrate that climatic conditions in the Triassic were indeed warm and arid. There is certainly some evidence for a relatively dry climate in late Triassic times in areas of southern and northern Africa, North and South America and Europe. Having a single continental landmass at the time seems to have led to generally hot summers, cool winters and lower rainfall. There were no polar ice caps, so that the latitudinal zonation of climate seen today were not nearly so marked in the Triassic.

There does, then, seem to be a general level of support for the idea that the climatic conditions of the Triassic were very different from those that apply today. This should, in theory at least, have favored the reptiles, but whether it can explain the total dominance of reptiles over mammals remains to be seen.

The final proposal that we shall briefly look at relies on a belief that organisms tend to operate in an opportunistic way in order to take advantage of chance events.

In this case, it is argued that something (the precise causative agent is not agreed upon) caused the widespread extinction of numerous groups of land-based animals at the end of the Triassic. The victims appear to have been the mammal-like reptiles, rhynchosaurs and some later archosaurs. Whatever caused the extinctions left the dinosaurs relatively unaffected and gave them a perfect opportunity to evolve very rapidly indeed and to take advantage of the 'spaces' vacated by the previous groups of animals.

The pattern of disappearance of groups and the appearance of others at the end of the Triassic is crucial to this argument. If there is a long period of overlap between groups about to become extinct and new groups beginning to evolve then the sudden widespread extinction argument, although not destroyed, would be significantly weakened. At the moment the analysis would appear to show little overlap of groups, and this lends support to this line of reasoning, though there continues to be some dispute about the figures.

What about the cause of such a sudden extinction of all these types of animal at the end of the Triassic? Two arguments are being used in conjunction. First, it is agreed that the climate was changing in the late Triassic to generally hot and dry conditions worldwide; secondly, it is thought that the climatic change altered the sorts of plants upon which the animals fed. Dinosaurs then become the animals that were best able to cope with the new hot climate and the new types of plant. From the point of view of this argument, it is a pity that the earliest dinosaurs are carnivorous rather than herbivorous!

There is no firm concensus on the cause of the takeover by dinosaurs at the end of the Triassic, and it may well be that the fossil record will never be able to provide us with the crucial evidence which will allow us to choose between the competing hypotheses outlined above. Whatever the actual answer, the late Triassic was clearly a time of fundamental change in climate, vegetation type (with the decline of the seed-fern-dominated wet, lowland areas to floras dominated by conifers and cycads) and a dramatic change in the types of animals on land. The events led to the rise of the dinosaurs, from among a stock of rather promising-looking archosaurs (*i.e.* the agile, nimble creatures) in the late Triassic. The dinosaurs were a stock of reptiles which were to dominate the world for the next 150 million years and produce some of the most extraordinary creatures that have ever walked the Earth.

Left The Namib Desert. Was this what the Triassic world was like?

Above *Glossopteris*, a very characteristic member of the flora of the southern Hemisphere during the Triassic.

Right This chart shows peaks of origination and extinction of vertebrates across the Triassic/Jurassic divide. It reveals not a clear-cut, single extinction and origination event, but several events. The end result was the rise of dinosaurs.

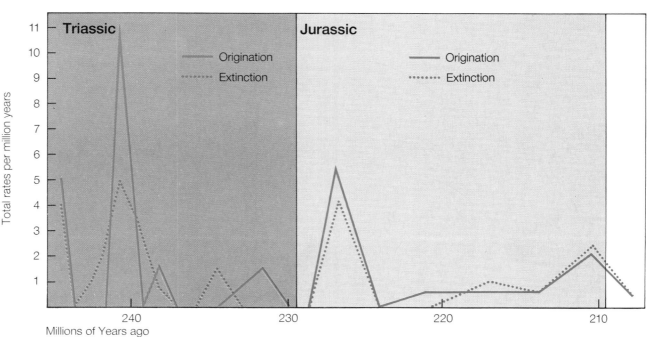

CHAPTER 4

The Early Jurassic Period

The early Jurassic Period has in the recent past always featured as something of a mystery when it comes to the study of dinosaurs because there seemed to be only a limited number of areas where dinosaur remains had been collected. However, the last decade has seen a considerable change – not because of new discoveries of fossils, but because the restudy of many of the deposits, which had been traditionally thought of as late Triassic, has revealed that they are most probably early Jurassic in age. As a result we now appear to know much more about the dinosaurs of this Period. Before going on to look in some detail at the variety of dinosaurs, we will briefly look at what we know of the world wide changes that had taken place since the time of origin of the dinosaurs in the late Triassic some 10 to 15 million years earlier.

Continental movements

Surprisingly little change had taken place in the early Jurassic. The formation of Pangea in late Carboniferous/early Permian times (290 million years ago) had resulted in an extremely stable land mass and the forces acting within the Earth's crust took a long time to start to break up the land mass into separate con-

Above Fronds of fossil ferns are quite abundant in rocks of early Jurassic age. Indeed, fossil ferns had been well-established in lowland areas since the Carboniferous Period. *Alethopteris* is pictured.

Left In some areas considerable thicknesses of fern remains are preserved, as this example of *Todites* shows. Ferns have the advantage of living in low, well-watered areas bordering rivers and lakes, which greatly improves their chances of being preserved.

Top right The fruiting body (cone) of a cycad. This group evolved in the early Mesozoic and became particularly abundant.

Right The very distinctive leaves of the maidenhair tree, *Ginkgo*. Although rare today these were very abundant in the Jurassic. All of the plants pictured here would have undoubtedly formed part of the diet of some herbivorous dinosaurs.

tinental blocks. However, in the early Jurassic times, changes were beginning to take place. In particular, there is evidence that the sea levels, which had been at an all time low, were beginning to rise, covering the continental shelf areas of the continents and beginning to flood over the low lying marginal areas of land. In this way the sea began to constrict the connection between the southern continents (South America, Africa, India, Australasia and Antartica – together referred to as Gondwanaland) and the northern lands (North America, Europe and Asia – collectively known as Laurasia). Complete separation of these two continental areas took place in the middle Jurassic.

Most fossil discoveries have been made in North America, southern Africa and China, and seem to show that the faunas were still very similar, and that there were presumably no barriers to migration north and south across the supercontinent.

Climates and floras

Evidence from plant remains across the Triassic/Jurassic boundary seems to show little sign of great change. Several types of seed fern (generally low, shrubby, fern-like plants found predominantly in the southern continents) became extinct at the end of the Triassic, but at least one new type evolved in the latest Triassic

Left Large conifer trees appeared in the Mesozoic, but rarely are such large specimens as these preserved.

Below Bennettitalean cycad, another of the many varieties of cycad which formed the food of some dinosaurs.

Right *Dimorphodon*, an early pterosaur, has been studied extensively by Dr Kevin Padian, who supervised this reconstruction as a bipedal runner.

Center right These are some of the bones in the hip region of the small early mammal *Megazostrodon* from southern Africa. The original fossil was found and excavated in the 1960s by John Attridge (University of London).

Bottom right The well-preserved skeleton of *Megazostrodon* has allowed quite an accurate reconstruction to be made of one of our own earliest ancestors.

and spread during the Jurassic both in Laurasia and Gondwanaland. Added to this, a variety of true ferns appeared in latest Triassic times and continued to spread in the early Jurassic. Larger and more substantial potential food plants for dinosaurs include the bennettitalean cycads (short-trunked trees with a crown of palm-like leaves) which became abundant during the Jurassic, and a variety of horsetails, ginkgos and coniferous trees (both pines and cupressus-like forms).

The early Jurassic seems to represent a period of consolidation for the plant communities. The seed fern dominated, and the well-watered and lush environments of the middle Triassic seem to have given way to a much more mixed vegetational type, with a substantial number of tree-like cycads and conifers becoming established.

The climate can be deduced from the sorts of plants found at this time. The numbers of seed ferns and ferns as well as horsetails suggests warm, or even hot, and moist conditions. But upland areas seem to have been dominated by conifers and cycads which are better able to cope with the drier conditions. The discovery of large-leaved ferns in quite northerly latitudes also indicates that, as in the late Triassic, conditions were warm over large areas of the globe, and there were no polar ice caps.

Mammals

Early mammals (dating from the earliest Jurassic) are known from a variety of widely spaced localities: southern Africa, China, India, North America and Europe. All the mammals recovered seem to be of the same general type, such as *Eozostrodon* and *Megazostrodon*. All are small (no more than about 4 inches [10cm] long) and shrew-like creatures; their skulls are narrow and pointed and the jaws are equiped with a variety of special teeth, as are all mammals. Small nipping teeth (incisors) are at the tip of the jaw; larger stabbing teeth (canines) behind the incisors; and, behind these a variety of premolars and molars, with complicated spikey surfaces, which were able to grind up the tough cuticles of the insects upon which they fed. This arrangement of teeth is rather similar to those of a cynodont, but the crucial difference is that the mammal has premolar teeth behind the canines – the premolars are the teeth that replace the milk molars. The milk teeth

indicate that during their early life these little animals were suckled on milk from their mothers. The suckling of young on maternal milk is the hallmark of all true mammals, and allows us to be sure that these tiny creatures must have been mammals, rather than reptiles which lay eggs and do not suckle their young, but generally leave them to fend for themselves as soon as they hatch.

Pterosaurs

The fossil record of pterosaurs at this time is a little limited because of the small number of their fossils known from this age. There is, however, one very well preserved and described pterosaur: *Dimorphodon*, which comes from the early Jurassic of southern England.

In general details the skeleton of *Dimorphodon* is not too different from that of *Eudimorphodon*. The arms and hands are similarly modified to form wings, whose membranous surfaces were supported by an incredibly elongated fourth finger. The tail was a long and slender series of vertebrae, supported along the sides by

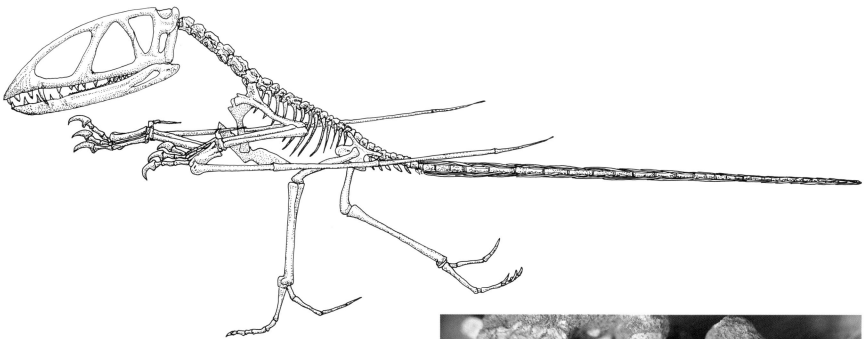

further thin bone rods, which presumably kept this structure relatively stiff, during flight. The hindlimbs would seem to be relatively slight, particularly when compared to the arms, and the feet are quite slender and five-toed.

The torso is short and compact in front of the hips, and the neck, too, is quite short, but the bones of the neck are large when compared to those of the back. The reason for this is the large head of *Dimorphodon*, whose weight had to be supported, as well as the muscles to move the head in flight and while feeding. The head is very characteristic in this animal, because unlike almost all other pterosaurs it is very deep; the normal skull shape in pterosaurs is rather long and thin. Despite its large size, the skull of *Dimorphodon* would not have been exceptionally heavy because it uses a light-weight construction. Most of the bones of the skull, apart from those which carry the teeth and those which surround the brain, are very thin and light and this honeycomb effect

combines strength with lightness, which is so important to any flying creature. A similar effect can be seen in the long bones of the wing, and elsewhere in the body. The bones are hollow – almost like drinking straws – with airspaces running through them, but the internal surfaces are criss-crossed by very thin spars of bone. These act as special supports to prevent the bones from kinking when bending, as they must have done, during flight.

The habits of pterosaurs have been the subject of much debate, ever since they were discovered. While it is now agreed by all that pterosaurs were aerial fliers (rather than swimmers), the debate is now about how competent they were at flying, and also about their ability to walk or run on the ground. It is understandable that pterosaurs have been compared with bats (which are mammals), and some have gone so far as to illustrate pterosaurs with bat-like legs and feet. By this, I mean that pterosaurs are given backwardly twisted legs and feet, which are, as in the case of bats, not at all suitable for motion on land. Bats are as a rule very poor walkers, being able to crawl when on the ground using their arms and claw-like thumbs to drag themselves around.

The most recent work in this area has been done by Kevin Padian (Berkeley, California) and he has been able to show that pterosaurs were active fliers, *i.e.* that they flapped their wings, rather than glided – as has been frequently suggested. He has also shown that pterosaurs were able to flap their wings by using a system of levers and muscles that is amazingly similar to that which is used by birds today; and that the wings of pterosaurs tended to be rather narrow, being attached to the waist area of the torso, rather than to the hind leg (as in bats, and other gliding mammals) as is almost always shown in illustrations. Finally, Kevin Padian believes that the hindlimbs of pterosaurs were not at all like those of bats, but resembled very closely the hindlimbs of birds and theropod dinosaurs. As a consequence, pterosaurs walked and ran like dinosaurs and birds on their hindlegs.

Some of these suggestions have been accepted very readily, as a much needed improvement in our knowledge and understanding of the group. Notably, the most accepted ideas are that they were active fliers, that they had sophisticated muscle systems for moving the wings, and that some species had narrow wings. However, there is some fossil evidence, for example, that the wing membranes of *some* pterosaurs, which have been preserved as impressions in the rock, were broad and attached to the legs. Also the greatest amount of controversy has surrounded the issue

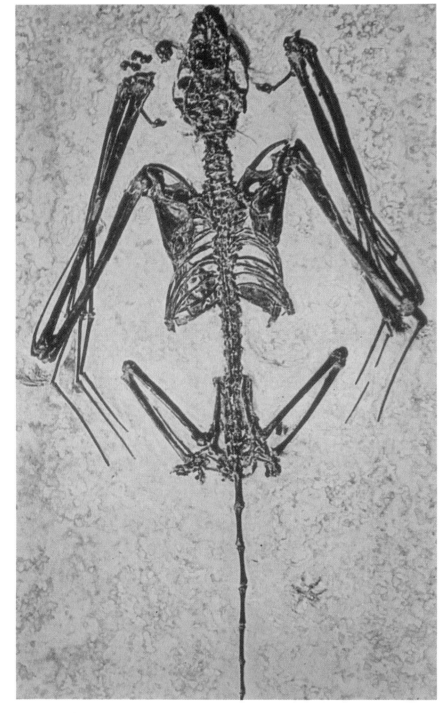

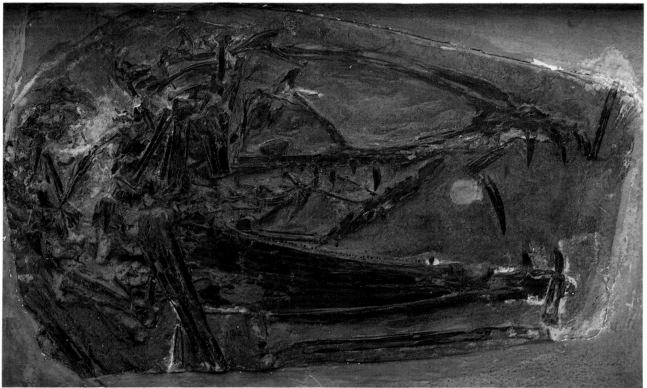

Above This is one of the earliest bat fossils known. It is complete and comes from the early Cenozoic and shows no evidence of a running ability.

Left The skull of *Dimorphodon* was large, but extremely light, being held together by a series of thin, rib-like bones.

Top right Modern bats have short hindlegs which also support the wing membrane.

Right Birds have narrower wings and legs which are free to be used for running or paddling.

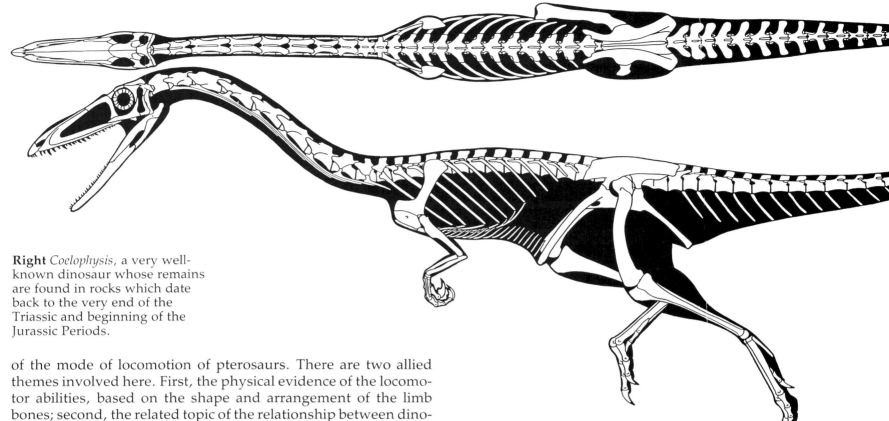

Right *Coelophysis*, a very well-known dinosaur whose remains are found in rocks which date back to the very end of the Triassic and beginning of the Jurassic Periods.

of the mode of locomotion of pterosaurs. There are two allied themes involved here. First, the physical evidence of the locomotor abilities, based on the shape and arrangement of the limb bones; second, the related topic of the relationship between dinosaurs and pterosaurs.

Padian has shown that the structure of the hips, leg bones, joints and feet are in nearly all respects similar to those of dinosaurs. The conclusion which can be derived from this is that pterosaurs, and in particular *Dimorphodon*, the main subject of Padian's work, walked and ran in a dinosaur-like way. A reconstruction based on Padian's work and featuring *Dimorphodon* running bipedally, shows its wings folded back along the sides of the tail. The tail is shown being used in typical dinosaur fashion to balance the body at the hips. As more pterosaurs are being investigated to confirm Padian's work, it is becoming clear that not all had such clearly dinosaur-like hindlimbs. It may well be that pterosaurs exhibited a range of walking or running abilities. The early ones, particularly forms such as *Dimorphodon*, retained a locomotor system reminiscent of dinosaurs, while those from later times (particularly the tail-less forms such as *Pteranodon*) became less and less able on the ground.

The question of the closeness of the relationship of pterosaurs to dinosaurs is also raised by Padian's work. In particular, the similarity in the form of early pterosaur legs and hips to those of early dinosaurs seems to indicate a closeness of ancestry, despite the striking differences to be seen in the forelimb.

The diet of *Dimorphodon* is difficult to determine with confi-

dence. Its remains are found in rocks which were laid down in shallow seas, suggesting that they may have lived upon fish caught either by scooping them from the sea surface, or diving upon them in the manner of a gannet. However, their teeth are a curious mixture of sharp stabbing types and small spiky ones. Many pterosaurs (such as *Rhamphorhynchus*) that are thought to have been fish eaters, have long, forwardly-pointed teeth for piercing the bodies of fish. It may have been that *Dimorphodon* spent at least a part of its time feeding on aerial insects, which it would have caught in the air over water or on land, or on the ground.

Dinosaurs

By early Jurassic times the various groups of dinosaurs become much more clearly separable into representatives of the two great groups, the Saurischia and the Ornithischia.

Saurishian dinosaurs are divided into two major types. First, the theropods which we have already seen at the end of the Triassic. These dinosaurs all tend to be bipedal and meat eating. The second type are the sauropodomorphs which are plant eaters and tend to be rather large and four-footed.

Left This moderately-well-preserved *Coelophysis* skull from New Mexico shows the sharp curved teeth and large eye socket of this accomplished killer.

Right *Dilophosaurus*, the largest of the early Jurassic theropods so far discovered. It comes from rocks of a similar age to those from which *Coelophysis* have been recovered. At first it was thought to be an early version of *Megalosaurus*.

Theropods

Unfortunately there are relatively few well-preserved, early Jurassic theropods. The best-known examples are *Coelophysis* which is known from rocks dating back to the very end of the Triassic and from the very earliest part of the Jurassic. Variants of the North American form of *Coelophysis* are known, such as *Syntarsus* (= *Coelophysis rhodesiensis*) from southern Africa. The differences are very slight, though, and reflect the fact that the supercontinent of Pangea still existed, and there was relatively free movement of animals from one area to another. The other type of theropod is *Dilophosaurus*.

The first remains of *Dilophosaurus* (two-ridge reptile) were discovered in 1942 during an expedition to northern Arizona organized by the University of California at Berkeley. Curiously the discovery was not made by the 'experts' on the expedition, but by a local Navajo Indian. Several skeletons, in varying degrees of completeness were found, including a nearly complete one that measured some 20 feet (6m) in length. Some years later, after the material had been examined in detail, it was described as a new species of a dinosaur named *Megalosaurus*, which is a theropod of similar size which had been known from the late Jurassic of western Europe for well over a century. Several years later still Dr Sam Welles, who had been involved in the first discovery, returned to the area where the first remains had been discovered. He was fortunate enough to discover yet more material, including a rather well-preserved skull.

Left *Massospondylus*. This specimen is mounted in the South African Museum, Cape Town. It is extraordinarily slenderly built compared to most other early sauropodomorphs and has been given a remarkably upright posture. This posture may only have been possible while it was leaning against a tree to reach the higher foliage. Other specimens of this dinosaur show evidence of the presence of a stone-laden gizzard for pounding up tough plant food.

Right This is a restoration of the skull of *Megalosaurus* (from the late Jurassic) based as far as possible on the material described by Buckland in 1824. It is clearly not at all like that of *Dilophosaurus*. Much of the skull outline is based on that of *Allosaurus*.

Below This fine skeletal restoration of *Dilophosaurus* is from the Museum of Paleontology at Berkeley, the University of California. Despite its large size, this was quite an agile dinosaur.

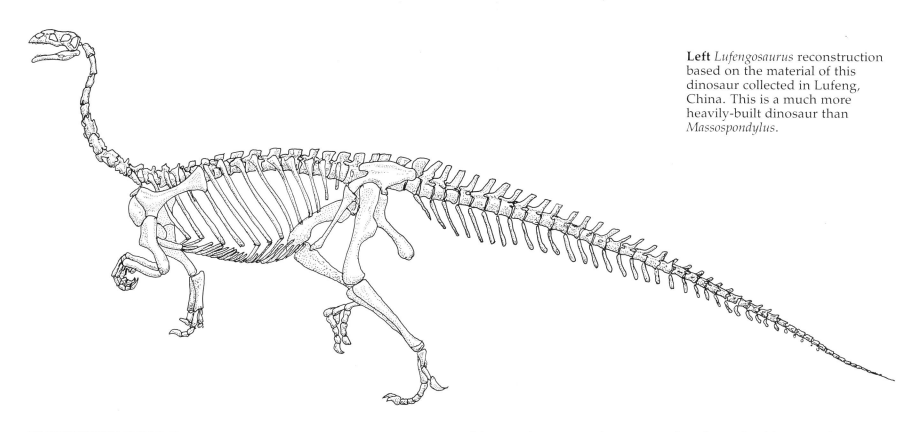

Left *Lufengosaurus* reconstruction based on the material of this dinosaur collected in Lufeng, China. This is a much more heavily-built dinosaur than *Massospondylus*.

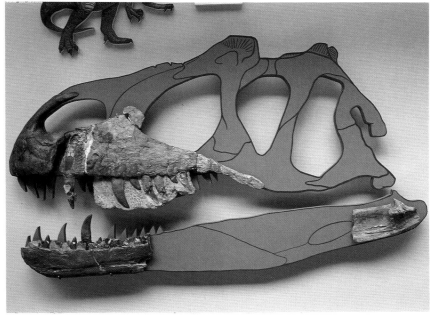

The new material indicated that the 'Megalosaurus' was much more unusual than at first thought. In particular, the skull was shown to have a pair of thin crests running along its length – the animal was therefore renamed *Dilophosaurus*. *Dilophosaurus* looks much like a wide variety of large theropods. It is the largest early theropod known to date, and can be seen as a replacement for the large and ferocious archosaurs which developed during the very late Triassic.

The hind legs were long and powerful, to support the heavy body, and the tail was long and muscular to counterbalance the front part of the body. The torso was quite short, as were the fore-limbs, but these were powerfully built, with heavy muscles and the hands had powerful talons for tearing at their prey. The neck was quite long, compared with typical archosaurs, where the pro-portions of back and neck tended to be reversed. The head was also large compared with the size of the animal, and clearly dedi-cated to a carnivorous way of life. The jaws were very long and lined with long, curved, serrated edged teeth, perfectly adapted for slicing through flesh, and operated by large muscles which ran to the top of the head through openings at the back of the skull immediately behind the eye socket. One slightly unusual feature was the curious notch in the line of the upper jaw. This is very similar to a notch that can be seen in the upper jaws of large croco-

diles, and seems to be a way of making doubly sure that prey, once caught between the jaws, is unable to struggle free.

Although it has been suggested that *Dilophosaurus* may have been a scavenger of the carcasses of dead animals, this seems un-likely to me. This was a powerfully built predator and it would have been a fast runner over relatively short distances. It would not have been a fast pursuit predator, in the way that the more lightly built *Coelophysis* may have been, but it would use stealth to get close to its prey and then catch them in a quick rush. Once caught between the jaws the prey had no chance and would have been torn and slashed by the talons of both fore- and hindlimbs, while mercilessly trapped within the jaws.

Sauropodomorphs

By contrast with the theropods, there are a variety of reasonably well-known early sauropodomorphs scattered widely, ranging from North and South America, to Europe, southern Africa and China. As with the theropods, these early herbivores seem to straddle the Triassic and Jurassic boundary. For example *Plateo-saurus* appears in both the latest Triassic and early Jurassic faunas of Europe. Representative examples of these early sauropodo-morphs include *Massospondylus* and *Lufengosaurus*, which are described below, and a variety of other forms that will be men-tioned in passing.

Massospondylus (massive vertebra) was fairly typical of one range of these early dinosaurs. They were rather lightly built, ranging up to about 20 feet (6m) in length. They were longer bodied than typical theropods, and tended to walk on four rather than two feet, although they appear to have had the option to walk in either way when it suited them.

The tail was reasonably long, enabling the body to be balanced at the hip. The hind leg resembled that of theropods, except that the foot was broader and had a very large and sharply clawed inner toe. The torso tended to be long and deep, to accommodate a large gut (essential for a plant eater) and the forelimbs tended to be only moderately long. The hands were multipurpose, being capable of acting as 'feet' for walking upon, but also having a fine set of grasping hands for picking up and holding things. The arms were considerably shorter than the legs, which suggests that much of the power and weight support came from the hindlimb. The neck was very long and slender, while the head was small and light, in marked contrast to an equivalent sized theropod, which would be expected to have a massive head.

The mode of life of these animals would appear to have been relatively mundane. Their limbs were proportioned in such a way as to suggest that they were not particularly fast runners, so could not have out-run the large predatory dinosaurs such as *Dilophosaurus* which lived at the same time. Their only likely means of defense would appear to have been the long tail, which may have served as a whip-lash at close quarters, and the large, clawed hands and feet.

Lufengosaurus (reptile from Lufeng) was an early Jurassic dinosaur from China and was considerably larger and more heavily built than *Massospondylus*. However, in most of its details it is very similar to *Plateosaurus*, so I will not spend long on a description of its anatomy.

The general body proportions of *Lufengosaurus* were similar to those of *Massospondylus*, except that it was larger and consequently, the bony skeleton more robust. Most notably the hands

Above An incomplete *Massospondylus* skeleton.

Left *Lufengosaurus* flesh restoration based on the skeletons recovered from China.

Right and far right *Massospondylus* skulls as preserved and reconstructed.

Bottom right A *Plateosaurus* specimen mounted in the American Museum of Natural History.

were large and heavily clawed, and these would have been formidable weapons of defense, as well as being used to grasp and break foliage while they were feeding.

Remains of *Lufengosaurus* seem to have been relatively common in China at this time, and this would seem to suggest that, as was the case with *Plateosaurus*, these animals were abundant, perhaps herding, creatures.

Sauropodomorphs were very successful at this time, so far as we can tell, because their remains are frequently found as fossils – which suggests that they were naturally abundant. It is possible that as in the case of *Plateosaurus* they lived in herds, so that they gained a certain amount of safety in numbers. It is also likely that the abundance of these early herbivores in various parts of the world at this time, reflects one very important feature which they all had and which no animal had previously possessed – height! The early sauropodomorphs were the first creatures that could reach high into the foliage of trees and browse unhindered. This presumably opened up a whole range of dietary niches that had never previously been exploited, and permitted the almost explosive evolution of these early, plant-eating dinosaurs.

One consequence of the dietary change undertaken by this group of dinosaurs (after all it does seem that all the earliest dinosaurs were carnivores, rather than herbivores), was the need to be able to cope adequately with a diet of plants. The teeth of all these forms are quite small when compared to those of typical carnivores. The edges of the teeth are coarsely serrated (rather than finely serrated as in the case of theropod teeth) and are well suited to tearing and cutting coarse plant fibers. However, apart from a fairly limited amount of biting and cutting, the plant tissues were not chewed up in the mouth prior to being swallowed, as is the case in mammals like ourselves. Instead, the cut lengths of plant tissue were swallowed immediately and passed into the spaceous gut. Here the food was left to slowly ferment in a bacterial broth, in a similar way to which food stays in the complex stomach of a cow. However, unlike a cow, sauropodomorphs had another set of 'teeth' in the gut. Either in the stomach walls, or in a specialized part of the gut, like a gizzard, a large number of stomach stones (gastroliths) were to be found. These gastroliths were stones that had been selected and swallowed deliberately by the animal during its life, and held in the gut to act as mill stones to pound up the plant food to a pulp, ready for digestion. The reason that we know this is that just occasionally a skeleton of this type of animal will be found with a pile of polished, angular stones, preserved in the approximate position of the stomach.

It should be noted that some scientists have proposed that these dinosaurs were in fact carnivores and scavengers. However I think that this is extremely unlikely given the type of teeth these animals had (clearly adapted for dealing with plants) and the small size of the head, compared to the body, which is unlike all other theropods of comparable size. If they were carnivores then they would seem to be singularly poorly designed for such a way of life.

The range and variety of sauropodomorphs is quite considerable, but this is in part a reflection of our relatively poor understanding of the group as a whole and the incomplete nature of at least some of the remains.

The size ranges from *Mussaurus* (mouse reptile) the complete skeleton of which I have held in the palm of one hand (this is almost certainly a very juvenile specimen), to forms such as *Rioja-saurus* (reptile from Rioja) and *Melanorosaurus* (black reptile) which grew to lengths of 36 feet (11m) or more and were very large, heavy limbed creatures. The latter types are rather similar to the sauropodomorphs of the later Jurassic, and show the very pronounced evolutionary trend toward gigantism seen among these types of dinosaurs.

Gigantism, seen early on among sauropodomorphs, would appear to be a consequence of the adoption of both an herbivorous diet and an arboreal feeding habit. Feeding upon large quantities of plant food requires a large 'fermenting tank' type of stomach, which in turn requires a large body to support it. Equally a large (and tall) body is required to reach foliage high in the trees. If the trees which found themselves subjected to such new browsers responded in the predictable way, which is to become taller to outgrow the 'new' predators of their leaves, then we have a positive reinforcement in a biological system which would result in the gigantism seen in the sauropodomorphs of the later Jurassic.

Obviously this is a self-fulfilling piece of reasoning, because we know the outcome. However, it would be interesting to know if the trees of the late Triassic and early Jurassic did show a trend toward increasing height and whether this was in response to browsing pressure. At present we – or rather I – do not know.

Ornithischians

Several types of ornithischian dinosaurs appear in the early Jurassic, ranging in type from small, slender, agile forms to rather heavy, armored types. Two of the best examples come from southern Africa (*Lesothosaurus* and *Heterodontosaurus*) although other material is known from elsewhere: *Scutellosaurus* from North America and *Scelidosaurus* from England.

Lesothosaurus (reptile from Lesotho) was a small, 3 feet (1m) long creature, typical in its body proportions of a whole range of ornithischian dinosaurs, known as ornithopods.

In its outward appearance, *Lesothosaurus* was not too dissimilar to a small theropod. It was extremely lightly built, with long, slender hind legs, and considerably shorter forelimbs. The tail was long in order to counterbalance the rest of the body at the hips, so freeing its hands for other purposes such as digging and

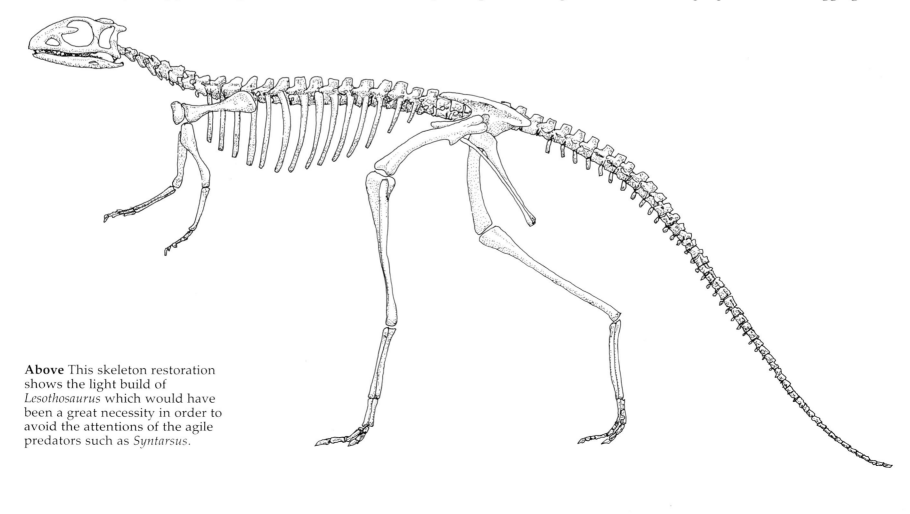

Above This skeleton restoration shows the light build of *Lesothosaurus* which would have been a great necessity in order to avoid the attentions of the agile predators such as *Syntarsus*.

Right These drawings of *Lesothosaurus* show some of the material which has been referred to in this general group of ornithopod dinosaurs. The skull is small and triangular and the teeth are similarly small and leaf-shaped in order to cut up plant tissues.

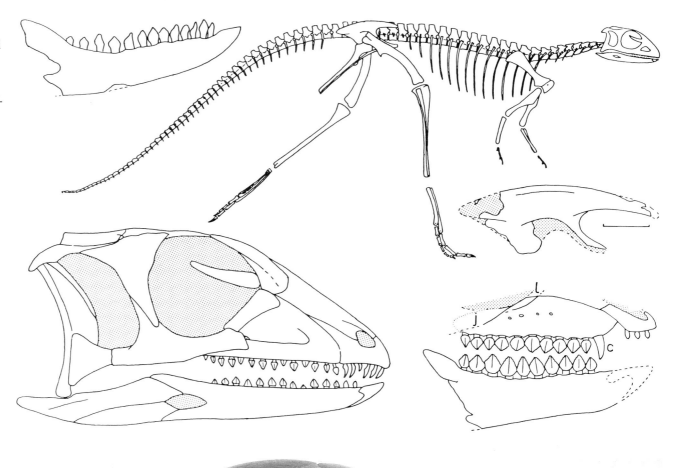

Right and below Gastroliths were stones which some herbivorous dinosaurs swallowed to help grind food in their stomachs and thus aid digestion.

collecting food. The head was small and triangular, with a large eye. The tip of the lower jaw was capped by a small triangular bone named a predentary bone, covered by a tough horny beak. Behind this, the jaws were lined with small, leaf-shaped teeth. Although a little more squat in shape, the teeth were very similar to those of early sauropodomorphs and were undoubtedly used for cutting plant, rather than animal, tissues.

It seems likely that *Lesothosaurus* was a selective feeder choosing succulent shoots, which it nipped off using its sharp horny beak. The simple teeth would have broken the food a little, but

the main job of digestion would have taken place in the gut, as was the case with the early sauropodomorphs. One very significant feature of ornithischian dinosaurs, compared with saurischian ones, was the arrangement of the hip bones. As was pointed out in Chapter 1, the pubic bone was rotated backwards to lie parallel and close to the ischium. The most important consequence of this difference was that in ornithischians the gut was able to extend further back, so that it was positioned between the legs and below the hips. As a result, in many cases ornithischians were able to retain agility and high speed by running bipedally,

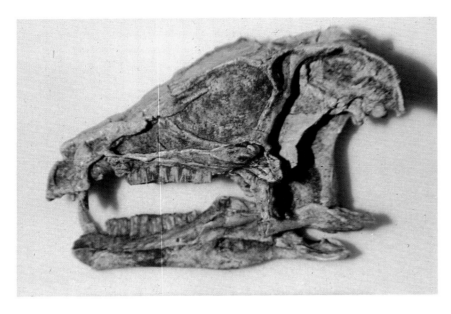

even though they were herbivores and had a heavy gut. It is notable that the only saurischian herbivores which retained any bipedal ability were the early sauropodomorphs, but even these spent only short periods of time on their hind legs alone.

The great length of the hind legs of *Lesothosaurus* would have given it a high top speed. Add to this the fact that the back and tail were held stiff by thin bony rods and what we appear to have is a very gazelle-like dinosaur. High speed would undoubtedly have been its only means of defense, and would have been necessary to avoid the attentions of high-speed predators such as *Syntarsus*, which has been found in similarly aged deposits in the same area.

Similar in size to *Lesothosaurus*, *Heterodontosaurus* (mixed tooth reptile) was a small ornithischian now rather better known because of the description of the entire skeleton which appeared just a few years ago. Although it appears very similar to *Lesothosaurus*, there are a number of very important differences. The hands were large, and very reminiscent of early sauropodo-

Far left The cast of the skull of *Heterodontosaurus* shows the large, canine-like tusks.

Right The complete skeleton of *Heterodontosaurus* as found, a very well-preserved example.

Below An early Jurassic scene featuring *Scutellosaurus* (left foreground) and two *Heterodontosaurus*.

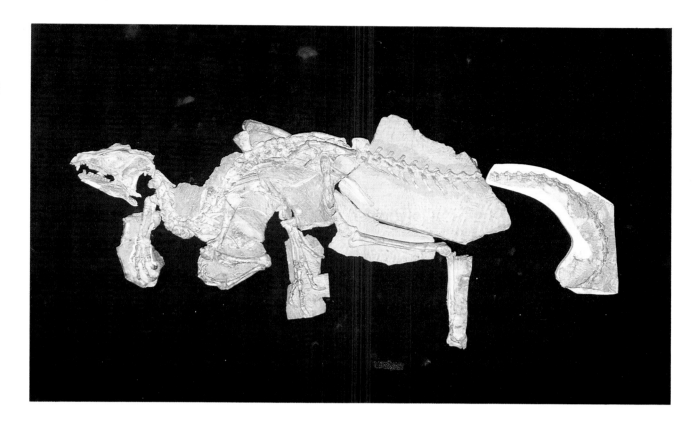

morphs, and it is not possible to say with confidence that *Lesothosaurus* had equally large hands. Most of the important differences reside in the head, however.

The skull is solidly constructed, and much stronger than that of *Lesothosaurus*. It has a predentary beak, as is usual for ornithischians, but behind this the jaw is very different. The name of this dinosaur comes from the fact that, unlike most reptiles whose teeth tend all to be the same, the teeth of this dinosaur are quite different along the jaw. At the tip of the upper jaw there are small, spiky teeth, behind which there is a large, curved, stabbing tooth, and behind this there is a row of closely-packed, chisel-edged teeth. The chisel-edged teeth are also unusual, when compared to the arrangement seen in *Lesothosaurus*, because they are set into recesses along the length of the jaws – so-called cheek recesses.

From the structure of the skull, teeth and jaws it is clear that *Heterodontosaurus* was very different from *Lesothosaurus* in the way that it fed upon plants: *Heterodontosaurus* was a chewer! Pieces of vegetation were nipped off using the tough beak and small nipping teeth, and then passed back into the mouth to be chewed between the chisel-like cheek teeth. The presence of fleshy cheeks outside the jaws prevented food being chewed from falling out of the sides of the mouth, and this important feature is seen in the majority of ornithischians. It is likely therefore that *Heterodontosaurus* was able to feed on tougher food than *Lesothosaurus*.

The large stabbing teeth have not yet been explained. These are normally found in meat-eating types, which this clearly was not. They were most probably used, as tusks are in pigs and wild boars, for defense against predators, or as social signals. It may be that tusks such as these are only found in males of the species, but the evidence for this is not yet entirely convincing.

An approximate contemporary of *Dilophosaurus* and *Coelophysis*, as well as the other ornithischians described here, is *Scutellosaurus* (bony plated reptile) from Arizona. From a partial skeleton

that has been described, it is clear that this was again a small dinosaur. It appears to have been very similar to *Lesothosaurus* in most respects, but differed in one crucial aspect, which is that it possessed armored skin. Many small cap-shaped bony plates were found associated with the skeleton, which are the remnants of this armoring.

In general this dinosaur appears to have had slightly shorter legs than *Lesothosaurus*, and was therefore a little slower at running. Perhaps it relied upon its defensive armor for protection against carnivores, rather than great speed (as in the case of *Lesothosaurus*) or ability to fight back (as with *Heterodontosaurus*).

Discovered in the 1850s, *Scelidosaurus* (arm reptile) is similar to the more recently discovered *Scutellosaurus* in that it, too, was armor plated. *Scelidosaurus* is known from several skeletons in various states of completeness. The largest so far discovered is about 13 feet (4m) long, and this is far and away the largest of the early ornithischians discovered to date. In most respects *Scelidosaurus* was similar to the other forms so far described, except that its limbs, in order to support the heavier body, were rather heavier and therefore slower moving. The animal also appears to have moved on all fours rather than bipedally, as has been the case with the previous types.

The head was partly armored, with a large bony plate attached to the side of the lower jaw, and the beginnings of bony plating on the skull roof. The jaws and teeth were similar to *Lesothosaurus*, indicating that *Scelidosaurus* did not chew food in the way described for *Heterodontosaurus*, but simply snapped off pieces of plant and swallowed them whole, relying on digestion in a large stomach. To date it has not been possible to prove decisively that *Scelidosaurus* had gastroliths as an to aid digestion, as was the case in early sauropodomorphs.

The heavy armoring in this form would have been a useful defense against large predatory dinosaurs such as *Dilophosaurus*.

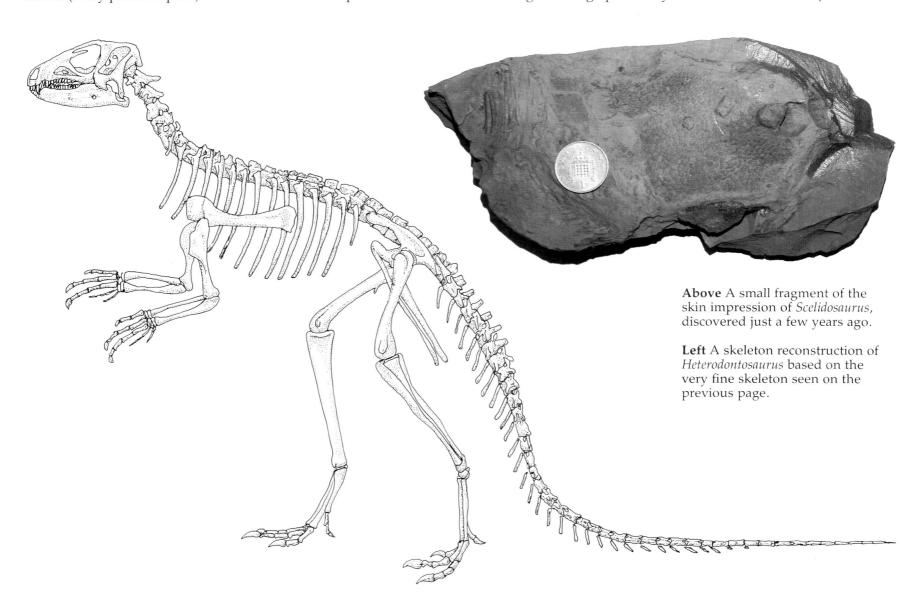

Above A small fragment of the skin impression of *Scelidosaurus*, discovered just a few years ago.

Left A skeleton reconstruction of *Heterodontosaurus* based on the very fine skeleton seen on the previous page.

In early Jurassic times dinosaurs were beginning to increase in number and variety on land. The saurischian theropods, which were among the earliest dinosaurs to appear, began to diversify into small nimble types (the general equivalent of small dogs and cats today) and larger more fearsome types (broadly similar to the large cats of Africa and Asia). The saurischian sauropodomorphs also began to diversify into small, medium and large sized types as a means of exploiting the full range of plants

Ornithischians appeared somewhat later than saurischians, making their debut in the earliest Jurassic, but already showing signs of an early rise in diversity in the fact that they are mostly small forms. But they show a surprisingly wide range of lifestyles: fast runners, fighters and armored forms, all of which can eventually be traced to types that can be seen in the later Mesozoic. As herbivores, the ornithischians were direct competition for the sauropodomorphs and it will be interesting to see how these two groups manage to coexist in later times.

Above The mounted skeleton of *Scutellosaurus*, as exhibited in the Museum of Northern Arizona.

Left Bones of the side of the face from a new specimen of *Scelidosaurus*, collected from Charmouth.

Below A reconstruction of the skeleton of *Scelidosaurus*, based on a nearly complete skeleton discovered in the 1850s.

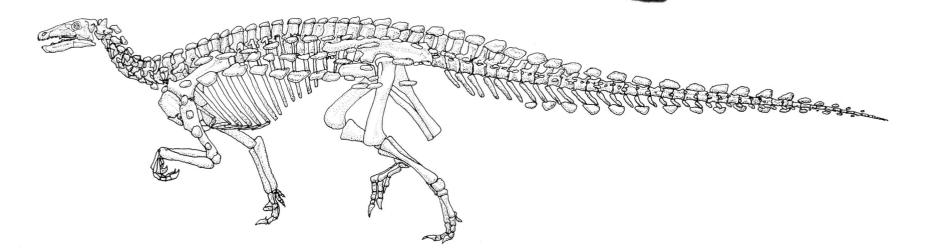

CHAPTER 5

The Late Jurassic: The Time of the Giant Sauropods

The late Jurassic saw dinosaurs become both numerous and enormously varied. It was in rocks of this particular age that the remarkable dinosaur discoveries were made in North America toward the end of the last century, bringing dinosaurs most forcibly to the attention of the whole world. In the same way, it has been the remarkable new dinosaur discoveries made in China over the last ten years, principally within the late Jurassic rocks of southern central China, that have reawakened much interest in these types of fossil.

The sheer size of many dinosaurs that lived at this time is one of the most extraordinary features. Land animals seem regularly to have grown to well over 65 feet (20m) in length, and their weights, which are singularly difficult to estimate with confidence, range upwards of 20 or 30 tonnes in some cases. So big and heavy are some dinosaurs that it is hard to believe that they ever managed to move around on land. Indeed for many years it was fashionable to illustrate some of the very largest dinosaurs wallowing in swamps for precisely this reason – so that their body weight could be offset by bouyancy in water. These views have changed completely over the past 20 years, and most of the skeletal adaptations in the very large dinosaurs can be seen to be specifically to allow them to move around on land with maximum efficiency. This is not to say that big dinosaurs never wallowed! The point is that they were not *obliged* to live in water habitually – it is quite possible that they wallowed in the same way that elephants do today, to cool themselves and clean and refresh the skin.

Continental movements

During the middle and into the late Jurassic Period the continental separation of Pangea into the northern land mass of Laurasia and the southern Gondwanaland continued. Rising sea levels following from the onset of tectonic movement produced an extensive shallow sea in the area between what was to become North America and Europe (the beginning of the Atlantic Ocean),

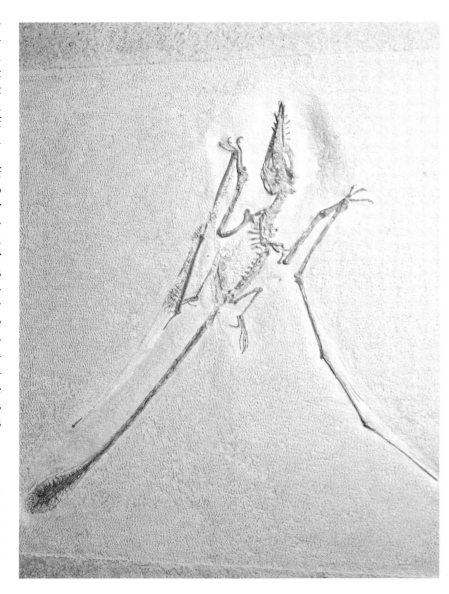

Above A well-preserved fossil skeleton of the late Jurassic pterosaur *Rhamphorhynchus*. It is preserved in fine-grained limestone which provides excellent preservation.

Left The map shows the continental positions in the Jurassic Period.

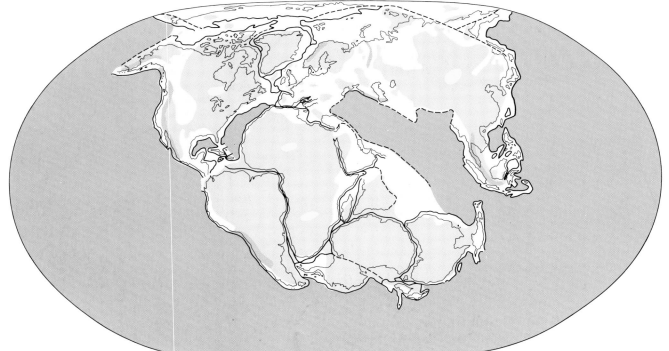

Late Jurassic Period
Kimmeridgian Stage (145 m years ago)

Vegetation		Tundra & ice
Mountain		Continental sea
Desert		Deep ocean

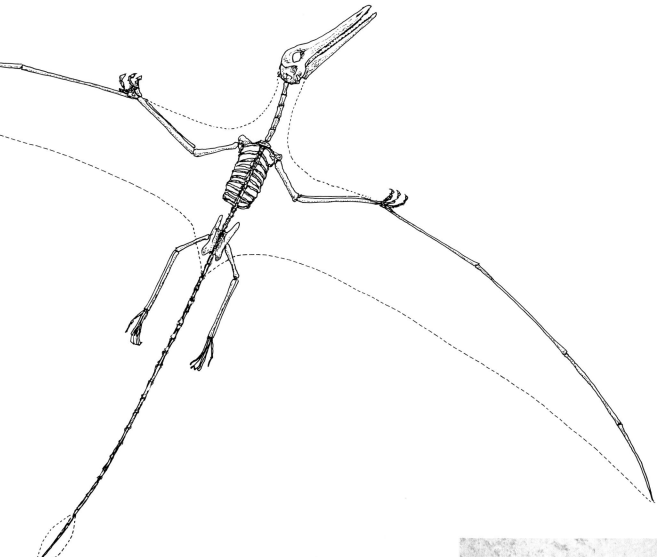

Left A *Rhamphorhynchus* skeleton reconstruction, showing the outline of the wing membrane and the small tail flap. The wings are not attached to the legs, unlike bats, so giving the legs much more mobility.

Below *Pterodactylus* is a smaller pterosaur built rather differently than *Rhamphorhynchus*, with a short tail and a more-slender and smaller-toothed snout. It seems likely that *Pterodactylus* was an insectivore, while the much larger-toothed *Rhamphorhynchus* was a fish feeder; the long, forwardly pointing teeth at the front of the jaws are ideal for spearing fish from the water surface.

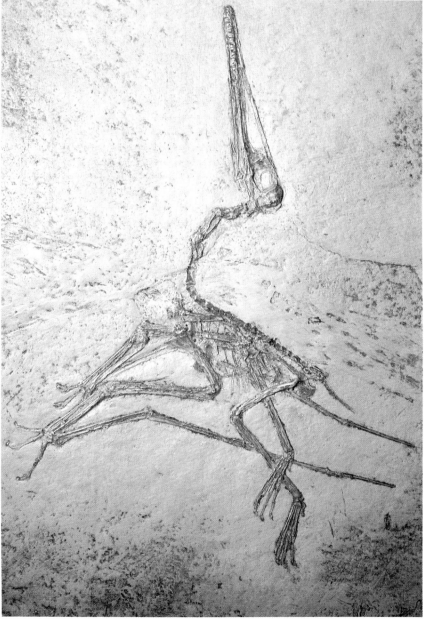

and the connection between southern Europe and northern Africa became very irregular as Africa began to move southwards. Also important at this time was what was happening in Asia. A large shallow sea (known as the Turgai Sea) ran from north to south separating Europe from Asia.

It is therefore apparent that there were a number of provinces, which were at least partly isolated by shallow seas during the later part of the Jurassic. Most important was the separation between North America and Europe from Asia, which led to the evolution in isolation of the Asian fauna of dinosaurs. This explains why it is that many of the dinosaurs recently discovered in the late Jurassic of China are new and different types. Of slightly less importance was the separation of North America and Europe from Africa and the other southern continents. This was not a complete separation until the Cretaceous Period and animals were therefore allowed to cross between these areas at least partly during the Jurassic.

Climates and floras

In general it seems that the Jurassic Period was one of very mild, warm climatic conditions, little different from the conditions established at the beginning of the Period. There were no polar ice caps, so the latitudinal bands were very broad, with warm conditions extending to high latitudes where today we would expect arctic or subarctic conditions.

As far as plants were concerned, ferns spread widely and formed much of the low ground cover (grasses did not evolve until long after the extinction of the dinosaurs, and it is at least possible that ferns served as the equivalent sort of low ground cover vegetation at this time). In addition the cycads, ginkgos, horsetails and coniferous trees of many types became abundant.

Mammals

These hardly differed from those that appeared in the latest Triassic and early Jurassic. All were small (in the region of 4-6 inches [10-15cms] long), shrew-like creatures, most of which were insectivores, although a few may have taken to a diet of plants, and had appropriately modified teeth to grind up tough plants.

Pterosaurs

During the late Jurassic two groups of pterosaur are found, examples of which are *Rhamphorhynchus* and *Pterodactylus* respectively.

Rhamphorhynchus (narrow beak) comes from the late Jurassic of West Germany, and is known from some very fine fossils, a few of which even preserve details of the wing membrane in the sediment surrounding the fossilized bones. In its general body form, this pterosaur was very similar to *Dimorphodon*, including the long stiffened bony tail. Again one or two of the better preserved specimens show that there was a small kite-shaped flap of skin on the very end of the tail, which was presumably a part of the flight control and guidance system.

The main difference with earlier pterosaurs such as *Dimorphodon* can be seen in the shape of the skull. In *Rhamphorhynchus* the skull is much lower and longer, and the teeth are fewer in number and arranged as forwardly-angled spikes. The diet of these pterosaurs was most probably fish, which could have been speared between the jaws either from the water surface as they skimmed over the waves, or by diving into the water.

The other example, *Pterodactylus* (wing finger), represents a new sort of pterosaur, which appeared in the late Jurassic, and its remains have been found in the same deposits that have revealed *Rhamphorhynchus*. The most obvious difference when these forms are compared is the lack of a long, bony tail. This suggests that *Pterodactylus* was much more unstable, and therefore a more maneuverable flier than forms with long tails. Another difference, which is a little less obvious, concerns the skull which is even longer than that of *Rhamphorhynchus*, and has fewer and smaller teeth. These differences represent the beginning of a trend within similar types of pterosaurs culminating in the complete loss of teeth and their replacement by a long horny beak similar to that of a bird. There are also slightly more subtle differences in the shape and length of the neck bones.

Pterodactylus was a small, sparrow-sized pterosaur, which undoubtedly fed upon flying insects, which it would have caught on the wing. They were bat-like creatures, except that unlike bats they relied on eyesight to see and catch their prey in daylight, rather than using echolocation at night as bats do.

Small though *Pterodactylus* was, it gave rise to some gigantic pterosaurs in the Cretaceous. The tailed pterosaurs seem to have been doomed once the short-tailed forms arrived because none survived the close of the Jurassic Period.

Dinosaurs

A great variety of dinosaurs are known in late Jurassic times, representing almost every conceivable terrestrial type. The best examples come from North America and China, but many others are known from most continents.

Theropods

Theropod dinosaurs can be divided into little ones (known as coelurosaurs) and big ones (generally known as carnosaurs). There are some very well-known examples of both of these groups in Jurassic times.

Above The fossil remains of the skeleton of *Compsognathus*, preserved in a limestone slab.

Right A new specimen of *Compsognathus* from Nice, France.

Left *Ornitholestes*. A reconstruction based on partial remains from Wyoming.

Two rather different types of coelurosaur (cavity tailed reptile) known at this time are *Compsognathus* and *Ornitholestes*. *Compsognathus* (pretty jaw) is known from two exquisitely preserved skeletons, one from Bavaria discovered in the 1850s, the other from southern France discovered a few years ago. The largest specimen, the one from France, is about 4½ feet (1.4m) long.

Reconstructions of this animal show it to have been lightly built, with long slender legs and narrow three-toed feet. The tail of *Compsognathus* appears to have been very long and whip-like, the torso short, the neck long and slender and the head large in proportion to the rest of the body. One particularly unusual characteristics of this creature is that it had only two functional fingers on each hand (there was a rudiment of the third finger, but this was not of any use).

It seems obvious that *Compsognathus* was a swift moving predator of small creatures. The teeth were rather few in number and quite small and spiky, suggesting that these dinosaurs may have taken insects as part of their diet (in the manner of modern lizards). There is some interesting additional evidence on the actual diet of this creature preserved in the fossil skeleton from Bavaria. In the area of the body cavity, approximately where the stomach would have been, there are the jumbled remains of the skeleton of a small lizard (*Bavarisaurus*), which was evidently the last meal of this dinosaur. The lizard itself was clearly small and must in life have been quite agile and fast moving. The fact that *Compsognathus* was able to catch and eat this little lizard is good testimony to the keen sight, agility and quick reactions of this dinosaur.

Swimming *Compsognathus*? The new specimen from Canjuers, near Nice in France has been the subject of a little controversy, because the original work on the skeleton led to the suggestion that this was an aquatic dinosaur. It was thought to have preserved the impressions of a flipper along the edges of its arms. This seemed to suggest that the dinosaur used to swim habitually – the first dinosaur ever to have been a swimmer. Detailed study of the material by others does not seem to agree with this suggestion, and it now seems generally agreed that the French specimen was simply a larger version of the Bavarian specimen and a fully terrestrial type. Rather, the remains of *Compsognathus* were found in shallow sea water sediments, along with many remains of pterosaurs, fish and other sea creatures, and its remains were probably washed in from the surrounding land.

Another very interesting fossil from the same deposits – *Archaeopteryx*, the first bird – shows a surprisingly large number of similarities between early birds and some small theropod dinosaurs. This subject will be fully discussed in Chapter 10.

The other example of a coelurosaur, *Ornitholestes* (bird robber), comes from late Jurassic rocks, among the remains of some huge sauropod dinosaurs. Most of what is known of this animal comes from a single, and incomplete, skeleton from Bone Cabin Quarry in Wyoming which was discovered just at the turn of the century.

In general details the skeleton of this animal is not too different from that of *Compsognathus* – though *Ornitholestes* was considerably larger, being over 6½ feet (2m) long. The body was balanced at the hips by the long whip-like tail, leaving the arms and hands free to be used as grasping organs. Unlike *Compsognathus*, the hand was long and has three sharply clawed fingers; this would have given the animal excellent reach and grasping ability, which may have been essential for tackling large and stronger prey. The

Left A very fine exhibition of the skeletons of *Allosaurus* (left) and *Camptosaurus*, its potential prey. Both of these species are found in quarries of the same age.

Top right A fine skull of the large carnosaur *Allosaurus* (see below also), showing the large teeth, spaces for jaw muscles (which also reduced the weight of the skull), and the curious 'knob' just above and in front of the eye. This may have been used for visual recognition of individuals. The lower jaw has been detached in this photograph.

Right Part of the upper jaw of *Allosaurus* in inner view.

Far right The entire right hind foot of *Allosaurus*, showing the sharp, talon-like claws used to rip open its prey.

skull was also larger and more strongly built than that of *Compsognathus*, the eye socket was large (indicating good vision) and the jaws were thicker and stronger, with large, serrated teeth.

Ornitholestes was clearly a more powerful type of predator than *Compsognathus*. It is often illustrated feeding on early birds since it lived at about the same time as *Archaeopteryx*, but judging from the skeleton, it would seem more likely that its prey may have been small herbivorous dinosaurs (such as *Dryosaurus* or even other small theropods if it could catch them).

Carnosaurs (meat reptiles) are larger types of theropod and, like the coelurosaurs, rather similarly built. Several carnosaurs are known, some in good detail, and a few of these will be mentioned below.

Allosaurus (strange reptile) was a very large theropod, the largest examples of which may have attained a length of 39 feet

(12m). Examples have been found in rocks of late Jurassic age in Colorado, Wyoming and Utah. In Utah, in particular, many thousands of bones from skeletons of this animal have been recovered. This is extremely unusual because large carnosaurs are very rarely found even as isolated fossil bones, let alone as complete skeletons.

The skeleton of *Allosaurus* is massive, compared to those of the coelurosaurs which we have seen so far. In similar fashion the tail is long and heavy to counterbalance the body at the hips. The legs are strong and pillar-like and the feet are very large, with three sharply-clawed, forwardly-pointing toes and a much shorter, backwardly-pointing first toe. The back is short and strong, as is the neck, which has prominent projections for the attachment of powerful neck- and head-moving muscles. The arms are very short, compared with the hind legs, and also compared to the

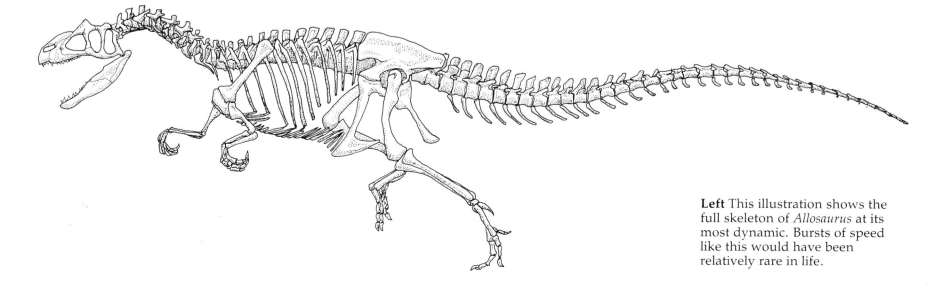

Left This illustration shows the full skeleton of *Allosaurus* at its most dynamic. Bursts of speed like this would have been relatively rare in life.

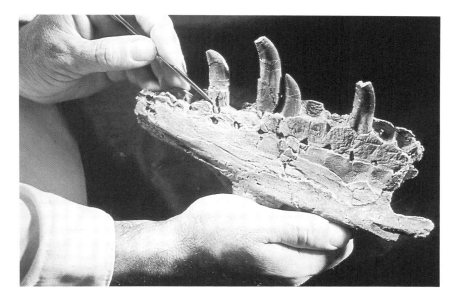

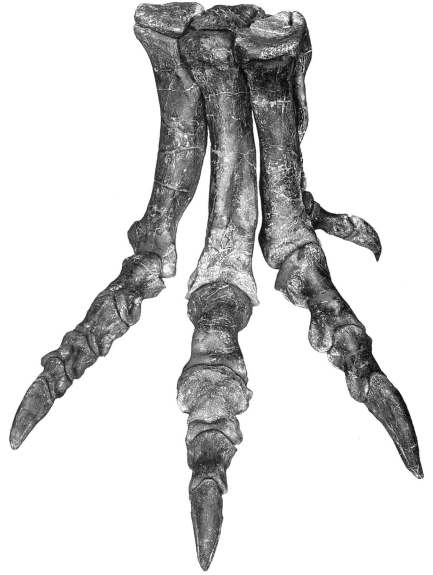

arms of coelurosaurs. The arms were clearly strong and well muscled, and had strongly clawed, three-fingered hands. Quite why the arms should be so small in these dinosaurs, when they would clearly be of use in grasping prey, is uncertain. Nevertheless the trend toward short forelimbs seems to be very strong among these types of dinosaur and culminates in the ridiculously small arms and hands of forms like *Carnotaurus* and *Tyrannosaurus*.

The head of *Allosaurus* was very large, almost 3 feet (1m) long in some examples. The jaws were heavy and lined with very long, curved, steak-knife-like teeth. The jaws could open very wide, in order to take massive bites at their prey, and huge jaw-closing muscles filled the spaces at the back of the skull, behind the eye socket. One slight peculiarity of this dinosaur is the fact that the top of the skull, just in front of and above the eye, has a curiously hollowed out lump of bone (like a short horn). Many theropods do seem to have some sort or ornamentation (such as *Dilophosaurus*) and this may well have been for social recognition purposes.

Allosaurus was clearly a devastatingly effective predator. Its large size and weight meant that it could attack most large animals of the time. If, as is suggested by the large numbers that have been discovered together, they lived and hunted in packs then they may even have taken huge sauropods if they attacked in cooperation with others. In the same way, a pack of Cape Hunting Dogs can today attack and bring down large adult Wildebeest.

It would seem that *Allosaurus* was so large that a sustained fast running way of life would have been unlikely. So the very dynamic image is one that it may have adopted for very short bursts of speed only in order to ambush and then rapidly subdue its prey.

Ceratosaurus (horned reptile) is a carnosaur which has been found in the same deposits as *Allosaurus*, but it is typically smaller, with a possible maximum size of 20 feet (6m), and great difference in outward appearance.

The skull had the main features of that of *Allosaurus*, but in addition to the small horns seen just above and in front of the eyes, there was a large horn in the middle of the snout, just behind the nose. The only logical function of such a horn was as a

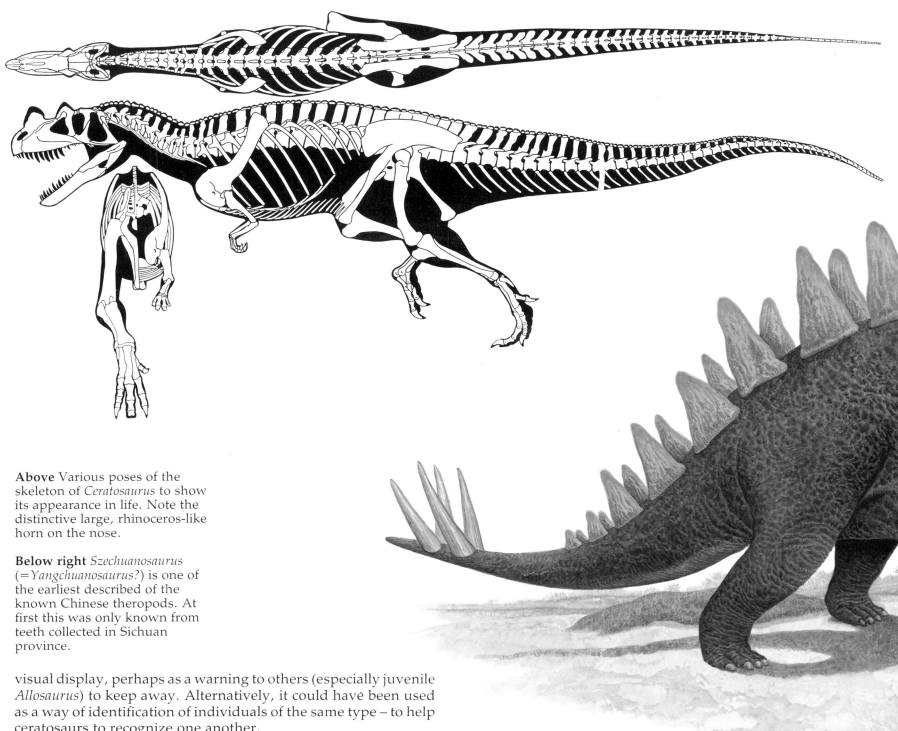

Above Various poses of the skeleton of *Ceratosaurus* to show its appearance in life. Note the distinctive large, rhinoceros-like horn on the nose.

Below right *Szechuanosaurus* (=*Yangchuanosaurus?*) is one of the earliest described of the known Chinese theropods. At first this was only known from teeth collected in Sichuan province.

visual display, perhaps as a warning to others (especially juvenile *Allosaurus*) to keep away. Alternatively, it could have been used as a way of identification of individuals of the same type – to help ceratosaurs to recognize one another.

The hand was also different from that of *Allosaurus* because it had four, rather than three fingers. And there appears to have been a row of small bony plates running down the back of the animal, above the spine – reminiscent of the arrangement in archosaurs in the Triassic.

The rarity of *Ceratosaurus* compared with the abundance of *Allosaurus* tends to suggest that *Ceratosaurus* may have been a solitary hunter, rather than a pack hunter. But the evidence for this is very slender and largely negative *i.e.* based on lack of evidence.

Yangchuanosaurus is an *Allosaurus*-like carnosaur from the late Jurassic of Sichuan, China. It is known from several specimens, including a nearly complete skeleton. In all of its most general details this dinosaur resembles *Allosaurus*, and can be considered as the Asian equivalent of the North American form. One skull of this creature is very large, measuring over 3 feet (1m) long, confirming that the size range of this dinosaur was similar to that of the North American allosaurs.

The most obvious visual difference between allosaurs and *Yangchuanosaurus* seems to be in the skull, where the tip of the snout is shorter and more sloping, and in the presence of a distinctly roughened ridge running along the snout in the area above the nose.

Another, smaller carnosaur from Sichuan, is *Gazosaurus*,

Left A late Jurassic scene from China with the stegosaur *Tuojiangosaurus* to the left and its probable predator *Yangchuanosaurus*, both of which have been collected in Sichuan.

known from several partial skeletons. Although it would seem to fit into the size range occupied by *Ceratosaurus* in North America, this type did not have the characteristic horned snout of the latter species.

Numerous other late Jurassic carnosaur names are known in the literature, but many are based on rather poor remains (odd bones, rather than complete or near complete skeletons) and this makes comparison with forms from elsewhere very difficult, if not impossible.

Some particularly well known forms are: *Megalosaurus*, the earliest described dinosaur from the late Jurassic of England; *Eustreptospondylus* from England and *Priveteausaurus* from France; *Marshosaurus* from North America; and *Szechuanosaurus* from China.

Sauropodomorphs

The herbivorous saurischians were particularly abundant at this time in Earth's history, and from what we can see of their remains they dominated the late Jurassic in all ways. After their begin-

nings in the Late Triassic, the early sauropodomorphs rapidly gave way to the gigantic sauropods in the later Jurassic. They can be divided very approximately into two general types, depending upon the way that their bodies were constructed: the high-shouldered, giraffe-like, brachiosaurs and the low-shouldered apatosaurs. There are of course, as with any man-made distinctions such as this, examples which do not fit neatly into either category, but this at least gives us a way of coming to terms with the range and variety of animals involved.

The best example of the brachiosaurs is the animal which gave its name to the group: *Brachiosaurus* (arm reptile).

The name comes from the prodigious length of its arms (forelimbs) compared to its hindlimbs. The remains of this animal were first described from material collected from Colorado. The information was very incomplete, but, fortunately both fore- and hindlimbs were preserved intact. The bones of what was left of this animal were enormous; those of the back showed signs of having been sculpted especially to reduce their weight and the legs were immensely long. When finally described, around the turn of the century, it was proposed that these sorts of animals were fully terrestrial (rather than swamp dwellers, as was thought at the time) and fed on high browse in the tree tops, in the manner of enormous giraffes. A few years later more remains of brachiosaurs were recovered, but this time in Tanzania (east Africa) and within a varied fauna of dinosaurs. The material was taken to Berlin, where it proved possible to reconstruct an entire brachiosaur, which is today still the largest dinosaur on display anywhere in the world – it measures some 74 feet (23m) long and stands almost 39 feet (12m) high.

The full skeleton confirms that *Brachiosaurus* was remarkably giraffe-like in its proportions. The immense arms raise the shoulders higher than the hips so that the back slopes upward (unlike all other sauropods) and into the huge neck. The neck bones are very long and were controlled by a system of neck muscles and long tendons (like the steel hawsers of a crane). In fact, it is probably best to visualize the whole animal as an immense crane in order to understand its structure better. The neck was like a crane jib, which could raise the head up into the tree tops; the main part of the body served as the stable base for balance, while the head was being lifted, and also as a storage area for the food as it was collected. The legs gave them mobility to visit other trees, and the tail was used to assist with balance while walking. The tail is shorter than most sauropod tails, but is important not

only as a balancing aid, but as the place of attachment of the important leg moving muscles and so could not be lost altogether.

The head was quite large, being up to 3 feet (1m) in length, even though it appears small compared to the size of the animal itself. The teeth are large, blunt, chisel-like pegs, which were presumably very effective at nipping off pieces of vegetation. As was described in the earlier sauropodomorphs, little chewing of food took place in the mouth, the food being passed almost immediately to the stomach which acted as a gigantic fermentation tank, aided by a stone-laden gizzard no doubt.

One slightly curious feature of the head of *Brachiosaurus* is the that fact the nostrils are very large and found near the top of the head, just in front of the eyes. This, and the very long neck of this creature, were used as the main argument in favor of an aquatic way of life. They were reconstructed walking on the bottom of lakes, using their long necks to reach the surface to breathe.

Many illustrations found in older books on dinosaurs show *Brachiosaurus* in just such a scene. It is now, however, generally accepted that they were neither aquatic nor even amphibious animals. Instead, they had narrow, elephant-like feet for walking on firm ground, rather than the broad feet necessary for walking on soft mud; they also had narrow chests typical of land animals, rather than broad, barrel-like ones. More important still, it has been calculated that the water pressure at the depths at which

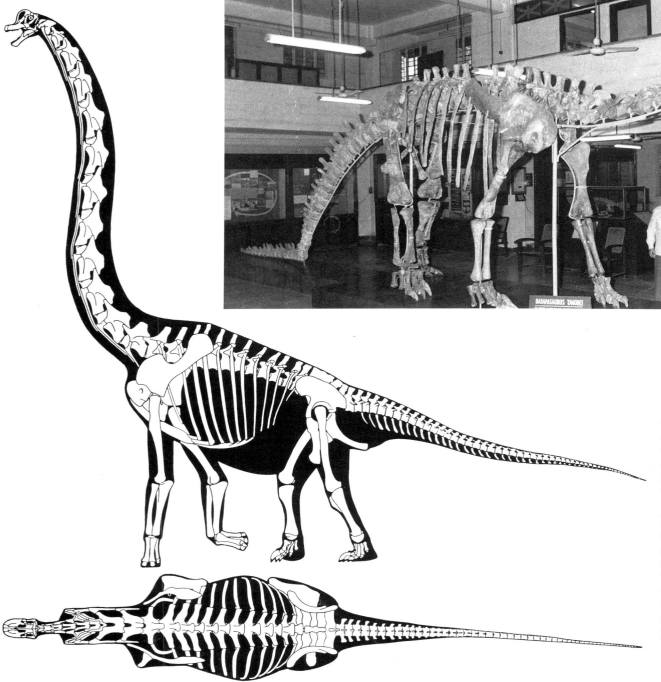

Above *Barapasaurus*, the only well-known sauropod from India, on display at the Indian Statistical Institute, Calcutta.

Left Skeleton restorations of the enormous dinosaur *Brachiosaurus*, showing its extremely giraffe-like appearance. Note the very large neck bones and the shortness of the tail.

Right The first and only skeleton of *Brachiosaurus* to be mounted and displayed in the world. This specimen was collected from Tanzania in the early years of this century by a team of German geologists, and is now displayed in the Museum of Natural History, East Berlin.

15

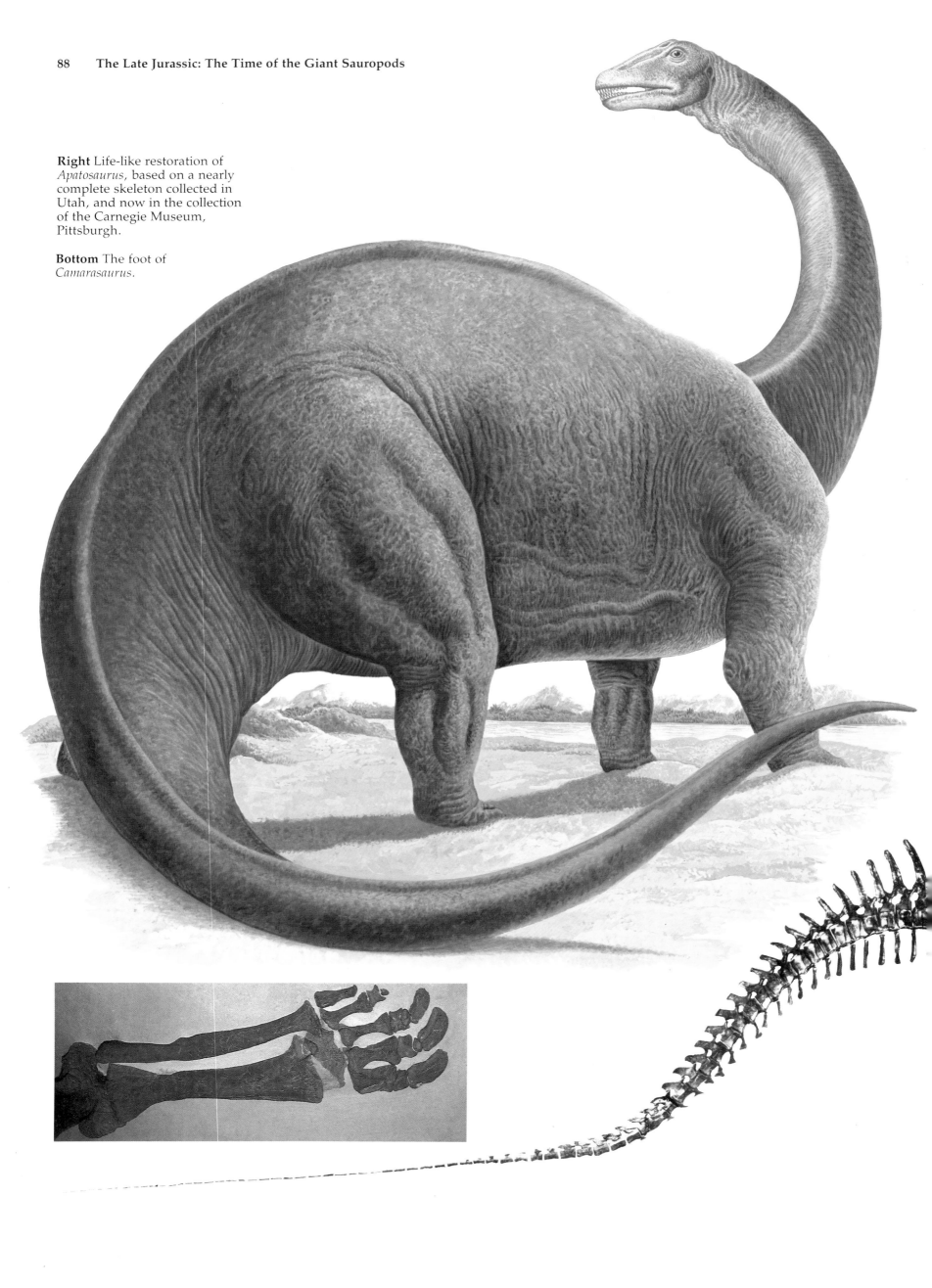

Right Life-like restoration of *Apatosaurus*, based on a nearly complete skeleton collected in Utah, and now in the collection of the Carnegie Museum, Pittsburgh.

Bottom The foot of *Camarasaurus*.

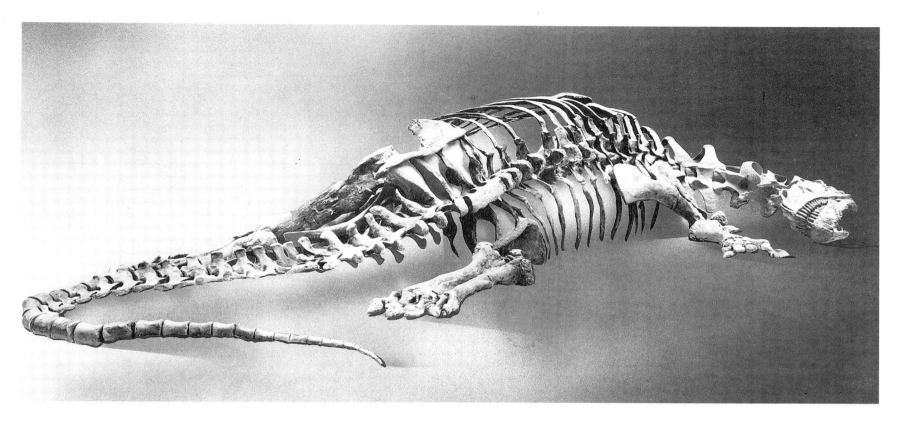

Brachiosaurus was imagined to have lived would have crushed the rib cage and lungs of the animal – it would have been impossible to breathe!

Another sauropod which is often grouped with brachiosaurs is *Camarasaurus* (chambered reptile). This dinosaur is best known from a complete skeleton of a young individual about 20 feet (6m) long that was found in Utah at the Dinosaur National Monument and described in the 1920s. It is probable that the carcass of this animal was rapidly buried in a river or estuary after it had died, otherwise the carcass would have been scavenged by predatory dinosaurs and its bones scattered.

The proportions of the animal are different from those of *Brachiosaurus*; the neck was not so long and the forelimbs, although quite long, did not exceed the length of the hindlimbs, so the back was roughly horizontal in life, rather than sloping upwards. The greatest resemblance is to be found in the head. The head of the young *Camarasaurus* was very similar to that of *Brachiosaurus*, except that the snout region was not so long, and the nostrils not as prominent. It should be noted, however, that these differences were less in the skulls of larger, adult camarasaurs. The teeth were also very similar, being the same sort of blunt, chisel-like teeth which were clearly used for nipping off vegetation. This type of tooth is very different from the long, narrow, pencil-shaped sort found in apatosaurs. Large skulls of *Camarasaurus* collected in Utah, suggest that this dinosaur may have attained lengths of 58 feet (18m) or more.

Very distinct from the brachiosaurs are the apatosaurs. The group takes its name from *Apatosaurus* (formerly named *Brontosaurus*), which was recovered from quarries in Colorado, Wyoming and Utah. Much confusion surrounded the early discoveries

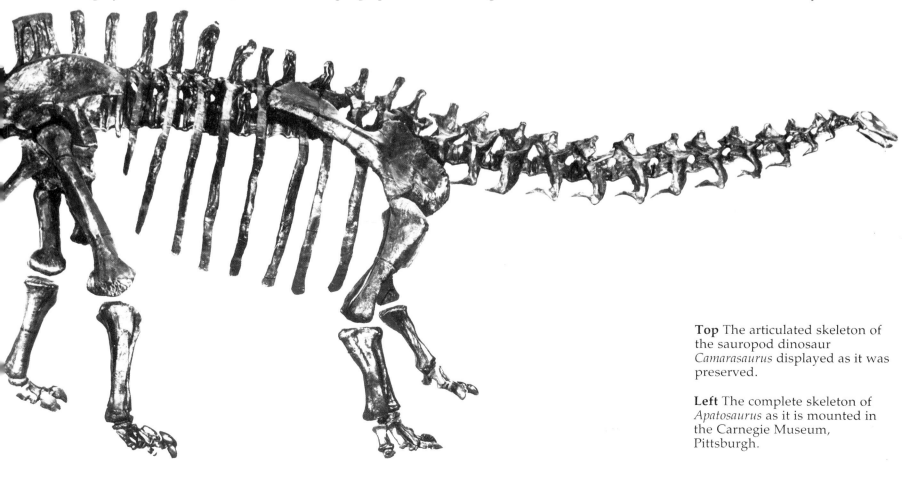

Top The articulated skeleton of the sauropod dinosaur *Camarasaurus* displayed as it was preserved.

Left The complete skeleton of *Apatosaurus* as it is mounted in the Carnegie Museum, Pittsburgh.

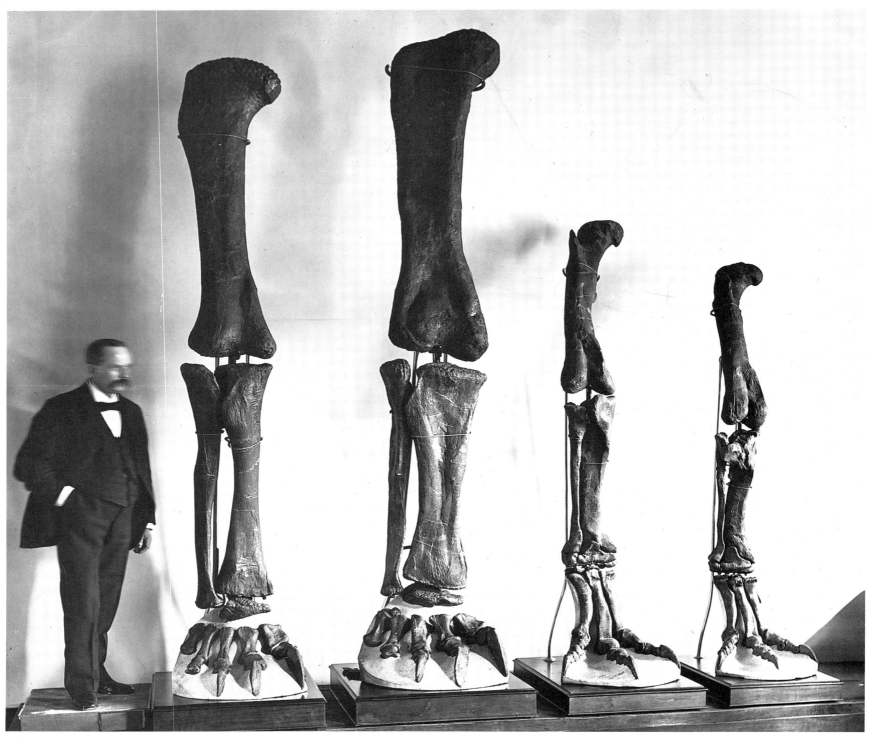

Left Unusual display of the giant sauropod *Diplodocus* in the Senckenburg Museum, Frankfurt.

Bottom left Hindlimbs of sauropods and theropods. Left to right: *Diplodocus, Apatosaurus, Tyrannosaurus, Allosaurus.*

Right A *Diplodocus* skull.

Below A *Diplodocus* foot.

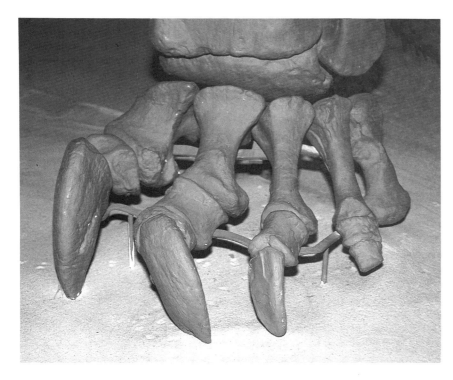

of *Apatosaurus* made in the late nineteenth century, largely because the first remains were very scrappy and difficult to compare with other types. Most of these problems were resolved in the 1930s following the remarkable discovery of an almost complete skeleton in Utah at the Dinosaur National Monument.

At first the head of *Apatosaurus* was thought not to have been found, and a model was made of one, which was based, rather loosely on the skull of *Camarasaurus*! It was not until the mid-1970s that the mistake was realized, following the discovery of the real head of *Apatosaurus* in the collection of dinosaur fossils at Pittsburgh's Carnegie Museum. *Apatosaurus* had a very long tail, forming a long whip-lash end. The hips were very high, held up on massive pillar-like legs; the back was strong, to support a large gut, and sloped down toward the shoulders – the arms being about two thirds of the length of the hindlimbs. The neck was long, and massively built (compared with *Diplodocus*, see below) and ended in a quite large head, which was rather long and low compared with that seen in brachiosaurs.

The jaws and teeth of *Apatosaurus* seem much more feeble than those of brachiosaurs. The teeth were confined to the ends of the jaws, and were narrow and pencil-like, forming what appears to be a sort of rake or comb structure at the front of the mouth.

Apatosaurs were clearly very different to brachiosaurs, having different body proportions, and presumably feeding in different ways. Apatosaurs were not apparently able to use a powerful nipping action of the teeth to cut off pieces of vegetation, but instead probably used their teeth quite literally like rakes, to drag in leaves and conifer needles, which could be swallowed and then digested slowly in the gut.

Although it would seem that apatosaurs did not have such a high browsing ability as brachiosaurs, this may not be completely true. It seems quite possible that apatosaurs were able to rear up on to their hind legs, and use the tail as a balance and prop, to reach the higher branches. The undersurface of the tail seems to have skid-like bones, which may well be an adaptation to allow for just this type of feeding position.

Diplodocus (double beam) lived at the same time as *Apatosaurus* and has been found in the same quarries in various parts of North America. It was similar to *Apatosaurus* in most details, except that it tended to be longer and much more lightly built – while *Apatosaurus* may have reached lengths of about 71 feet (22m), *Diplodocus* attained 88 feet (27m) or more.

The skulls of these two dinosaurs are very similar and this was the reason that the true skull of *Apatosaurus* lay unrecognized in the collections at Pittsburgh for so long.

The feet of apatosaurs need a little comment. First they tended to be rather short and rounded, being supported from behind by a large pad of tissue, rather like a wedge heel. The front foot tended to lose all but its inner claw which was quite large, and may well have been used by the animals as a defensive weapon. This seems especially likely if they were able to rear up and lash out with their forelimbs. They may also have been used as a digging tool, perhaps for nest building. The hind feet tended to retain several of their inner toes, usually three, sometimes only two, as in the case of *Diplodocus*.

Other apatosaurs include names such as *Barosaurus* (from similarly aged deposits in North America), *Dicraeosaurus* (found with *Brachiosaurus* in Tanzania), *Cetiosauriscus* (from the late Jurassic of

England), *Antarctosaurus* (from the late Jurassic of Argentina) and *Nemegtosaurus* (from the Cretaceous of Mongolia).

One of the most spectacular of the new finds from the late Jurassic of China has been the the probable apatosaur named *Mamenchisaurus*. This was an extraordinary sauropod because it had a disproportionately long neck. The total length of the body is approximately 73 feet (23m) in one individual, and of this approximately 35 feet (11m) is neck alone. Unlike other apatosaurs, the tail of this species does not seem to have been extended into a whip-lash. It has also been reported in a conversation with Dr Dong Zhiming (Beijing) that the skull of *Mamenchisaurus* is not as long and low as is seen in the majority of apatosaurs. There are therefore some reasons for doubting the closeness of relationship between *Mamenchisaurus* and other typical apatosaurs.

Several other puzzling sauropods are known, particularly from the middle to late Jurassic of China. These include *Omeisaurus*, *Shunosaurus* and *Datousaurus*. These are mostly known from complete skeletons, which are now on display in various museums in China, notably the Beipei Museum in Chongqing, Sichuan. All of

Left A late Jurassic scene from China, with the giant sauropod *Mamenchisaurus* in the background and the theropod *Gazosaurus* in the foreground.

Above *Dicraeosaurus*. This dinosaur was found in Tanzania, with the remains of *Brachiosaurus*. In many respects it is similar to other apatosaurs such as *Diplodocus* and *Apatosaurus*.

Right Some very fine sauropod dinosaurs have been found in China. This display shows two skeletons of *Shunosaurus* in Zigong Dinosaur Museum. It has been reported that *Shunosaurus* may have had a tail club, somewhat like those of ankylosaurid ornithischians, but the evidence has not yet been published.

these forms seem to show some resemblance to camarasaurs, but at present, not a great deal of work has been done to clarify their relationships with other dinosaurs from the West.

Barapasaurus is another sauropod which comes from the middle Jurassic of India, but again its relationship with dinosaurs from elsewhere is uncertain.

Ornithischians

A wide variety of ornithischians are known in late Jurassic times. Some of these types can be traced almost directly to the early forms described in the early Jurassic. Others are new developments. At this stage it is possible to discern several distinct types of ornithischian: ornithopods, stegosaurs and rare ankylosaurs.

Ornithopods tend to be bipedal types, little changed in shape from those seen in the early Jurassic. They were relatively small – 10-13 feet (3-4m) long was a maximum – though they became larger in the Cretaceous Period. They were also agile forms which relied on speed to escape from predators.

Dryosaurus (wood reptile) comes from the late Jurassic of North America and southern Africa and similar forms have been found in western Europe. *Dryosaurus* was relatively small, reaching a maximum length of about 10 feet (3m), and retaining the body proportions of early forms. The tail was long and muscular, the hind legs were long, too, and the feet and toes narrow, indicating a good running ability. The gut swung down between the legs, so that the dinosaur did not pitch forward onto all fours when running. Such a position also meant that the dinosaur's hands were left free for other purposes.

The head was perched on a short neck, and was compact, with a toothless, horny beak for nipping off plant shoots. Behind the beak was a row of sharp chewing teeth, and outside these a set of cheeks to hold the food in the mouth while the teeth were doing their work. The large eye indicates alertness in order to avoid the attentions of the many predators, such as young allosaurs or adult *Ornitholestes*.

Left A fine display of juvenile and adult specimens of *Camptosaurus* which is currently on display at the Smithsonian Institution.

Bottom left *Camptosaurus* featuring as the lunch item for *Allosaurus*!

Right The skeleton of *Stegosaurus* as it was preserved in the quarry clearly shows the enormous size of the plates which ran down the back. There were also a series of small armor plates associated with the head, which may have served as protection for the throat.

These dinosaurs seem to have been quite successful at this time, since their remains have been found almost worldwide. A similar type to *Dryosaurus* is found in the late Jurassic of China: *Xiaosaurus*, sometimes known as *Yandusaurus*. This differed very little from dryosaurs, apart from the fact that the hind foot of *Xiaosaurus* had four toes, while that of *Dryosaurus* had only three toes.

Camptosaurus (flexible reptile) is a somewhat larger ornithopod, which has so far only been found in western North America and Europe. *Camptosaurus* reached a maximum size of about 20 feet (6m) and was clearly a slower and more cumbersome creature than dryosaurs. It would presumably have been easy prey to the large carnosaurs of the time since it was not particularly fleet of foot, and lacked any obvious defensive weapons.

By comparison with *Dryosaurus*, *Camptosaurus* was a much more dedicated herbivore. The skull was longer and lower, the jaws longer and stronger and packed with larger teeth, and the jaw muscles were more powerful. If we are looking for a comparison with animals living today, then it is probably best to consider *Camptosaurus* as a little like the goat, capable of eating a wide range of plant types with ease.

Stegosaurs may have had their origin in the armored types, such as *Scutellosaurus* and *Scelidosaurus*, of the early Jurassic. However, the stegosaurs were much more elaborate in their armoring, having developed some very bizarre plates and spines in some cases. The group takes its name from *Stegosaurus*, an extremely well-known dinosaur from the late Jurassic of North America. Stegosaurs seem only to have flourished during the latter half of the Jurassic Period: a few fragmentary fossils are known from the early Cretaceous of Europe, China and Africa, but these seem to be the remnant of a once flourishing group.

Stegosaurus (roof reptile) was first discovered in the latter half of the nineteenth century, in quarries in Colorado, Wyoming and Utah and it is instantly recognizable by the row of high, angular plates which run in a row down the back.

The head was low and long and quite small for such a large animal (*Stegosaurus* reached lengths of 23 feet [7m] or more).

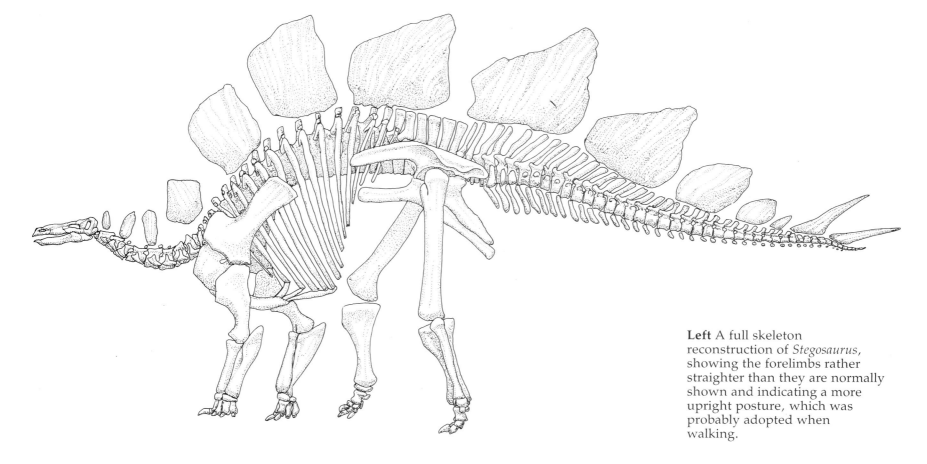

Left A full skeleton reconstruction of *Stegosaurus*, showing the forelimbs rather straighter than they are normally shown and indicating a more upright posture, which was probably adopted when walking.

tip of the snout was a horn-covered beak, as usual, and behind this were numerous small leaf-shaped teeth, which were quite small and weak compared with those of the much smaller *Camptosaurus*. Although these animals seem to have had cheeks, there is little evidence that they were able to chew plants at all effectively. They undoubtedly relied on a large fermenting stomach to digest the plant food, but whether this was supplemented by a stone-laden gizzard is not known.

The remainder of the skeleton is strikingly different from other ornithischians. The hind legs were very long and pillar-like, and the forelimbs were barely half their length, even though they were clearly used for walking upon. The back therefore slopes very sharply down from the hips and the head is carried quite low to the ground. The tail was not very long, but the end carries at least two pairs of long (up to 3 feet [1m]) pointed spikes, which served as defensive weapons. The plates running down the back were quite small near the head, but over the rump they were very large angular plates, which overlapped one another slightly on either side of the midline.

There has been much discussion concerning the function of the large plates in *Stegosaurus*. Opinions have varied between their use as defensive spines, which stuck out from the body (as in a porcupine), or as armor plating (with the plates folded down over the sides of the body), to their use as solar panels or radiators of body heat. The ideas about their being for defense seem flawed because the plates themselves are thin and spongy in texture, and not at all the thick, hard plates that they appear to be at first sight. Today, most people believe that the plates acted both as solar panels and as radiators, to control the body temperature of the animal. The texture of the plates only makes sense if they were covered by a thin layer of skin and and were infiltrated by blood. The shape of the plates has also been tested in a wind tunnel, and they have been seen to be a most effective shape for cooling in a breeze. On cool days, the plates could be filled with blood and turned toward the sun so that the blood could be warmed in order to warm the rest of the body.

All in all, *Stegosaurus* was a most unusual dinosaur. It was a slow-moving herbivore, probably capable of rearing up to feed on high browse on occasion, but spending most of its time feeding on the low ground cover ferns. The large plates along its spine were used to regulate its body temperature (and probably served for visual recognition at the same time), and for defense they were

Above right A mounted skeleton of *Stegosaurus* showing the extremely small size of the head and narrowness of the snout. Undoubtedly this would have been a low browser of ferns and cycads.

Left *Dryosaurus*, a smaller and more agile ornithopod than *Camptosaurus*.

equipped with quite vicious tail spikes, which could have inflicted a severe wound if swung with force against the flanks of an attacker.

Other stegosaurs show a variety of spine and plate patterns. *Tuojiangosaurus* from Sichuan has a double row of more conical shaped plates down its back, which seem much more defensive in function, although the remainder of the skeleton differs very little from that of *Stegosaurus*.

Kentrosaurus from the late Jurassic of Tanzania (a contemporary of *Brachiosaurus*) is smaller than either of the two previous stegosaurs, but is far more prickly, having a set of long and very sharp spines along the tail and over the hips, but broader plates over the back and shoulders.

A number of other stegosaurs are somewhat less well-known, including *Huayangosaurus*, known from a partial skeleton from the middle Jurassic of China. This dinosaur seems to have had a set of rather narrow plates along its back, rather like *Tuojiangosaurus*. But it did have a larger and deeper skull. Unlike the typical

stegosaur skull, it is rather reminiscent in some ways of the skull of the early Jurassic *Scelidosaurus*. There are also European stegosaurs such as *Lexovisaurus* and *Dacentrurus*, but these are frustratingly poorly known at present.

The ankylosaurs are quadrupedal, heavily armored dinosaurs which made their main appearance in the Cretaceous. The earliest remains appear in the late Jurassic, but only to the extent of odd fragments. One of the best known of these is an incomplete jaw from England, long thought to be that of a theropod. Unfortunately there is not enough information to allow a reconstruction of such an animal, though the early Jurassic *Scelidosaurus* cannot be far away in overall body form.

The late Jurassic, then, was most definitely the time of the sauropod dinosaurs. These huge four-footed animals must have dominated the land, roaming either in herds or as individuals, almost invulnerable as adults, unless attacked by a pack of most determined allosaurs or equivalent large theropods.

Left A skeleton reconstruction of *Kentrosaurus*. This dinosaur was also found with the remains of *Brachiosaurus* and *Dicraeosaurus* in Tanzania.

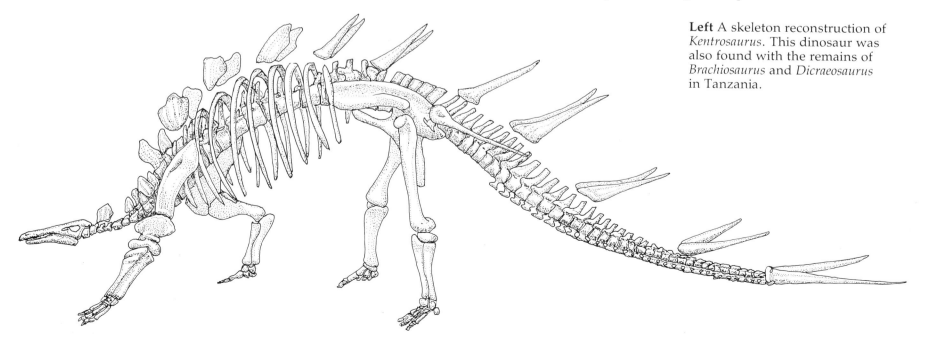

CHAPTER 6

The Early Cretaceous: The time of the Ornithopods

The early Cretaceous Period is slightly unusual in that it marks a time of very significant change in the world of the dinosaurs. During the Jurassic it is clear that the dinosaurs came very rapidly to dominate terrestrial habitats. By the end of the Jurassic, however, terrestrial communities were clearly topped by the gigantic sauropods on the one hand, which appear to have been well represented in communities worldwide, and the large carnosaur theropods on the other.

In early Cretaceous times, communities do not seem to have been structured in the same way. Sauropods seem to have been relatively rare members of any community, theropods are not so abundant as fossils, but other groups, in particular the ornithopod ornithischians, seem to have been far more numerous.

Continental positions

The break up of Pangea into distinct continental areas was now well progressed. Europe and North America were separated from both Asia and the southern continents by substantial shallow seas. Africa and South America were still connected to Antarctica and Australia, but India had begun to move away from the other continents and begin its long journey across what was to become the Indian Ocean before finally colliding with southern Asia many millions of years later (a collision that resulted in the formation of the Himalayan mountain range).

Therefore during the Cretaceous we would expect to see increased provincialism in the faunas of the world, as the species in Asia, or North America/Europe, or South America/Africa evolved in their own particular ways.

Climates and floras

The introduction of seaways between many of the land masses during the late Jurassic, and their continuance in the Cretaceous must have had some effect on the climatic conditions. So far – as can be seen from the plants – the climatic conditions seem to have remained virtually the same. That is to say, the world climates were warm and mild with very little seasonality. There were still no polar ice caps, which means that the latitudinal bands of climate were very broad and tropical and subtropical conditions extended far to the north and south of the equator – conditions which seem almost incomprehensible to we who live in a world with two polar ice caps and much narrower climatic zones.

The floras at the beginning of the Cretaceous Period show no significant change from the conditions of the late Jurassic, but there was a marked dominance of ferns, conifers, cycads, horsetails and ginkgos. However, a short time into the Cretaceous a completely new type of plant appeared for the first time: the angiosperms, or flowering plants. These new sorts of plants started as small shrubby types of bush which, because they were able to reproduce much more quickly than ferns and many of the

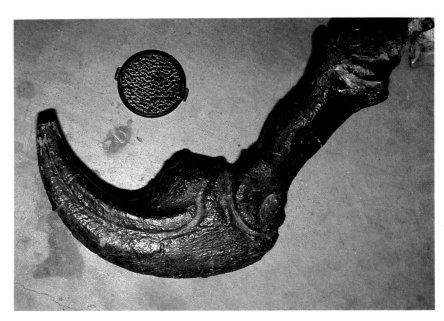

Above The claw of the large theropod *Allosaurus* is rather similar to that of *Deinonychus*.

Right Ferns of various types were still abundant.

Far right The trunk of a cycad. A crown of palm-like leaves would have sprouted from the top.

Left Continental positions in the early Cretaceous Period.

Early Cretaceous Period
Hauterivian Stage (125 m years ago)

Vegetation	Tundra & ice
Mountain	Continental sea
Desert	Deep ocean

other plants of the time, were able to colonize areas of disturbed land very quickly. It has actually been argued that the effect of trampling and disturbance to the ground and undergrowth by the giant browsing herbivorous dinosaurs of the late Jurassic may have provided the opportunity for flowering plants to get established in a world dominated by plants of the Jurassic Period.

Whatever the actual cause, which we may never know with absolute conviction, the effect of the appearance of the flowering plants was dramatic. Flowering plants of various types began to appear in ever greater numbers during the Cretaceous Period, and must have had a profound effect on the diets of the herbivores. Could it be a coincidence that the giant sauropods declined during the Cretaceous as the flowering plants spread? Or are we seeing the interaction of plants and animals on a global scale? It is certainly the case that different types of herbivorous dinosaurs came to dominate in the Cretaceous Period; perhaps they did so because they were better able to cope with the new diets afforded by the new species of flowering plants.

Mammals, pterosaurs and birds

As the only other significant groups of essentially land-based animals, these three groups continued to evolve, but the changes that were taking place within these groups were relatively insignificant compared with what was happening with the dinosaurs.

Mammals continued to survive as various types of largely nocturnal insectivorous forms, none bigger than about the size of a rat. They appear to have had little or no impact on the dinosaurs, though they may have attracted the attention of some of the smaller and more agile theropods, as potential prey.

Rather like the mammals, pterosaurs continued to evolve along the lines of those seen in the Jurassic. The main evolutionary trend was the disappearance of the long-tailed pterosaurs and their replacement by a variety of short-tailed forms. The trends toward increasing size and loss of teeth continued, and by the end of the early Cretaceous, some substantial pterosaurs had evolved.

Birds which first appeared in the late Jurassic are very rarely found as fossils, and as far as can be told from fossil evidence, do not seem to have had any significant impact on the pterosaurs which were clearly their main competitors in the aerial world in the early Cretaceous.

Dinosaurs
Theropods

This group of dinosaurs are frustratingly poorly represented in the early Cretaceous. Why this is so is not certain, but their fossils appear only rarely and when they are found are almost always very fragmentary. Fortunately there are one or two exceptions to this rather gloomy picture of the predators of the early Cretaceous, and these are described below. The strange thing about them is that those which are well known all seem to have some peculiar characteristics: they appear to be rather bizarre when compared to the types of theropod seen in the late Jurassic.

We will concentrate on three particular theropods. Two are carnosaurs and comparative new comers: *Baryonyx* from southern England and *Carnotaurus* from South America; the other is a small/medium sized theropod from Montana (and close relatives from Mongolia) named *Deinonychus*.

Deinonychus (terrible claw) belongs to a group of theropods which are referred to as dromaeosaurids (after a dinosaur, from the late Cretaceous of Canada, named *Dromaeosaurus*, which was known in only sketchy detail until quite recently).

Deinonychus, which reached a length of about 10 feet (3m), first came to light in 1964, following the discovery of several part skeletons in early Cretaceous rocks in Montana (USA). The dinosaur proved to be entirely new to science, and does much to complicate the apparently simple classification of theropods into carnosaurs (big ones!) and coelurosaurs (little ones!). Quite simply, it has features which are typical of both groups and others which are unique to itself.

Looking in some detail at the skeleton of this dinosaur, the skull

is quite large, though lightly built, with thin struts of bone surrounding large openings for the eyes and jaw muscles. The teeth
are typical of those of theropods, being curved, narrow daggers
with serrated edges. The neck is strongly curved and powerful
and the back short and quite stiff; the tail is long and also supported by a pack of long thin bones, developed as extensions of
processes on the vertebrae, which could be used to hold the tail
stiff if required so to do.

The arms are unusually long with large three-fingered hands
and powerful claws; these were clearly used for grasping their
prey very powerfully. As we shall see, the ability to hold prey
very tightly is explained by the curious way in which they killed
their prey. The hindlimb is at first sight typical of any fast-running
theropod, in that it is quite long and slender. However, the foot is
most extraordinarily constructed: the inner toe is a small, hooked
claw (as is the case in the majority of theropods); the second toe is
modified into an enormous sickle, which was held clear of the
ground (to keep it sharp); and the third and fourth are normal
walking toes with smaller, more flattened claws.

What do all these unusual features tell us about the life style of
this animal? Clearly these were fast-running, sharp-eyed predators. The tail, which could be held either stiff or loose was used
as a dynamic stabilizer (when held stiff, so that these animals

Above This marvelous skeletal
mount of *Deinonychus* in a
leaping attack was produced by
the Peabody Museum, Yale
University. It creates a very vivid
image of the dynamic abilities of
this dinosaur.

Right Early Jurassic scene from
North America. Two
Deinonychus attack the large, but
practically defenseless,
ornithopod *Tenontosaurus*. The
sharp teeth and vicious sickle
claws give the prey no chance.

could 'jink' or sidestep while running at speed, in order to catch evasive prey), and as a balancer (for balancing on one leg, in order to be able to kick out viciously with the sickle claw at the soft underbelly of prey held firmly in the hands).

These amazingly sophisticated killers bring home very vividly just how active and dynamic were the lives of some dinosaurs. Indeed, the discovery and interpretation of *Deinonychus* did much to stimulate much of the debate which has gone on over the past 20 years on the subject of the physiological status of dinosaurs. Were they warm-blooded and active in the way that mammals are today, rather than sluggish and cold-blooded as reptiles living today?

It is quite possible that *Deinonychus* hunted in packs or small groups in order to bring down larger prey, such as full-grown *Tenontosaurus*, whose remains have been found in the same deposits as those of *Deinonychus*. There is also some evidence from the large number of bones collected in Montana that male and females may be distinguishable. It seems that a heavier and lighter version of the same dinosaur can be distinguished among the remains. Rather than proposing separate names for otherwise extremely similar animals, it seems at least possible that these represent male and female versions of the same creature.

Sex differences among dinosaurs are very difficult to identify with confidence, especially among dinosaurs like this which do

not show any obvious secondary sexual characters, such as the horns of male deer. Some crested ornithopods seem to show sexual differences (see crested hadrosaurs in chapter 7), but these are the exception rather than the rule.

Another, apparently quite closely related dromaeosaurid, known as *Velociraptor* has been found in the late Cretaceous of Asia (Mongolia) and has very similar proportions to *Deinonychus*. This suggests that this development to a predatory sickle-clawed dinosaur was very successful once it had appeared in the early Cretaceous.

Baryonyx (heavy claw) was discovered in 1983 in a claypit in southern England. The first indication of this dinosaur was a large claw weathering out of a clay slope and discovered by William Walker, an amateur fossil collector. The claw was eventually taken to the Natural History Museum in London, where it was recognized as belonging to a theropod dinosaur. Further excavation at the clay pit revealed more bones of this animal and a full-scale excavation with a team of people involved was organized. Two tons of rock and fossils were collected and taken back to the Museum during the spring of 1983 and this has now been almost fully prepared in the paleontology laboratory at the Natural History Museum.

What has been recovered is about 40 percent of the skeleton of a completely new type of large theropod, approximately 23-26 feet (7-8m) long. The main body of the animal appears to have been broadly similar to most other large theropods: the tail was probably long and heavy, to balance the body at the hips; the hindlimb

was strong and pillar-like to support the heavy body; the neck appears to have been curved and strong. The main differences lie in the head and hand. The head is unusually long and flat, unlike almost all other theropods which have rather deep, short faces by comparison. The jaws are also very long, and have large numbers of small, spindle-shaped teeth for much of their length. However, near the tip of the snout the teeth of both upper and lower jaws have become decidedly larger and fan out slightly to form what is known as a rosette – a similar feature is seen in the snout of some crocodiles. The nostrils are found surprisingly far back on the snout – they are usually positioned right at the tip – and there is an unusual knob on the snout in the midline, in front of the eyes.

The arm and hand are unusual, too, because the upper arm bone (humerus) is very large and powerful – unusually so for theropods which normally have relatively small forelimbs. Also there may have been an enormous claw on the hand. This cannot be proved at the present time, because there is no clear association of the bones of the skeleton, but it is believed that the large claw may go with the massive humerus, rather than being a large toe claw similar to that seen in dromaeosaurs. It would seem unlikely that theropods as large as *Baryonyx* would have been as acrobatic as dromaeosaurs seem to have been.

The unusual shape of the head and possibility of a large claw on the hand have provoked some interesting suggestions concerning the way of life of this dinosaur. Currently, the most popular idea is that this dinosaur may have been a fish eater. The shape of the jaws, the pointed teeth and low snout are very similar to those

Left The final stages of excavation of the mortal combat of *Protoceratops* and *Velociraptor*, preserved in sandstone in the Gobi Desert.

Bottom left The skull bones of the new and remarkable dinosaur, *Baryonyx*, from England.

Right The long, slender, lower jaw bones of *Baryonyx*.

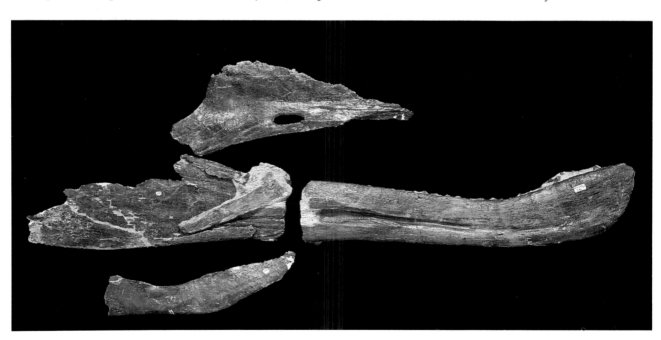

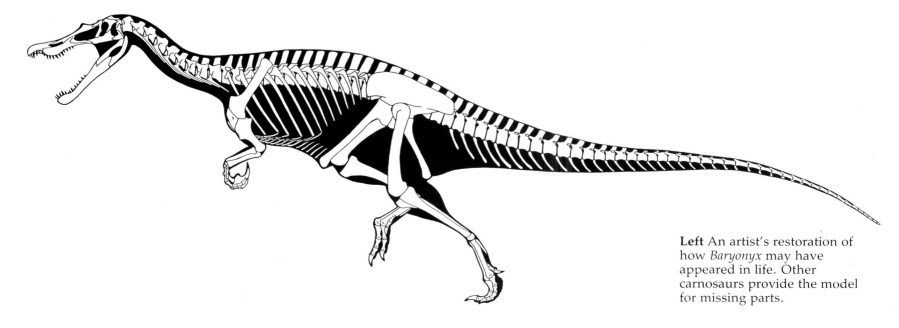

Left An artist's restoration of how *Baryonyx* may have appeared in life. Other carnosaurs provide the model for missing parts.

of crocodiles; in addition the large claw may have served as a gaff with which to hook fish out of the water. The idea is that these dinosaurs were the broad equivalent of the grizzly bear. It is also possible that the shape of the snout would fit with a scavenging way of life, the long snout being able to probe into the body cavity of carrion and the large claws being used to fully dismember carcasses for careful picking over.

Clearly we are dealing with a very unusual dinosaur, but more skeletal material is needed before we can be sure of both the appearance of the dinosaur and its way of life. This really emphasizes how important any new finds can be in the paleontological world. The rocks from which these remains were recovered have been scoured regularly by paleontologists and geologists, both amateur and professional, for the best part of 200 years, and yet until William Walker stumbled upon these remains in 1983 we had no idea that such an unusual dinosaur lived at this time and in this part of the world.

Carnotaurus (meat-eating bull) was another very large theropod from the latest part of the early Cretaceous. It is known from an almost complete skeleton, of which the skull is the only part to have been described in any detail.

The skull is unusually short-snouted compared with all other theropods of this size and is very deep. Immediately above the eye sockets are a pair of large conical horns, which give the skull a remarkably bull-like appearance, explaining its name. The remainder of the skeleton is similar to that of all large theropods, but for one feature: the forelimbs. In this feature there is a similarity to tyrannosaurs (see next chapter), but this is a deceptive similarity, because the details of the structure of the arm and hand are very different. In *Carnotaurus* the upper arm bone has the appear-

ance of being normal, even though it is rather small for the size of the animal. However beyond the elbow, the forearm bones are incredibly short, to the extent that the wrist seems to come out of the elbow. The hand is short and three fingered and well clawed. The overall effect is to provide a very short forelimb, as in tyrannosaurs, but in a totally different way.

It is a curious fact that we know precious little about theropods, be they carnosaurs or coelurosaurs, at this time in Earth history. Odd bones, vertebrae, limb bones, claws and teeth have been found, of course, but all that these remains tell us is that animals of this general type existed. They tell us nothing about how the animals looked in detail, and certainly give us no information about any peculiarities of their way of life.

The one slight exception to this observation has to be the remains of an animal named *Spinosaurus* (spine reptile), which is known from some back vertebrae and some jaw fragments, collected from north Africa. The one extraordinary feature of this form of dinosaur is that it has extremely long spines on its back. The jaw fragments which have been attributed to this dinosaur do look very similar to those of the snout of *Baryonyx*, which is very unexpected. However the spines of the back of *Baryonyx* are very short and stubby and not at all like those of *Spinosaurus*.

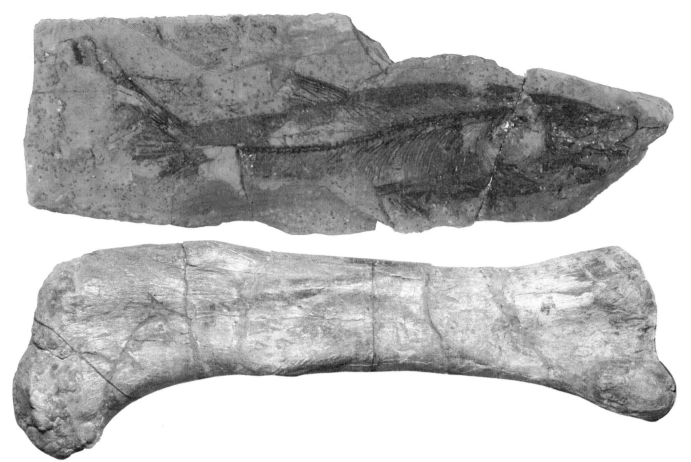

Below left *Carnotaurus*, a new and very unusual theropod from the early Cretaceous of South America.

Top right A bony fish from the early Cretaceous, which differs little from bony fish today.

Right Cetiosaur bones rather like this one have been found in early Cretaceous rocks.

Below This is the humerus (upper arm bone) of *Pelorosaurus*, a sauropod collected by Gideon Mantell from a quarry near Cuckfield, England.

Sauropodomorphs

It is an unfortunate fact that the sauropodomorphs are also rarities in the early Cretaceous. There are no complete, or even partly complete, skeletons of these types of animals known, and our knowledge of them is taken from the odd scrappy remains that have been collected. These can be interpreted by comparison to the excellent skeletons of sauropods which are known from the late Jurassic, but this is a most unsatisfactory state of affairs. The best dinosaur-bearing rocks of early Cretaceous age in the world are those from southeast England, but even here sauropod remains are rare and generally poorly preserved. Three species are known in a little detail: *Pelorosaurus*, *Ornithopsis* and *Cetiosauriscus*.

Pelorosaurus (monster reptile) was discovered in the first half of the nineteenth century in a quarry near Cuckfield in Sussex by Gideon Mantell. It consists of a single upper arm bone (humerus), which is very long. Several other remains were also discovered at this quarry which may belong to the same dinosaur, including a few tail vertebrae, but they cannot be definitely associated with this particular bone. In general details, the humerus resembles

that of brachiosaurs (see chapter 5), as do the tail vertebrae. So it can be seen that brachiosaurs survived into the early Cretaceous, though we can not tell much about them as yet.

Ornithopsis (bird-looking) was also discovered in the last century, but this time in similarly aged rocks on the Isle of Wight (just off the south coast of England). The remains include a set of back vertebrae and part of the pelvis of a large sauropod. Once again these bones seem to resemble those of a brachiosaur, and may in fact belong to *Pelorosaurus*, but this cannot be proved as none of the remains of either dinosaur coincide and comparisons are therefore impossible.

Finally *Cetiosauriscus* (whale-like reptile) is even more tantalizing than the previous two because its known remains consist merely of an isolated tail bone. This type of bone is quite distinctive of apatosaurs, such as *Apatosaurus* and *Diplodocus* (chapter 5), and again provides evidence that this type of dinosaur survived into the early Cretaceous. Again, what is really needed are some good skeletal remains in order to be able to discover how similar, or different, these early Cretaceous forms are to their Jurassic forebears.

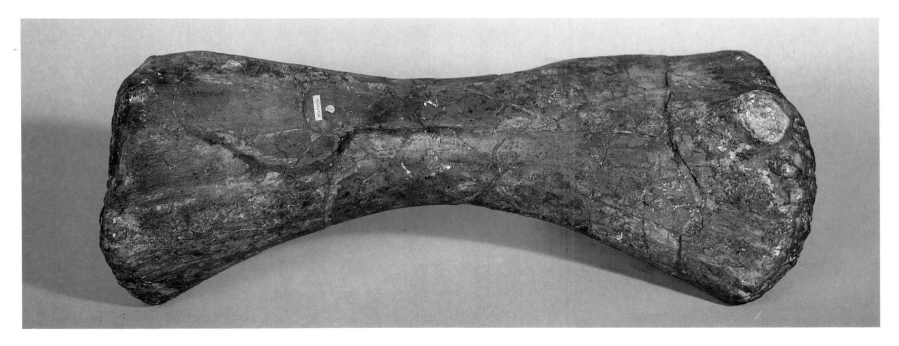

Left An interesting, but rather dated view of how *Hypsilophodon* may have looked and behaved in life. It was almost certainly a fast ground runner and not a tree-climber at all.

Below *Hypsilophodon*. A skeleton reconstruction based on material collected from the Isle of Wight, just off the southern coast of England and now on display in the British Museum (Natural History).

Right An early Cretaceous scene, with *Baryonyx* in the distance and *Hypsilophodon* in the foreground. Note the cycad with the branching stem just in front of the tail of *Baryonyx*.

Ornithischians

By comparison with the saurischians, the ornithischians seem to be reasonably well represented in early Cretaceous times. Although not particularly varied (yet! – wait until chapter 7) they seem to have been quite abundant and fossils abound, contrasting markedly with the rarity of saurischians. Quite why this change should have occurred at this time is uncertain. It may reflect the unreliability of the fossil record, but while this is a distinct possibility, I doubt that this is the reason. My suspicion is that the early Cretaceous marks a change in fortune of the various groups which may be associated with the appearance of the flowering plants. The ornithischians may well have been better able to adapt to the new diets that these plants offered than the sauropods. The latter group became, as a result, more restricted in their distribution, sticking to a diet of plants descended from the Jurassic, rather than exploiting the new plants.

Among the ornithopods of the early Cretaceous, *Hypsilophodon* (high ridged tooth) was found on the Isle of Wight as well. This dinosaur is in most respects similar to *Dryosaurus* as it was small, by dinosaur standards, reaching a maximum length of about 6½ feet (2m), but extremely agile and fast moving. These small, fast running, highly maneuverable ornithopods seem to have been a very stable group because animals of this type persist right through to the end of the reign of dinosaurs. In almost all respects these ornithopods follow the body plan of coelurosaurs. The body was balanced at the hips, on long, slender legs; the balance having been made possible in the herbivore (despite the need for a bulky gut) by the reorganization of the pelvic bones, allowing the belly to be slung between the legs.

The tail was long, and acted not only as a counterbalance to the front half of the body, but also as a dynamic stabilizer as was discussed in the case of *Deinonychus*. This development is analogous to that which was seen in the theropod. The end of the tail was stiffened by bony rods as it was in *Deinonychus*, but the bony rods

were not formed from the bony processes of the tail bones themselves, but were derived from long spine tendons, which had turned into thin strips of bone. These bony tendons (ossified tendons) formed a tight lattice around the end of the tail, but the base of the tail (near the rump) was quite flexible. This meant the tail could be held stiff and straight for fast, balanced running in a straight line, or if needed could be sharply swung to one side or the other to make the body twist, veer sharply to one side, or sidestep. Such agility would have been of great value to these animals and would have assisted their escape from predatory theropods.

The fact that both predator and prey developed similar adaptations for running fast and combining this with an ability to move ellusively indicates that the 'struggle for survival' was operating just as it does today: each improvement of the one (prey or predator) being countered by a similar change in the other – failure to keep up with this constant round of changes and improvement would result in the extinction of either species.

A rather curious story surrounds this little dinosaur and its habits. The first remains of this dinosaur were found as early as 1849, but for almost exactly 20 years it was thought to be the remains of a young *Iguanodon*! The discovery of several skeletons eventually proved this assumption to be incorrect; and, when the animal was finally described, it was noted for its long fingers and toes, which suggested to the experts of the time that it probably used them to clamber over rocks and climb trees. So powerful was the impression left by these views, that *Hypsilophodon* came to be regarded as an arboreal dinosaur. It was compared to the living tree kangaroo of Papua New Guinea, a rather clumsy animal which scrambles among the branches of trees and eats their leaves – the kangaroo uses its long, fairly stiff tail for balance, and has long back legs and short, grasping forelimbs. In following years other characteristics of *Hypsilophodon* came to be used to demonstrate its tree-climbing ability, including the shape of its arms, and the fact that it had feet in which the first toe was re-

versed very much like that of a perching bird, so that the foot could gain a very firm grip on a narrow branch. The image of *Hypsilophodon* was that of a tree-climbing dinosaur until comparatively recently, since when views have changed totally.

A thorough review of this dinosaur was undertaken by Dr Peter Galton (Bridgeport, USA) in the 1960s. One of the main results of this work was the demonstration, beyond reasonable doubt, that *Hypsilophodon* was anything but a clumsy tree-dwelling dinosaur, but that it was a very finely adapted cursor – fast-running animal. The most important discoveries that were made were that the tail was a stabilizer, associated with high running speeds; that the leg had the proportions of a typical fast-running creature; that the arm did not show the bowed forearm bones typical of other climbing animals; and, perhaps most telling of all, the fact that the foot did not have a reversed toe which could be used to grasp branches. It was discovered that the toe had been reversed by mistake, and was anyway far too short to have been able to grip on to branches at all effectively.

An apparently fairly close relative of *Hypsilophodon*, *Tenontosaurus* (sinew reptile) has so far only been discovered in western North America, and remains have been discovered associated with those of the sickle-clawed theropod *Deinonychus*. *Tenontosaurus* was considerably larger than *Hypsilophodon*, measuring up to 15 feet (4.5m) long, and appears to have been a little less agile, its legs are considerably heavier, and in proportion to the body, somewhat shorter. The forelimbs were also quite large and may well have been used for walking upon for at least part of the time. The tail was very long, and its tip was surrounded by a bundle of tendons, as in the case of *Hypsilophodon*.

Linked to the larger size of this dinosaur, was the differing proportions of the head. The jaws were longer and heavier, the snout was longer, to accommodate more and larger teeth, and the jaws were operated by larger sets of muscles. These were clearly far better 'food processors' than smaller ornithopods such as *Hypsilophodon*, and it is perhaps not surprising to find that their remains are in some places quite numerous.

The size of *Tenontosaurus* was not entirely beneficial however. As larger and more cumbersome animals they may well have easily fallen prey to the faster and more agile *Deinonychus*. While individual *Tenontosaurus* may have been too strong for a single *Deinonychus*, if – as has been suggested – this theropod hunted in packs then this larger ornithopod would have stood little chance

Top A whole skeleton mount of *Tenontosaurus* which is now on display in the American Museum of Natural History, New York. Note the bundle of bony rods around the tail.

Left A carefully made drawing of the skeleton of the dinosaur *Iguanodon*, as it appeared when discovered during coal mining in Belgium in the 1870s.

Above right *Tenontosaurus*. The skull still encased in its plaster field jacket, which served to protect it during transportation back to the laboratory.

Far right A skeleton restoration of *Iguanodon*. This is one of 11 which can be seen mounted, together with another 20 lying on their sides, in the Royal Institute of Natural Sciences, Brussels, Belgium.

of survival. What this type of dinosaur clearly lacked was any form of defense, apart from being able to run away.

The next ornithopod that we shall be looking at was bigger still than *Tenontosaurus*, and may have been even more slow moving, but it had developed a rather unusual defensive weapon.

Iguanodon (iguana tooth) grew to lengths of 33 feet (10m) and was the largest of the early Cretaceous ornithopods. It is an extremely well-known dinosaur, because abundant remains, including many complete skeletons, have been recovered from various parts of western Europe. Very recently *Iguanodon* remains have also been recovered from North America, and a very *Iguanodon*-like creature has been discovered in Mongolia, so it would appear that this dinosaur, or its very close relatives, were not only very abundant, but were surprisingly widespread.

In appearance, *Iguanodon* differed little from the ornithopods that have been described so far, apart from the fact that it was yet longer and heavier. The legs were long and very powerful, ending in quite large, three-toed feet. There is no smaller inner toe as there was in *Tenontosaurus* and others (and this actually resembles the foot of the late Jurassic form *Dryosaurus*). The tail was thick and very heavy, to counterbalance the front part of the animal. It is evident that, as was the case in *Tenontosaurus*, the forelimbs

were also used for walking upon. In the case of *Tenontosaurus* the forefoot was quite broad, and the fingers had quite sharp claws; however in the case of *Iguanodon* the hand was remarkably specialized to perform a variety of functions. For walking, it was able to use the three center fingers (numbers two to four), which were thick and provided with hoof-like nails. The fifth finger was unusually long, and sprouted out sideways from the wrist, and this seems to have been the one real finger, in the sense that it could be used to grasp things with, as our fingers can. The first finger (the equivalent of our thumb) is the most extraordinary of them all as it was modified into a very narrow and tall, conical spike of bone jointed directly to the wrist. In life this thumb spike would have been covered by a sharp horny sheath in the form of a gigantic stilleto, which may have been as much as 20 inches (50cm) long in the largest individuals.

The lifestyle of *Iguanodon* would have been that of an abundant, possibly herd-dwelling, herbivore. The front of the jaws was provided with a hard, horny beak, which was ideal as a perpetually growing, self-sharpening tool for nipping off pieces of vegetation, which could be pulverized between rows of powerful cheek teeth before being swallowed.

As young individuals, *Iguanodon* were probably quite agile and

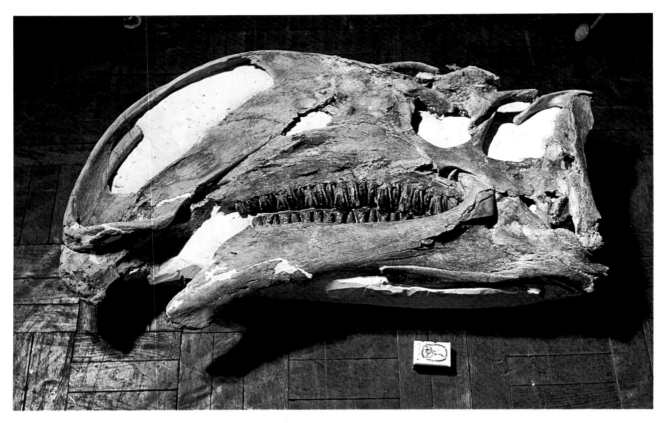

Left *Iguanodon orientalis*. The skull of a very *Iguanodon*-like ornithopod from the early Cretaceous of Mongolia. It has a particularly large nose.

Below The left hand in outer view of *Iguanodon bernissartensis* showing the remarkable thumb-spike.

Right *Iguanodon atherfieldensis*. A species which was collected from near Atherfield Point on the Isle of Wight.

fast-moving bipedal creatures, not too dissimilar to the smaller *Hypsilophodon* living at the same time. But as they grew, these dinosaurs would have become increasingly prone to move about on all fours, only relying on bipedal running for short sprints, perhaps to escape from predators. Full-sized individuals would obviously not have been particularly agile and, although they would have been invulnerable to small theropods, the larger theropods (of which, we unfortunately know precious little – apart from the odd few teeth and bones) may well have preyed upon them. *Iguanodon* was not the easy prey that *Tenontosaurus* may have been for *Deinonychus* because it had the stilleto weapon on its hand. The one disadvantage possessed of all large theropods was their short arms, this meant that in order to catch and kill their prey they had to lunge in head first to get in a telling bite. This approach would have been fraught with danger in the case of an attack upon *Iguanodon* because, armed with the stilleto-like thumb spine, it could lash out at close quarters into the eyes or neck of an attacker – with devastating results. The fact that these dinosaurs may well have lived in large social groups would also have added protection for the young and potentially more vulnerable individuals.

Left A skeleton restoration of *Ouranosaurus*, a bizarre ornithopod with its extraordinarily long spines running down its back. The function of these spines is still a mystery today.

One of the most bizarre of the early Cretaceous ornithopods is *Ouranosaurus* (valiant reptile), whose remains have been recovered from the early Cretaceous rocks of Niger (West Africa). As in *Iguanodon*, this dinosaur had a thumb spike on the hand. The body proportions were also quite similar, although it seems only to have reached about 23 feet (7m) in length.

The differences can be seen in the skull and back of this animal in particular. The skull had a beak which was flat and quite broad, looking more than anything like that of a duck (in doing so it resembles some of the crestless hadrosaur ornithopods of the late Cretaceous – see chapter 7). It also had a pair of small lumps on top of the head, just in front of the eyes, which looked for all the world like a pair of horn buds – but were not! The back is most extraordinary because the spines grew to quite ridiculous lengths. They must have formed a high ridge down the center of the back, which looks awkward on an animal of this size.

While the shape of the duck-like beak may be explicable as an adaptation of shape to suit a particular food preference of the animal, and the bumps on the top of the head may well be associated with a visual display for social reasons (much as in the case of theropods with peculiar headgear – chapters 4 and 5), the spines almost defy explanation. The only half reasonable attempt to explain what they may have been for is that they were something like the plates on the back of *Stegosaurus*, perhaps acting as heat radiators or absorbers.

The other really puzzling observation concerning this dinosaur is the fact that spinosaur (see earlier in this chapter) remains have been reported from the same area at the same time. Why should two such different animals both develop similar tall spines on their backs? It may be that we are seeing some sort of common adaptation to some aspect of the environment in which they lived in this part of the world. Tempting though this explanation may seem, it is fatally flawed by a new piece of research.

Another ornithopod has been collected from Niger, in the same deposits as *Ouranosaurus* and has been described by Dr Souad Chabli in Paris. It is larger and more heavily built than the latter species, but *lacks* the long spines on the back. At the moment the research on this dinosaur is nearing publication and we await the report on this animal with considerable interest.

The only stegosaur which is known in any detail from the early Cretaceous is *Wuerhosaurus* from China. As far as we can tell from the fragmentary remains so far described this was very little different from the stegosaurs of the mid to late Jurassic (*Huayangosaurus* and *Tuojiangosaurus*).

The more heavily armored ankylosaurs of the early Cretaceous, which appear as very fragmentary forms in the latest Jurassic, are unfortunately not very well known at present. The ones of the early Cretaceous are generally known as nodosaurs and the two best known types are *Hylaeosaurus* and *Polacanthus*, both known from part skeletons (neither of which can be compared directly) and both coming from the famous early Cretaceous rocks of southern England.

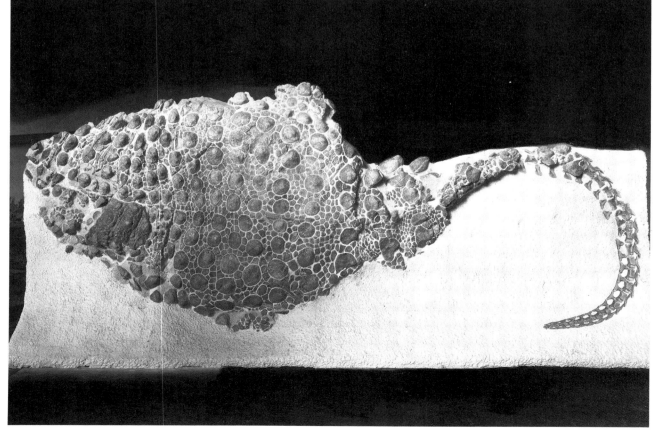

Above Part of the middle of the back of a new dinosaur from Australia, which shows evidence of small bony armor. It may have been a small nodosaur.

Left This is a view of the armor-plating that covered the back of *Sauropelta*. The other side shows much of the skeleton; the belly was not so armored as the back.

Right A surprisingly complete skeleton of a very young psittacosaur collected from Mongolia, and now on display in the Museum at Ulan Bator, Mongolia.

Hylaeosaurus (wood reptile) was one of the three that Richard Owen based his Dinosauria on in 1841. It is known from the front half of the skeleton of a dinosaur embedded in a large piece of rock. It is clear from the preserved remains that the animal was armored, because a row of large spines are preserved alongside the bones of the neck and back. To date the material has not been prepared out of the rock, so precise details of its anatomy are unknown.

Polacanthus (many spines) was discovered in the 1860s on the Isle of Wight. This discovery and the comparison with the form from Cuckfield is exactly the same as the situation with the brachiosaur remains referred to earlier in this chapter. *Polacanthus* comprises the remains of the rear half of an armored dinosaur, again characterized by the presence of spines along the back. The legs and back of this dinosaur have been prepared out of the rock, and the form is therefore known a little better than *Hylaeosaurus*. The fact that one dinosaur is known from the front half and the other from the back half is very frustrating, again because there is no proof that the one belongs to the other, no matter how much we may suspect this to be the case.

From what is known of this sort of dinosaur from the late Cretaceous, it seems that they were quite low-slung quadrupedal forms, moderately heavily armored. The armoring has a characteristic fringe of large spines on the flanks, the remainder of the back being covered with a mosaic of smaller rounded, interlocking plates.

The representations shown here are largely guess work, based on a minimal amount of factual material (more for *Polacanthus* than for *Hylaeosaurus*). Much more needs to be done on these animals before we can have a reasonable knowledge of them, but this requires more material.

The only other dinosaur of this type of which there are reasonable remains is *Sauropelta* from the early Cretaceous of Montana. Unfortunately, this dinosaur still has to be described, even though there is the better part of a skeleton of this dinosaur in the American Museum of Natural History in New York.

Another group of ornithischians makes its first appearance in the very closing stages of the early Cretaceous of China and Mongolia. The earliest representatives are known as psittacosaurs (parrot reptiles) because of their peculiarly parrot-like beaks, and are small, ornithopod-like creatures.

First discovered in expeditions to China and Mongolia in the 1920s by a crew of geologists from the American Museum in New York, these are curious little dinosaurs. They may have lived in Europe, if the remains of one scrappy skeleton are to be believed, and Dr Eric Buffetaut in Paris has recently reported that these dinosaurs may have been discovered in Thailand. They seem to have reached lengths of little more than 5 feet (1.5m). Like ornithopods, they were bipedal, and had a long tail to counterbalance the front half of the body. The hindlegs were long and slender, indicating good running abilities and they had four-fingered, powerful hands. The most curious feature of these dinosaurs was their beak, made of a special bone in the upper jaw known as the rostral, which opposes the predentary bone found at the tip of the lower jaw of all ornithischians. The rostral was narrow and pointed and gave the beak a decidedly parrot-like appearance. It can only be assumed that the beak reflects some dietary preference of these animals among the plants of the time, but precisely what this may have been is uncertain.

The importance of this particular group of dinosaurs is that they were the predecessors of the ceratopians of the late Cretaceous, a group which became both larger, considerably more numerous and varied in late Cretaceous times.

So, the early Cretaceous seems to have been a time of profound change. The world of the Jurassic, dominated by sauropods, was replaced largely by one dominated by herds of smaller, more mobile ornithopods. It is possible that the change mirrored, or tracked changes in the plants of the time. Paradoxically, the reason for such changes, in particular the evolution of the flowering plants, may have been a response to the heavy predation on plants by the giant sauropods of the late Jurassic.

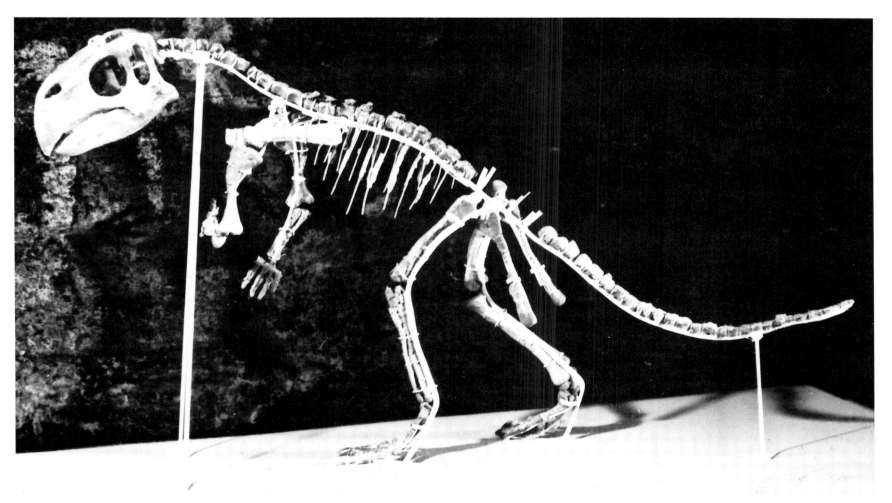

CHAPTER 7

The Late Cretaceous:
The Flowering of the Ornithischians

The late Cretaceous saw the final blossoming of the dinosaurs, prior to their mysterious extinction at the very end of the Cretaceous Period. It was a time of consolidation of the ornithischian group of dinosaurs, in particular, as they increased markedly both in number and variety (some of which are positively bizarre to our eyes). By contrast the saurischian group had mixed fortunes.

The theropods, after what appears to have been an extended period of conservatism, in terms of their body design, appear to have 'cut loose' biologically speaking, because during the late Cretaceous a surprisingly large number of extremely puzzling types appeared. Some of these, such as the ostrich mimics (ornithomimosaurs), are well known because they are represented by good skeletal specimens, but many others (particularly from Asia) are known by tantalizingly fragmentary pieces. It is hoped that the next decade will see the discovery of much new material of these enigmatic dinosaurs to fill in many gaps in our present knowledge.

The sauropodomorphs appear to have been quite rare members of the fauna at this time, which is in marked contrast to the situation in the late Jurassic. The group as a whole is widely spread across the continents, but remains are again rather poorly known, based as they are on incomplete skeletons, or isolated bones rather than good complete skeletons. Late Cretaceous sauropods also show some unexpected features, such as the armor plating found in some South American forms, but our knowledge of these forms is still frustratingly sketchy at this time.

Among other groups, changes were seen in the type and variety of species, but these give no clear indication as to why so many groups became extinct at the end of the Period.

Continental positions

The increasing provincialism that was seen in the earlier part of this Period continued into the Cretaceous as a result of two processes. First the continents continued to split and move apart. Europe and North America began to pull apart, and the northern part of the Atlantic Ocean began to develop. Africa and South America separated as the South Atlantic Ocean developed, and South America began to lose contact with Antarctica and Australia. All the major continental areas that we recognize today had separated, even though they were not in the positions that they are today.

The second process was that of transgressions by the sea: that is to say the flooding of low-lying areas of land as sea levels rose. This process had already been seen in the early Cretaceous, with the formation of the Turgai Sea separating Western Europe from Asia. In late Cretaceous times the rising sea level also resulted in a broad seaway separating western and eastern halves of North

America, and another separating western and central southern Africa.

The reason for the rise in sea level appears to have been related to the extent of continental movement through the sea floor spreading. The more movement there is, the greater the activity and size of the ridges separating the huge tectonic plates upon which the continents float. The effect of an increase in the size of the ridges is to decrease the total volume of the oceans, so that the water level rises and can flood low areas on the continents.

Climate and flora

The late Cretaceous was a time of continued warm and pleasant conditions over most of the Earth. There were still no polar ice caps because there were neither continents sitting on the poles and trapping ice (as in the case of Antarctica, today) nor an enclosed sea (as is the case with the present North Polar ice cap). As a result, the latitudinal climatic bands continued to be very broad, and warm conditions prevailed into high latitudes which today we would associate with sub-arctic or arctic conditions.

However, it does seem likely that climatic conditions would have been less stable than those that applied in the earlier Periods of the Mesozoic. The presence of seaways separating most of the continents and, furthermore, the presence of shallow seas dividing some of the other continental areas (Asia from Europe, North America, and Africa), would have undoubtedly contributed to more changeable climatic conditions. It seems likely, too, that the seasons would have become progressively more marked during the late Cretaceous. There would have been a shift to more obvious summer and winter times, not as extreme as today particularly in the higher latitudes, but nevertheless noticeable for both the animal and plant communities, whose activities would be timed by the onset of such seasons.

The plants of the late Cretaceous do not differ particularly from those of the earlier part of the Period, except for the fact that the flowering plants (angiosperms) continued to evolve into an increasingly wide variety of types. As a result they gradually came to replace many of the seed ferns and some of the conifers, cycads and gingkos that had become so common in the landscape of the

Left One of the biggest changes which took place in the Cretaceous was the arrival of the flowering plants. At first just small shrubby plants, they rapidly spread and developed into forms that ranged from small flowers to large trees: these are large fossil angiosperm tree trunks.

Above Magnolia leaf from the Late Cretaceous of Alabama.

Above right A modern magnolia.

Right The continental positions in late Cretaceous times. Note the extent of the transcontinental seas (pale blue).

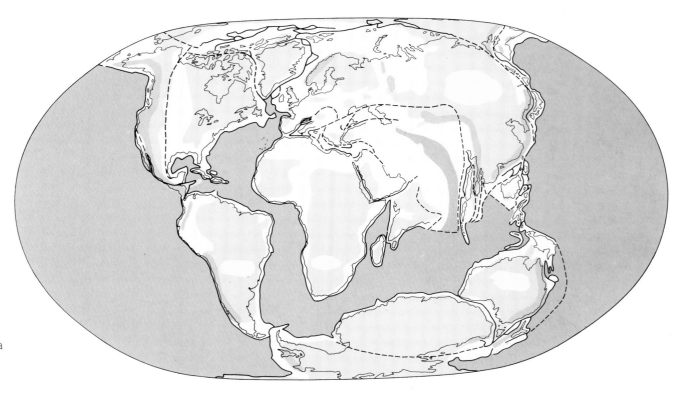

Late Cretaceous Period
Senonian Stage (90-80 m years ago)

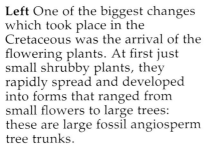

Vegetation	Tundra & ice
Mountain	Continental sea
Desert	Deep ocean

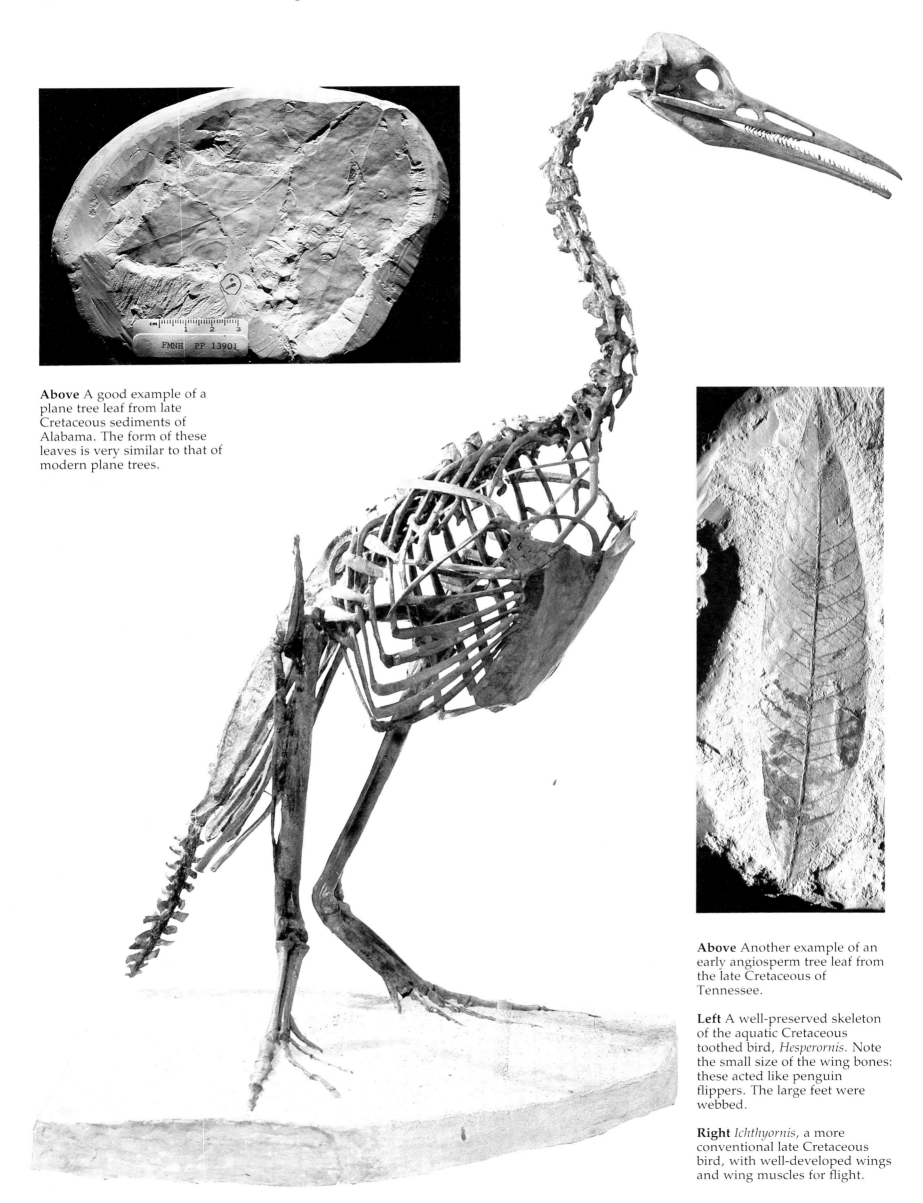

Above A good example of a plane tree leaf from late Cretaceous sediments of Alabama. The form of these leaves is very similar to that of modern plane trees.

Above Another example of an early angiosperm tree leaf from the late Cretaceous of Tennessee.

Left A well-preserved skeleton of the aquatic Cretaceous toothed bird, *Hesperornis*. Note the small size of the wing bones: these acted like penguin flippers. The large feet were webbed.

Right *Ichthyornis*, a more conventional late Cretaceous bird, with well-developed wings and wing muscles for flight.

Jurassic and early Cretaceous. However, it should be mentioned as a point of fact, that one group of flowering plants that are particularly common today never appeared during the time of the dinosaurs: the grasses. The grasses did not appear until midway through the Cenozoic Era (the Era immediately succeeding the Mesozoic), so there were never any precise dinosaur-equivalents of the grazing animals – horses, cattle, sheep, deer – that are so common today. The nearest to such animals would have been the low browsers (stegosaurs, ankylosaurs, ornithopods and ceratopians) which were able to feed upon the low, shrubby, flowering plants, cycads, horsetails and ferns of the time.

The flowering plants, after their beginnings as relatively small, shrubby plants, were opportunistic colonizers of disturbed ground. They would have ranged from the smaller, ground cover plants – the 'flowers' of today – to the larger flowering trees. Many of these plants had distinctly seasonal activity patterns, perhaps showing a measure of adaptation to the conditions which prevailed during their time of origin in the Cretaceous. Small plants died off, overwintering as seeds which germinated the following spring. By contrast the deciduous flowering trees were able to shut down their bodily activities in winter, losing their leaves and essentially slowing down all their normal activities so as to 'sleep' through the least hospitable time of the year.

Mammals

The story of mammals throughout the Mesozoic had been that of a shy, retiring group, almost entirely nocturnal, most being small insectivores (though there were small groups such as the multituberculates which where obviously herbivorous, mouse or rat-like creatures). In the late Cretaceous this pattern continued to hold true until right at the end of the Period (within the last 5-10 million

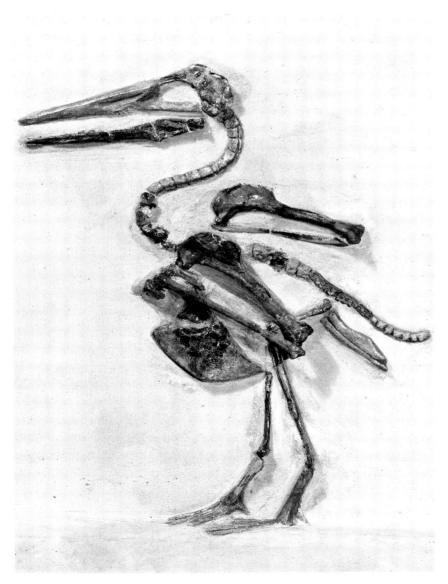

years), when the mammals began, at last, to show some signs of evolving into more varied types (mostly herbivorous) and increasing in size. The largest mammals of this time would appear to have weighed as much as 44 pounds (20kg). Clearly this was nothing compared to the dinosaurs of the time, but nevertheless it was a very significant increase for mammals which had, for the past 150 million years or so, weighed considerably less than 1 pound (0.5kg)!

The very fact that there was this increase in the representation of mammals indicates that something rather subtle, but nevertheless important, was happening at this time in Earth history. It is surely no coincidence that one of the main features of mammals is that they are able to maintain a constant and warm internal body temperature, no matter what the prevailing climatic conditions. Mammals have a highly active physiology, which is able to generate heat within the body, and are able to insulate themselves against the cold with a hairy covering (fur) to the body and/or subcutaneous fat. These can be seen to be natural advantages to animals living at times of increasing seasonality.

Pterosaurs and birds

These natural aerial competitors are both moderately well represented in the late Cretaceous. The biggest problem as far as paleontologists are concerned, is that both groups are composed of very light, fragile creatures, whose remains are only rarely fossilized. Our knowledge of both groups is therefore incomplete.

Birds are probably best known from two fossils from North America: *Hesperornis* and *Ichthyornis*. *Hesperornis* (western bird) was large, measuring a little over 3 feet (1m) from head to tail. It resembled the earliest bird (*Archaeopteryx*) in that it still retained teeth in its jaws – compared to all living birds which have only a horn covered beak – but it was clearly a very specialized bird because it could not fly. The wings were too small to have lifted the bird off the ground. However, careful examination of the proportions of the bird and the shape of its feet suggest that it was penguin-like, the 'wings' acting as flippers for swimming through the water, and its feet being broad and webbed for swimming and steering with. The neck was quite long and snake-like and the long, sharply toothed beak was ideally designed for catching slippery fish.

Ichthyornis (fish bird) was a smaller, toothed bird of the late Cretaceous. The fossilized skeleton discovered is similar in shape to that of a small seagull. It had long wings and was clearly an excellent flier. As it has been found in sea deposits and resembles today's gulls, it has been suggested that this bird was probably a seabird, and may have dived to catch fish.

Pterosaurs are known from several examples, the majority of which are large or very large fliers. It may have been that toward the end of the Cretaceous the birds occupied the ecological niches of small, aerial forms and the pterosaurs were the large aerial types.

Pteranodon (winged toothless) was a large pterosaur with a wingspan of 16 feet (5m) or more. In general terms the construction of this creature was very similar to that of *Pterodactylus* of the late Jurassic. It had a very short tail, a long neck constructed of large, powerful vertebrae and an extraordinary head.

As the name suggests, this pterosaur was toothless. Its jaws were very long and narrow, ending in a sharply-pointed tip and the beak must have been covered with a horny beak in life. There is some evidence to suggest there was a pouch between the lower jaws, which may have been used to store fish, rather like that on the beak of a pelican. At the back of the head there is another peculiar feature: a large, thin bony crest.

These pterosaurs would seem to have been the equivalent of large albatrosses, spending much of their time gliding upon oceanic air currents. They were almost certainly fish feeders. The

Left A full flesh reconstruction of *Ornithomimus*.

Right This magnificent mounted skeleton *Daspletosaurus* is on display in the National Museum in Ottawa, Canada.

fish may have been caught either by diving upon them from the air, or spearing them as it swooped just above the sea surface. The long beak would have been an excellent spearing device, and the extraordinary crest would have served as a counterbalance against the weight of the long beak and to help lift the head back after it had been used to spear a fish. The crest may also have had a secondary function as an aerofoil for steering in flight.

Dinosaurs
Theropods

The theropods of the late Cretaceous are quite varied in type when compared with those seen in earlier times. Why this should be so is a mystery. I shall deal with a variety of types here, some known from complete and reasonably well-preserved skeletons, others are relatively poorly known types. The first to be described is probably the best known of all dinosaurs: *Tyrannosaurus*(tyrant reptile).

The first remains of this dinosaur to be found were some large teeth discovered in northern Montana (USA) in the early 1850s. At the time these were recognized as the teeth of a carnivorous dinosaur, but nothing more could be told about it until 1902, when a partial skeleton was discovered in the same area. The material was described and given the name *Tyrannosaurus* by the American paleontologist Henry Fairfield Osborn in 1905. In the following year more material was discovered and then a few years later an almost complete skeleton was found making this one of the best known of all late Cretaceous carnivorous dinosaurs.

The skull of this dinosaur is very large (over 3 feet [1m] in length) and very solidly constructed of bone. This is slightly unusual, because it is often the case that large dinosaur skulls are very lightly constructed with thin struts of bone in order to save weight. The reason for this is explained below. The jaws are very long, and equipped with massive serrated-edged teeth, which were clearly designed for slicing flesh.

The remainder of the skeleton is in most respects similar to that of the large carnosaurs of the late Jurassic (see *Allosaurus*, Chapter 5). The neck was thick and powerful, in order to hold the heavy head and swing it around as the animal tore large pieces of flesh from its victims. The back was short and quite stiff and the tail (the length of which is not known at present, because no complete tails have yet been found with this species) was heavy and counterbalanced the front half of the body at the hips. The hind legs were long and powerful and ended in a foot with three long, sharply clawed forwardly pointing toes, and a smaller first toe which pointed backward. The forelimbs were by comparison ridiculously small. The upper and lower arm bones are short and lightly built, and the hand probably consisted of two fingers, ending in modestly hooked claws. (I say *probably* because the hand is another part of this dinosaur that is not known from fossil remains. But close relatives, *Albertosaurus* [from Canada] and *Tarbosaurus* [from Asia] do have well-preserved hands and this is the model for this description.)

Another point of interest, seen in many other theropods but not previously mentioned, is the large, flat-ended foot to be seen on the pubic bone of the pelvis. This curious bone probably served as a support to protect both the lungs and belly while these dinosaurs were lying down. The immense weight of the animal would otherwise have crushed both the chest (making breathing impossible) and the organs of the belly (clearly undesirable) while lying prone. The supporting function of the pubic bone was aided by a row of narrow, rib-like bones (known as gastralia) which form a row along the midline from the belly to the shoulder region.

The life style of *Tyrannosaurus* was obviously that of a large carnivore. However it has often been argued in the past that this was a rather slow moving scavenger: an animal that was not particularly fast moving or agile and therefore had to content itself with carrion. I consider this not to have been the case. The legs of *Tyrannosaurus* are strong and long and could have moved this dinosaur quickly, especially over short distances. This dinosaur was probably an attacker of live prey, using short bursts of speed to launch itself, mouth wide open, at its prey. An attack of this

Left A plaster cast of the skull of *Gallimimus*, an ornithomimid dinosaur from Mongolia. It is very little different from the ornithomimids such as *Struthiomimus* from North America.

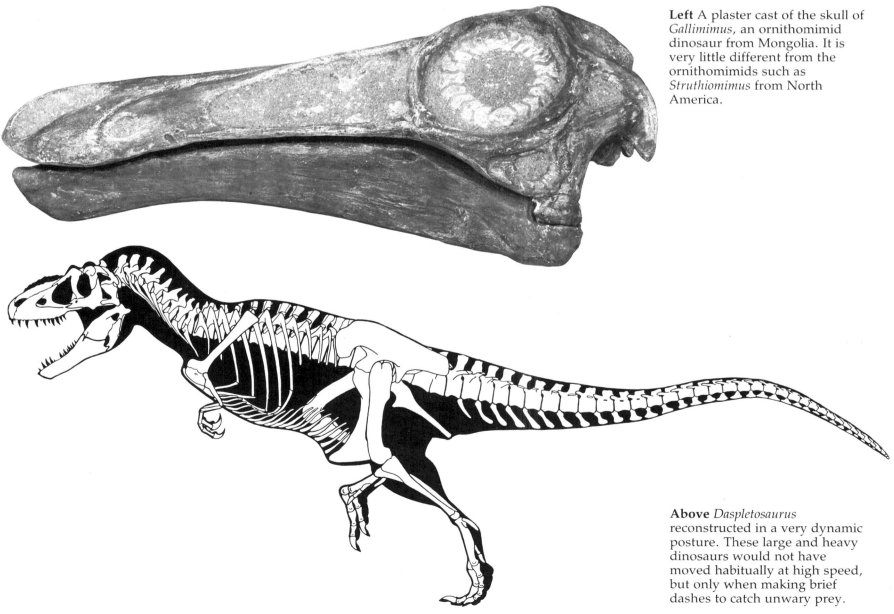

Above *Daspletosaurus* reconstructed in a very dynamic posture. These large and heavy dinosaurs would not have moved habitually at high speed, but only when making brief dashes to catch unwary prey.

sort would have left the prey little chance of either escape or survival once caught between the huge teeth-lined jaws of this dinosaur. This type of attacking strategy may well explain the very heavy and strong skull of *Tyrannosaurus*, which would have to be strong to withstand the enormous shock of the collision between predator and prey, and the desperate struggles of the doomed prey before it was finally subdued between the jaws. This is not to say that *Tyrannosaurus* never took carrion, or scavenged old carcasses at times, in the same way that African lions will do today if they have the chance.

There are a variety of theropods which are close relatives of *Tyrannosaurus* and found in different areas of the world at this time. These include *Albertosaurus* and *Daspletosaurus* from North America and *Tarbosaurus* from Asia. All of these dinosaurs were similar in their bodily details, but tended to differ in their build. *Albertosaurus*, for example, was quite a lightly built tyrannosaur, while *Daspletosaurus* was a particularly heavily built form. It is not improbable that these differences reflect differences in their feeding habits, the larger forms choosing heavier prey than the smaller forms.

Very recently some more large theropod remains have been discovered in South America. *Abelisaurus* (Abel's reptile) is a large theropod, known to date only from the skull which has been described. It was very large (the skull alone being over 3 feet [1m] long) and seems to have resembled the large theropods of the late Jurassic, *Allosaurus* and *Yangchuanosaurus*.

Almost at the other extreme, in terms of the specialization of theropods, come the next type of theropods: the ornithomimosaurs represented by *Struthiomimus* (ostrich mimic).

The remains of ornithomimosaurs were first recovered in the late 1880s from the late Cretaceous of Colorado and consisted of a partial foot. The proportions of the foot resembled those of a large ground bird, such as an ostrich, and this is the origin of the name. At first they were thought to be the remains of an ornithopod dinosaur (since they too were known to have rather birdlike legs and feet), but the later discovery of parts of the pelvis, soon proved that these were saurischian rather than ornithischian dinosaurs.

Just after the turn of the century an almost complete skeleton of one of these types of dinosaur was described and given the name *Struthiomimus*. The similarity in proportion between this dinosaur and a living ostrich are quite striking: small head with large eyes and a toothless beak, long neck, very long legs. However, unlike modern birds, these dinosaurs possessed a long bony tail, and arms with claws rather than wings (or remnants of wings – as in the case of ostriches).

The head, with its toothless, horn covered beak gave these animals an extraordinarily birdlike appearance – far from the predatory aspect of other theropods such as tyrannosaurs. The skull was particularly light and flexible, and could be moved with great precision. It seems quite possible that, as in the case of the living ostrich, these dinosaurs had a very broad diet, ranging from fruit and seeds to insects and small reptiles. The long and flexible neck is in complete contrast to the torso, which appears to have been rather stiff and short. The bones of the back seem to have been held firmly in place by stiff ligaments and the belly region was lined with belly ribs (gastralia), adding to the general inflexibility of this part of the body. The tail was long with a very slender tip.

The hindlegs were very long and three toed (like an emu), and were clearly designed for fast running. The forelimbs, too, were long and slender and their hands had three long, slender fingers ending in gently curving claws (rather that the sharply hooked claws seen in almost all other theropods). The arms and hands were clearly used for catching, holding and manipulating all manner of food.

Although there has been some dispute over the way of life of these animals in the past, ideas today are pretty well unanimous. Ornithomimosaurs were in all probability ground-dwelling animals, capable of very fast running. This fast running ability, coupled with agility and good vision no doubt helped them to avoid larger potential predators, but also made them able hunters of smaller animals, especially small reptiles and mammals.

Since the early years of this century a small number of ornithomimosaurs have been discovered, including *Ornithomimus* after which the group was originally named, and *Dromiceiomimus*, both of which come from North America. There are also *Gallimimus*, *Archaeornithomimus*, *Garudimimus* and an as yet poorly known dinosaur, which may belong to this group, known as *Harpymi-*

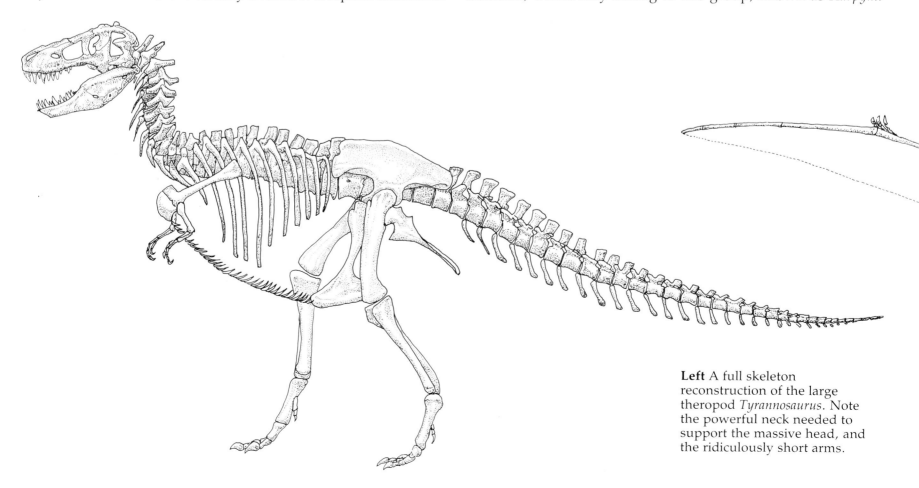

Left A full skeleton reconstruction of the large theropod *Tyrannosaurus*. Note the powerful neck needed to support the massive head, and the ridiculously short arms.

Right This fine specimen of the large tyrannosaurid *Albertosaurus* is on display in the Field Museum of Natural History, Chicago. Note the well-developed gastralia (belly ribs) shown in this specimen.

Below The remains of *Quetzalcoatlus*, a giant pterosaur, have been found in the late Cretaceous of Texas. It may have had a wingspan of 48 feet (15m) – the equivalent of a small aircraft. It is thought that these pterosaurs fed on carrion.

Right The very well preserved skull of the tyrannosaurid *Tarbosaurus* which has been collected in Mongolia. This specimen is in the Paleontological Museum at Ulan Bator, Mongolia.

mus. All of these forms originate in Asia and are known with varying degrees of completeness.

Another rather unusual group of theropods are the saurornithoidids (bird-like reptiles). These are found exclusively in North America and Asia and in their general details closely resemble ornithomimids. The most important difference between saurornithoidids and the latter group is the presence of teeth in the jaws in saurornithoidids. *Stenonychosaurus* (slender-clawed reptile) is one well-known example of this group. The body of these animals was clearly designed for fast running, the arms were long and grasping and the head was rather long and narrow, with small, but sharp, serrated teeth.

The head is rather interesting for two reasons. First the eyes are very large and forward pointing, which suggests that they had excellent stereoscopic vision; second, they appear to have

unusually large brains, comparable in size to those of birds. These were clearly fast-moving, highly sophisticated predators, and it has been suggested that their stereoscopic vision allowed them to catch small mammals in the twilight.

Saurornithoidids have also been the subject of an interesting thought experiment by two Canadian colleagues. They tried to imagine what dinosaurs may have looked like if they had not become extinct at the close of the Cretaceous Period. Their answer was the 'dinosauroid', an intelligent, bipedal and rather man-like creature. All the attributes are derived from saurornithoidids (their model being the Canadian specimen of *Stenonychosaurus*).

Another rather extreme form of theropod is represented by the animal which has been named *Oviraptor*, and its close relatives. This extraordinary creature also has the distinction of being another theropod which lacks teeth!

The first remains of *Oviraptor* (egg thief) were recovered from Mongolia in the 1920s and consisted of a skull and partial skeleton. The skull has toothless jaws, covered by a horny beak in life. It is much shorter and more compact than those of ornithomimosaurs, and has a curious crest in the middle of the snout.

The skeleton is much more poorly known, not ever having been properly described, but appears to have been of a fairly conventional theropod design: long slender legs for running, fairly long powerfully clawed hands and arms, and a long slender neck.

Since the original discovery, little more was known of these extraordinary creatures until the early 1970s, when a team of scientists from Mongolia found at least five better preserved skulls and skeletons. As yet these have not been completely described, but it is known that there is quite a wide range of form

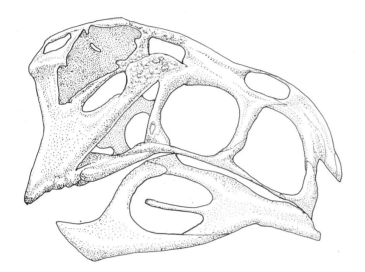

Above The extraordinary skull of the theropod dinosaur *Oviraptor* poses all sorts of problems of interpretation. It is toothless (what did it eat?); what was the crest for?

Top right The well-preserved skeleton of the ornithomimid *Struthiomimus* as displayed at the Museum of Paleontology at Drumheller, Canada.

Right A scene from Mongolia in the late Cretaceous. Two *Protoceratops* attempt to defend their eggs from the attentions of a pair of *Oviraptor*.

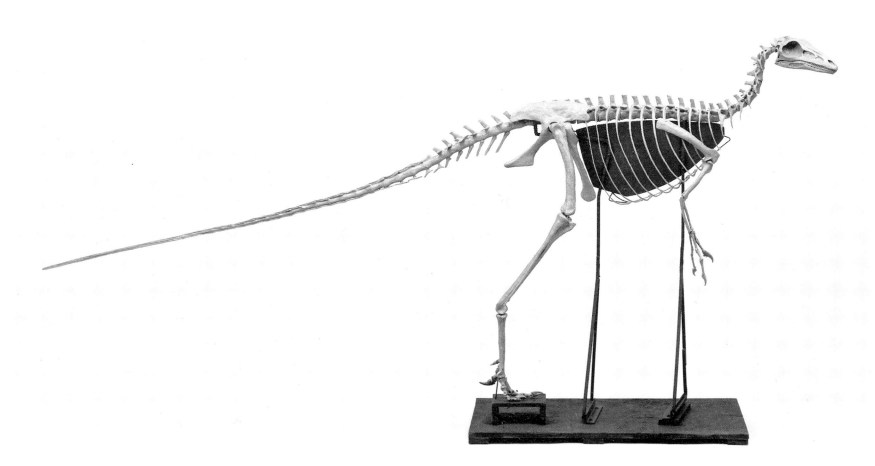

of the snout horn. It is quite possible that this will have changed shape significantly during growth, and what is being found is an age range of the same species, rather than lots of different species. The material from Mongolia also suggests that a variety of odd theropod bones discovered at various times in North America and Asia, and given their own names, may well be remains of oviraptors. These include *Caenagnathus, Macrophalangia, Chirostenotes, Elmisaurus* and *Ingenia*.

The circumstances of the original discovery of *Oviraptor* in Asia may shed some light on the habits of this unusual creature. Henry Fairfield Osborn, who described this dinosaur first, noted that its head was found somewhat crushed and on top of a nest of *Protoceratops* eggs. For this reason, he named this dinosaur *Oviraptor philoceratops*, which means 'egg thief, fond of ceratopian eggs.' He thought that the unfortunate creature had perhaps been caught in the act of stealing eggs from a *Protoceratops* nest, its skull having been crushed by an enraged parent!

It is certainly possible that this creature may have raided nests in this way, the short powerful toothless jaws could certainly have cracked open dinosaur eggs. The fact that they seem to have

had a pair of sharp toothlike structures in the roof of the mouth, which could have been used to crack open an egg once in the mouth (so that the nourishing juices could all be swallowed) seems to confirm this idea.

However, it has been suggested that these dinosaurs may, by contrast, have been herbivores. A parallel has been drawn between the structure of the mouth in these types of dinosaurs and those of dicynodonts, the mammal-like reptiles of the Permian and Triassic. At present I prefer to see these animals as egg eaters, but it is quite possible that they had a broad and varied diet.

Sickle-clawed theropods are also known from late Cretaceous times, both in North America and Asia. I will not spend long describing these, as they have already been considered in the previous chapter. Examples are *Dromaeosaurus* and *Velociraptor*.

Dromaeosaurus (fast reptile) was small (4½-4¾ feet [1.5-1.8m] long), and comes from the late Cretaceous of Canada and consists of a partial skull and an assortment of footbones, found in the early years of this century on the Red Deer River. It lay unappreciated as a special dinosaur (a sickle-clawed type) until *Deinonychus* was described in the 1960s.

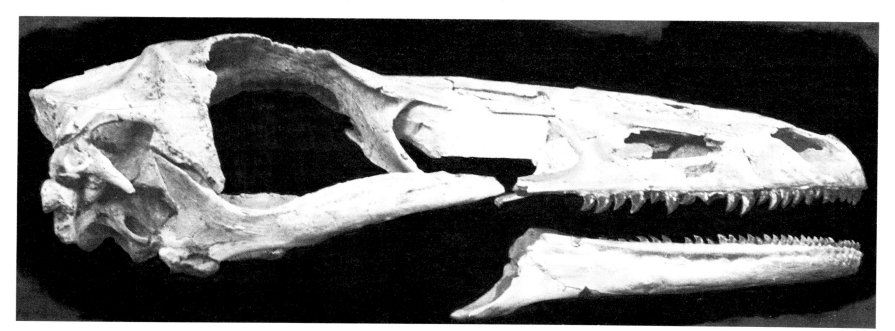

Left The skeleton of the very agile saurornithoidid theropod *Stenonychosaurus*. These resemble ornithomimids, but possess teeth.

Bottom left The well-preserved skull of the mongolian saurornithoidid *Saurornithoides*. Note the small, but sharp, curved teeth.

Right A pair of *Dromaeosaurus* gorge on the carcass of the ceratopian *Centrosaurus*.

Velociraptor (speedy thief) was similarly sized to *Dromaeosaurus*, comes from the late Cretaceous of Mongolia and was a contemporary of *Oviraptor*. It was first described on the basis of a well-preserved skull and partial skeleton, but is now supplemented by material discovered more recently by expeditions to the same areas of Mongolia by various team of scientists.

The predatory abilities of this dinosaur cannot be doubted and were similar to those already described for *Deinonychus*. One new discovery seems to have confirmed their predatory habits remarkably. This was the discovery of a pair of dinosaurs (a young *Protoceratops* [the prey] and *Velociraptor* [the predator]) apparently fossilized in a death struggle. How this came to happen we may never know, but it is very plain that *Velociraptor* had a firm grip on the head of its unfortunate victim and its legs tucked up as if in position to kick out with the deadly claws on its feet. Apart from rare evidence of stomach contents, this is one of the few clues about the diet of any dinosaur ever discovered.

Some really puzzling theropod remains have come from Asia over the last few decades. Not only the remains of quite well-preserved dinosaurs, but also those of tantalizingly poorly preserved ones, such as those mentioned below.

From the late Cretaceous of southern Mongolia comes *Deinocheirus* (terrible hand), which consists of a pair of huge arms (7¾ feet [2.4m] long) and shoulder blades which were discovered by a joint Polish-Mongolian expedition to the Gobi Desert.

In their general appearance, these arms seem to be closest to those seen in the ornithomimosaurs. The hand however differs in that the fingers are of almost equal length, while those in the hand of typical ornithomimosaurs tend to have a shorter and more twisted first finger. Whatever this theropod was it was clearly enormous. The arms are far larger than those of any other theropod known and imply an enormous skeletal frame to go with it. Quite why no one has found any more of this creature is a mystery. It would be wonderful to know more of this creature than just these arms.

Therizinosaurus (sickle reptile) is also from the late Cretaceous of

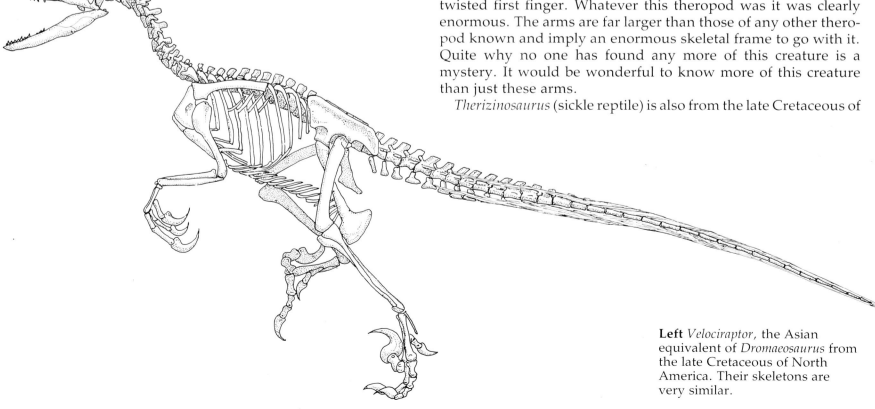

Left *Velociraptor*, the Asian equivalent of *Dromaeosaurus* from the late Cretaceous of North America. Their skeletons are very similar.

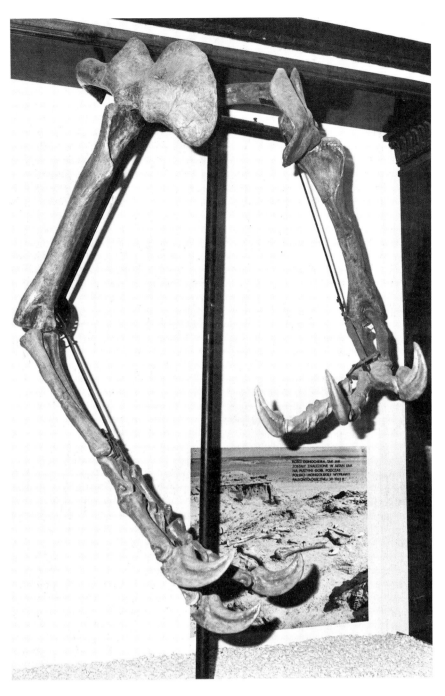

Mongolia, and was discovered by a joint Soviet-Mongolian expedition. The discovery consists of some more gigantic claws, pieces of forelimb and the hindlimb of another very large theropod. One of the claws alone measures 2¼ feet (70cm).

Another mystery, this dinosaur has been suggested as being a termite or ant eater – using its huge claws to break into termitaria. It seems very unlikely, however, that a diet of ants would sustain an animal the size of this!

Noasaurus (reptile from northwest Argentina) consists of a few fragmentary remains, including a jaw bone, some vertebrae and ribs and claw bones from the very latest Cretaceous. It would appear that this dinosaur may have independently evolved a sickle claw on its hindleg, and has some extraordinarily shaped neck bones, but until more is discovered of this creature it will remain a considerable puzzle.

Segnosaurus (slow reptile) is now known from a skull and part skeleton which was collected from Mongolia. This strange dinosaur is thought to have been a theropod, but if it is then it is a most extraordinary one. In the skull its teeth are rather small and confined to the rear of the jaws and there was a toothless beak (as in ornithischians). The pelvis looks ornithischian as well, with a backwardly pointing pubis. However the pubis is also known to be backwardly pointing in the sickle clawed dinosaurs as well, so it is possible in some cases to be a theropod and have an ornithischian type pelvis.

These dinosaurs appear to have been rather heavily built and may have been plant eaters, but their affinities to other groups are far from clear at the moment. One suggestion is that this is a long lost group representing the early members of a group which bridged the dividing line between early sauropodomorph and ornithischian groups of the late Triassic/early Jurassic. But quite why they appear so late in the Cretaceous is a puzzle.

Sauropodomorphs

Late Cretaceous sauropodomorphs are to be found on almost all continents, but are frustratingly poorly known for the most part. It would seem to have been the case that the group was able to survive in late Cretaceous times, but not to prosper. They were probably never particularly abundant in any habitats – but they were there!

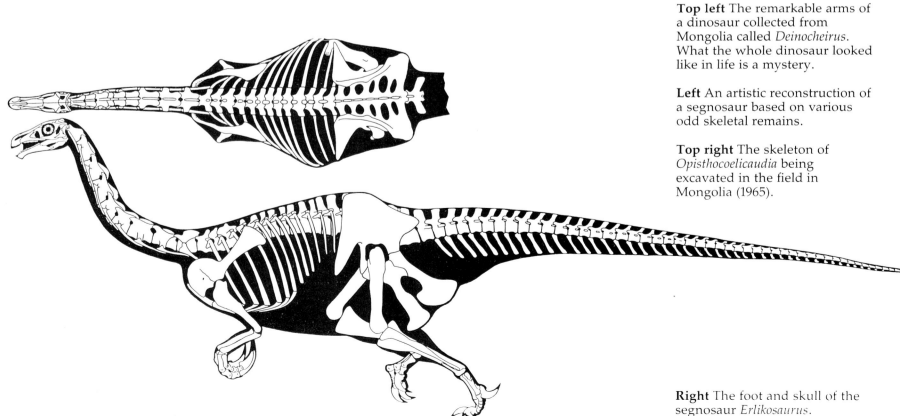

Top left The remarkable arms of a dinosaur collected from Mongolia called *Deinocheirus*. What the whole dinosaur looked like in life is a mystery.

Left An artistic reconstruction of a segnosaur based on various odd skeletal remains.

Top right The skeleton of *Opisthocoelicaudia* being excavated in the field in Mongolia (1965).

Right The foot and skull of the segnosaur *Erlikosaurus*.

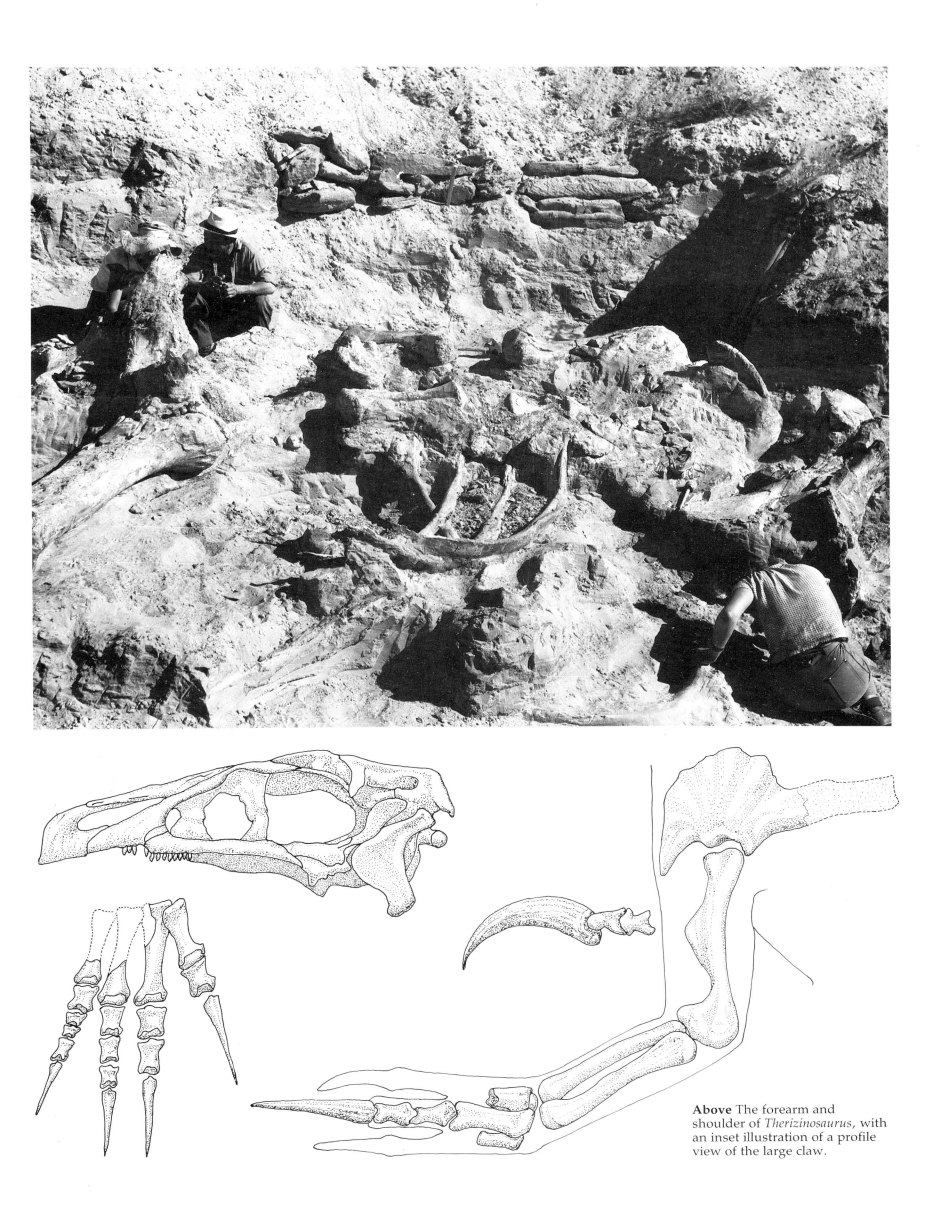

Above The forearm and shoulder of *Therizinosaurus*, with an inset illustration of a profile view of the large claw.

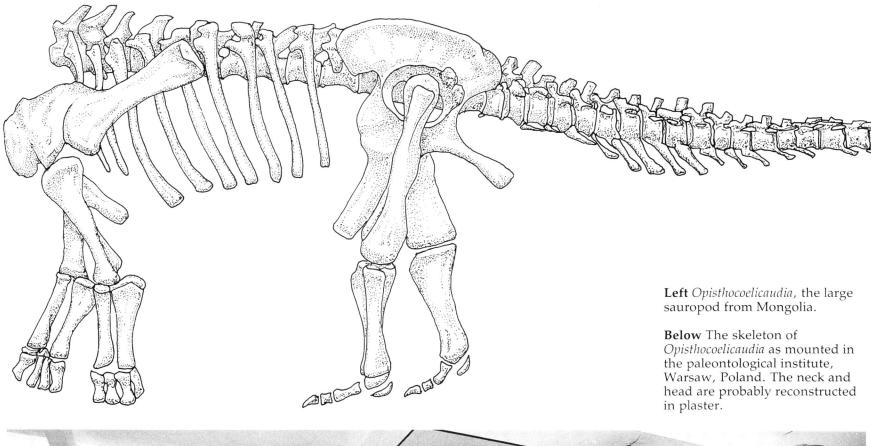

Left *Opisthocoelicaudia*, the large sauropod from Mongolia.

Below The skeleton of *Opisthocoelicaudia* as mounted in the paleontological institute, Warsaw, Poland. The neck and head are probably reconstructed in plaster.

In recent years, *Opisthocoelicaudia* (posterior cavity tail) has come to be one of the best known of this type of dinosaur. It is a typical sauropod, with heavy legs, a moderately long tail and stout chest and bears at least a passing resemblence to *Camarasaurus* of the late Jurassic. The frustrating thing is that the neck and head of this dinosaur were not found.

The remains of another sauropod have been found in rocks of the same age, and in the same area of Mongolia that produced *Opisthocoelicaudia*. This consists mainly of an isolated skull and has been named *Nemegtosaurus*. The skull is similar in shape to that of a typical apatosaur, and this does not seem to be consistent with the form of the skeleton of *Opisthocoelicaudia*. It will be interesting to see whether new material proves a relationship between the isolated skull and skeletons of these two dinosaurs.

One of the most surprising discoveries of recent years has been that made of *Saltasaurus* (reptile from Salta Province) in Argentina. Much of the skeleton of this dinosaur was recovered, and it proved to be typical of most sauropods in terms of its general anatomy. However, large and small plates of bony armor which appear to have been embedded in the skin were also found and are associated with the skeleton. At first these plates were thought to belong to an armored ornithischian dinosaur (an ankylosaur), but it became obvious that this was not the case. This is the first evidence of armor plating in these types of dinosaur.

Other sauropods of this time include *Alamosaurus, Titanosaurus, Loricosaurus* and *Laplatosaurus*. Numerous eggs of the late Cretaceous sauropod dinosaur *Hypselosaurus* have been recovered from Aix-en-Provence, southern France.

Ornithischians

Numerous ornithischians appear in the late Cretaceous. They appear to be the most numerous and varied than the sauropodomorphs in all habitats so far examined.

A considerable variety of ornithopods appear in late Cretaceous times. These range from small agile forms, very similar in most details to creatures like *Hypsilophodon*, seen in the early Cretaceous. Examples of these are *Thescelosaurus, Parksosaurus* and *Rhabdodon*. The iguanodon-like dinosaurs which were quite widespread in early Cretaceous times seem to have been replaced by a group known as hadrosaurs or 'duck-billed' dinosaurs, and were one of the most abundant and widespread of dinosaur groups at this time.

The hadrosaurs can be divided very crudely into two groups: those which have crests (known as lambeosaurines) and those which do not have crests (hadrosaurines). We shall look at some examples of both of these groups.

Parasaurolophus (parallel crested reptile) is a well-known lambeosaurine hadrosaur because of its distinctive tubular crest. It comes from the late Cretaceous of North America.

The body form of hadrosaurs was little different from that of most ornithopods so far described. The tail was long and muscular and the hindlimbs long and strong to take most of the body weight during walking (though they could also walk with ease on all fours, their hands have hoof-shaped claws). By comparison with the *Iguanodon*-like dinosaurs of the early Cretaceous, these ornithopods had lost the spike-shaped thumb, only having four fingers on the hand. And they tend to have rather more elaborate skulls.

In the case of *Parasaurolophus* the skull has a broad, downturned beak which – as in all dinosaurs of this group – is toothless and was used to gather plants into the mouth. Behind the beak there were massive batteries of teeth. These were arranged in straight rows of diamond-shaped interlocking teeth, which wore down to form flattened grinding surfaces for crushing up plant tissues to a

pulp before they were swallowed. These batteries of teeth were the equivalent of the powerful chewing teeth of horses and cattle living today and were an excellent way of grinding up plants to extract the maximum of nourishment. The jaws were operated by large muscles at the rear of the head.

Above the snout, the bones that normally cover the nose area of the snout were enormously enlarged, forming a crest. In this dinosaur they were a pair of hollow tubes which ran upward and backward from the nose openings in a long arc to the end of the crest. The tubes then turned sharply backwards on themselves, tucking down against the head above the region of the eye and leading down to the area that would have been at the top of the throat in the living animal.

There have been numerous suggested explanations for these crests. At first it was thought that the crests formed snorkels, that the top end of the crest was open (which, in fact, it is not) and that these animals could breathe through the open end while they were feeding on water plants with their noses under water. Another idea along similar lines, was that the crest tube acted as a reservoir of air for use when the dinosaur was totally submerged, but the volume of the crest was really too small to have allowed them to store enough air to have been worthwhile. Later it was suggested that the large area of the tubes was there to give them a very powerful sense of smell. None of these ideas is

Above The enormously elongated crest on this hadrosaur *Parasaurolophus* was used as a resonator for calling with.

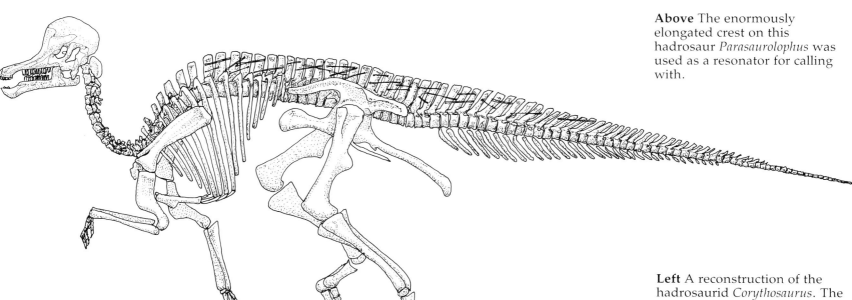

Left A reconstruction of the hadrosaurid *Corythosaurus*. The long and deep tail counterbalances the weight of the body so that little weight has to be taken on the hands.

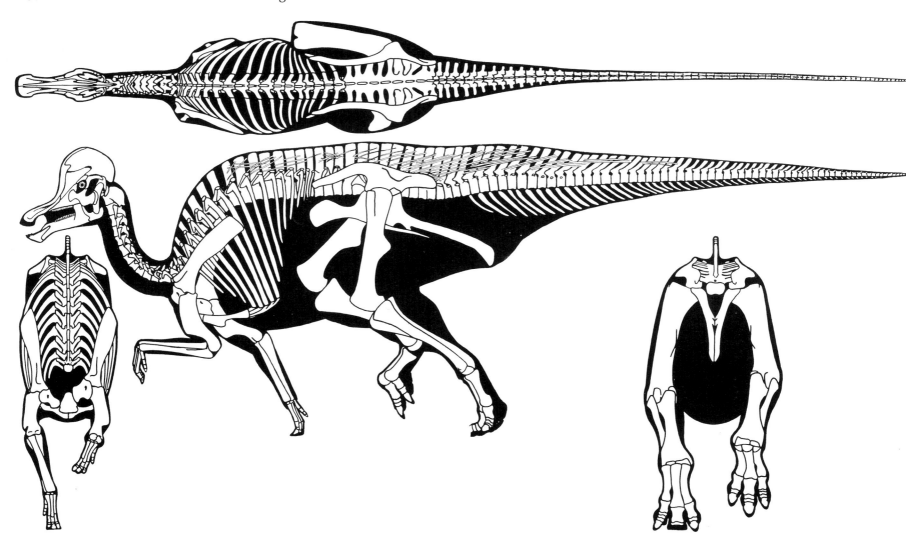

accepted today. It is now generally agreed that the tubes acted as resonators. That is to say that they were like the tubes of a musical instrument such as a trombone, and gave these animals the ability to produce loud and very distinctive calls for social purposes (establishment of territories, mating, warning, individual recognition, etc). The implication of this is that these were very social animals, akin in some respects to birds and mammals living today. In addition to the sound qualities of these crests, it is obvious that they will have had a visual role as well for recognition, since they are such large and distinctive features.

Corythosaurus (Corinthian Helmet reptile), a hadrosaur also from the North America, has yet another type of crest, this time shorter and higher than the previous example. The remainder of the skeleton is virtually identical with that of *Parasaurolophus*.

Corythosaurus was studied in some detail a few years ago because it was found that the skulls of several of these dinosaurs tended to differ a little in structure. For a long time this was thought to indicate species differences between them. A detailed study revealed that it was much more likely that the differences could be associated with either the age of the individuals (smaller young individuals had much smaller crests than the adults) or with the sex of the dinosaur (males had larger crests than females for example). When this was realized, it became evident that there were not nearly so many species of this sort of dinosaur living at the same time, just lots of young as well as old individuals and males and females.

This is not so startling a conclusion when you think about it, but as can probably be appreciated it is only very rarely that paleontologists can prove, as reasonably as possible, what the sex of a dinosaur may have been, or whether a specimen is just a young one of a larger dinosaur, or a new species of smaller dinosaur.

Saurolophus (crested reptile) was less prominently crested than previous examples. In this type of hadrosaur the crest consisted of a thin prong of bone projecting up and back from the eye region. In front of the prong, the area of the snout, above and behind the beak was broad and depressed on either side of the midline. It seems highly likely that the depressed area was covered by a layer of skin, which in life was capable of forming an expandable pouch; this would have formed a movable resonator, a little like the soft, flabby nose of an elephant seal, acting as a resonator for their roars.

This hadrosaur has been found in both North America and Asia – unlike the previous two which are so far confined to Western North America.

Hadrosaurines have a much more conventional appearance than the crested forms. Examples include dinosaurs such as *Edmontosaurus, Anatosaurus* (which is being renamed *Anatotitan*) and the gigantic Chinese hadrosaur *Shantungosaurus* which reached a length of some 45 feet (14m).

These dinosaurs were very little different in body shape from the previous types, but there were subtle differences in the shape of the pelvic bones. The principal difference lies in the structure of the skull: the snout tends to be considerably broader, and if anything more ducklike than the previous examples. This is particularly the case in *Anatosaurus*. The beak was presumably very important in that it was designed to allow these animals to feed in an

Left *Hypacrosaurus*
(=*Corythosaurus*) shown in a
series of skeletal studies to give a
complete picture of its anatomy.

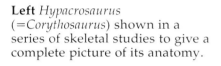

Bottom left A mounted skeleton
of *Corythosaurus*, this time
shown in a bipedal feeding
posture.

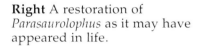

Right A restoration of
Parasaurolophus as it may have
appeared in life.

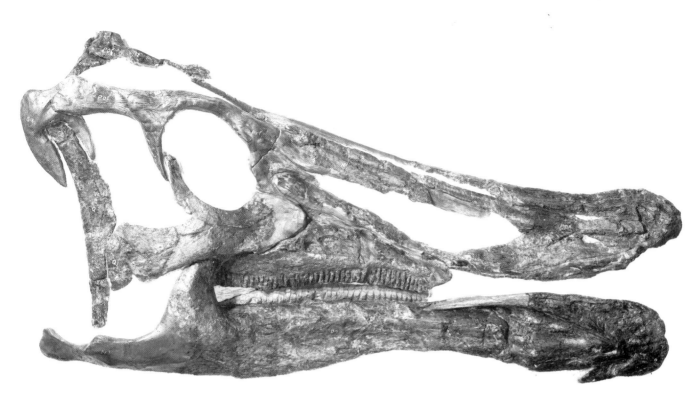

Left In this hadrosaur, *Prosaurolophus*, the crest is limited to a small prominence behind the eye. The beak is broad and duck-like.

Right An almost complete skeleton of *Saurolophus* displayed as a wall mount. Note the longer crest than that seen in *Prosaurolophus* (left).

Below A scene showing *Anatotitan (=Anatosaurus)* and *Saurolophus* (right).

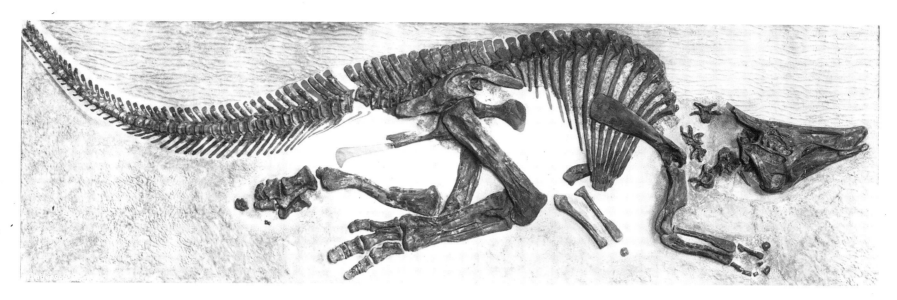

effective way on their preferred plants. So it is no doubt important to catalogue the precise difference in snout shape. Unfortunately it is not presently possible to tie food preference to snout type, though attempts are being made to do so.

Another group of dinosaurs which made its first appearance in the late Cretaceous are the pachycephalosaurs or 'bone headed dinosaurs.' These appear to have been bipedal dinosaurs, quite rare as fossils, which ranged in size from 6½ to 26 feet (2 to 8m) in length. There are at least three moderately well-known examples.

At present *Pachycephalosaurus* (thick headed reptile) is only known from an almost complete skull, lacking the lower jaw, and a few other large parts of the cranial dome. The skull is very large (over 2½ feet [80cm] long) and probably belonged to an animal that would have been in the region of 26 feet (8m) long.

The skull is dominated by the high-domed skull cap. This is made of solid bone, rather than indicating a very large brain. The purpose of the dome would appear to have been associated with their social behavior. It is thought that these animals had social lives as herding animals somewhat like those of living sheep and goats. That is to say that the head was used as a measure of the social status of individuals. In most cases the visual signal would have been sufficient. However when similarly sized individuals

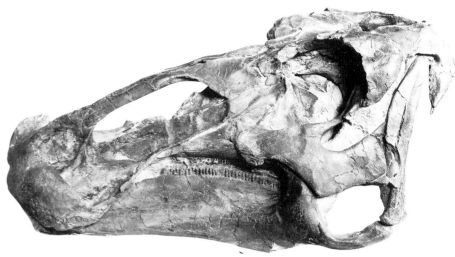

met, the seniority may have to have been settled by a head-to-head pushing contest, or by butting. The thickness of the dome in *Pachycephalosaurus* acted as a shock absorbing area for the enormous impact of large and heavy individuals head butting one another. It is a great pity that we still have not managed to find more of this dinosaur, because it is certain that parts of its skeleton, particularly its neck and back, would show a variety of other features associated with head butting.

Homalocephale (even headed) is another, better preserved, dome head. This one comes from Asia and is known not only from a quite well preserved skull, but also from parts of the remainder of the skeleton. The skull differs from the previous example in that it is strongly reinforced, but lacks a prominent dome on the top. The remainder of the skeleton shows that these were indeed bipedal, and that the backbone and tail were particularly reinforced by bony tendons. In addition the joints in the backbones were strongly reinforced to prevent the dislocation associated with their butting activities.

First of the pachycephalosaurs to be discovered, at the turn of the century, *Stegoceras* (horned roof) was based on a part skeleton,

with a well-preserved skull found in the 1920s. At about 6 feet (2m) in length (similar in size to the much more recently discovered *Homalocephale*) this dinosaur has a distinctive high dome on the skull roof.

Careful study of this skull and other fragments led to the realization that the dome of these dinosaurs was probably an adaptation for butting, and comparisons were made with modern sheep and goat lifestyles. It has even been suggested that these dinosaurs are relatively rare in the fossil record because they tended to

live in upland areas (as do goats), away from rivers and water courses that are so essential for the fossilization of animals. Until the better skeletal material of *Homalocephale* was discovered, it was very difficult to reconstruct the skeleton of this dinosaur because its skeleton was so fragmentary.

Pachycephalosaurs were quite widespread in Asia and North America, and one interesting discovery (*Majungatholus*) has been made in the late Cretaceous of Malagasy (Madagascar), which suggests that they also spread to the southern continents.

The earliest pachycephalosaur may have been a small creature known as *Yaverlandia* from the early Cretaceous of southern England. But at the moment this is only known from an extremely small and poorly preserved piece of skull roof, so nothing very definite can be said about this specimen.

Above left *Edmontosaurus*, a crestless hadrosaur, with a very thick and broad beak. The area around the nostrils is excavated and probably contained a resonating pouch.

Below A late Cretaceous scene with *Edmontosaurus* and the tyrannosaurid *Daspletosaurus*.

Following the appearance of the psittacosaurs in the latter part of the early Cretaceous, the ceratopians rapidly radiated in the late Cretaceous into a spectacularly successful group of dinosaurs. In some parts of North America layers of sediment are strewn with the bones and carcasses of these types of animal. They were clearly extremely successful at this time in Earth's history. Quite why this was so is not certain, but they may represent a group which had managed to adapt themselves to a very specific diet of plants, or so their jaws would seem to indicate.

Above A complete skeleton reconstruction of *Edmontosaurus* from the Smithsonian Institution, Washington.

Right The skull of *Pachycephalosaurus*, showing the extraordinary thickness of the skull roof.

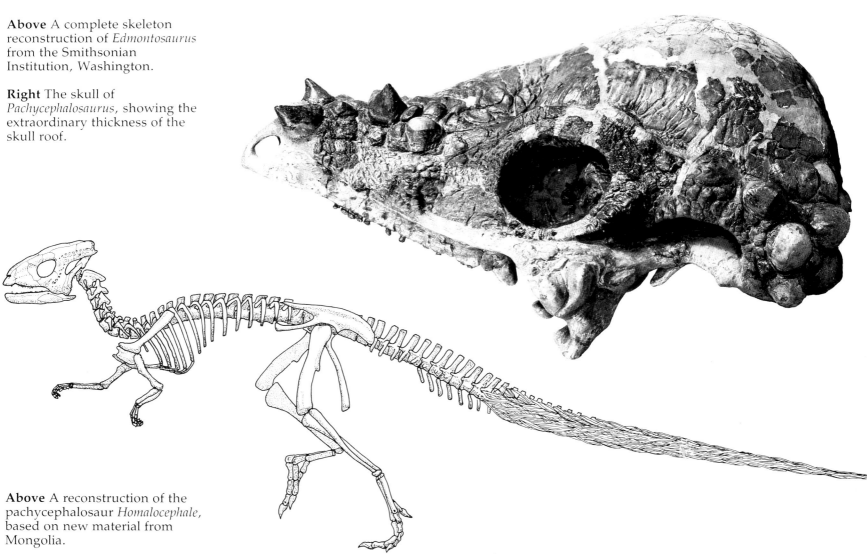

Above A reconstruction of the pachycephalosaur *Homalocephale*, based on new material from Mongolia.

All the ceratopians had similar jaws, which were very distinctive. The front of the jaws were dominated by a very large, horn-covered, parrot-like beak, which was narrow and sharply hooked. Behind the beak the jaws were arranged very close together and were operated by enormous muscles which ran up into the spaces at the back of the skull, and in some instances up onto the surface of the huge frill, which was so characteristic of these dinosaurs. The teeth were also modified into the equivalent of the tooth batteries seen in hadrosaurs, except this time, instead of forming broad grinding plates as the tooth wore down, they formed sharp guillotine-like cutting blades. These jaws must have been able to cut the toughest plant fibers into short lengths with ease and large muscular cheeks held the food in the mouth before it was swallowed.

Apart from the jaws, the ceratopians all possessed, to varying degrees, combinations of horns and frills on the skull. The horns were invariably found on the nose or over the eyes, while the frill rose as a broad sheet of bone from the back edge of the skull. The exact position, size, and shape of the horns varied from species to species, as did the size and shape of the frill and the degree to which it was ornamentated by small 'hornlets' (epoccipitals). These varying patterns allow paleontologists to distinguish species with some confidence, and presumably served the same purpose in the living animals.

The first remains of *Protoceratops* (first horned face) were found in the 1920s during the expedition to Asia, organized by the American Museum of Natural History. Many complete skeletons were found and collected and, of even greater importance at the time, nests of eggs laid by this dinosaur were also discovered. Many of the nests were very well preserved and showed that the eggs were laid in ring-shaped clutches in shallow depressions in the sand, and in what appeared to be colonial nest sites.

Protoceratops was not a biped, as was *Psittacosaurus*, but walked on all fours, even though it was little larger than the latter. The

Above The skull of the Mongolian pachycephalosaur *Prenocephale*.

Left A flesh restoration of the low-domed pachycephalosaur *Homalocephale*.

Left The large pachycephalosaur *Pachycephalosaurus* looks down upon the antics of two *Stegoceras*, which are head butting one another.

Right A nearly complete skeleton of *Protoceratops* preserved as it was discovered in the sandstone of Mongolia.

Below right The skull of another late Cretaceous ceratopian (*Leptoceratops*) from North America. This was a small, bipedal form and the skull here is somewhat flattened.

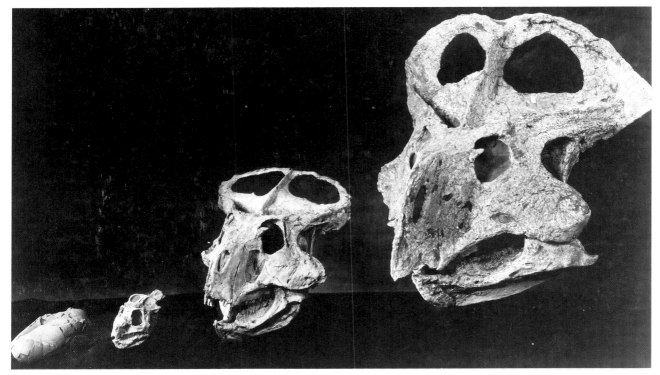

Left The discoveries in Mongolia include a complete size range of *Protoceratops* individuals from egg, through juvenile stages, to adult.

Below Adult *Protoceratops* attend the hatchlings at a nest.

Right *Euoplocephalus*. A large and well-preserved ankylosaurid from North America. Note the heavy armor and tail club.

Below right The skull of *Euoplocephalus* viewed from above.

beak was much more pronounced than in *Psittacosaurus*, and the head a great deal larger, with a high nose ridge, which in males almost took on the dimensions of a horn. The back of the head had a large frill of bone, unlike *Psittacosaurus*, where the frill was not at all obvious.

The skeleton is similar to that of *Psittacosaurus* in its proportions, and it is notable that the front legs are considerably shorter than the back ones, indicating that its ancestors were undoubtedly bipedal. The tail was still quite long in these types of ceratopian, but in later, larger forms the tail became shorter and less important, since it no longer performed the function of counterbalancing the body over the hips.

These animals were clearly low ground browsers, probably not very fast moving, relying on living in large social groups as protection against the many and varied predators which must have stalked them at this time. Evidence of their predators is graph-

ically illustrated by the marvellous fossil of a *Protoceratops* grasped in the arms of *Velociraptor* which was found in the Gobi Desert in recent years.

A variety of ceratopians similar in size and general shape are now known from deposits in North America as well as Asia.

Larger and altogether more heavily built than *Protoceratops* and relatives, *Styracosaurus* (spiky reptile) typified this general group. It comes from North America (as do all the large ceratopians to date – no large ones have yet been recorded from good material from Asia, which seems very surprising) and had a large heavy body, comparable in size to the largest living rhinoceros. The legs were stocky, indicating immense power, and the tail was quite short, as was the neck. The latter had shortened through the

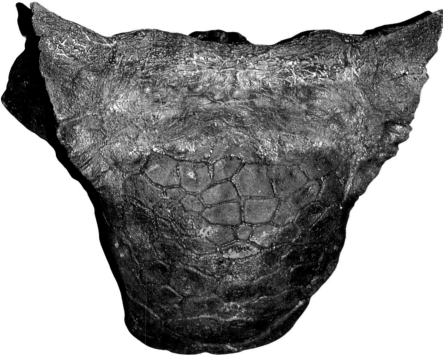

welding together of several of the neck vertebrae, as a way of adapting to support the weight of the huge and very heavy head of this animal.

The head was indeed huge, in proportion to the body, with a very narrow deep snout. The nose had a very large horn, which was straight and sharply pointed, and there were very small eyebrow horns (which hardly showed at all). The frill was large, with large openings in the front, where large jaw closing muscles were attached in life. But around the rim of the frill was a row of enormously long epoccipital bones, like a fan of horns.

The nose horn was clearly suitable for use as a defensive weapon, as it is in the living rhinoceros. The function of the frill and its subsidiary horns is less immediately obvious. It would seem likely that the frill was used as a defensive shield for the neck and shoulders. The fringe of spikes may equally have acted as deflectors, or even as offensive spikes. However, the frill spikes would seem to have been rather susceptible to blows from the side, which might easily have snapped them off. It seems much more likely that these structures may well have had a social function as well, acting as visual signals of social behavior. Male individuals may have faced one another and displayed their frills rather than direct fighting and risking serious injury, in order to establish their social ranking. Other individuals may well have been ordered in the manner of a 'pecking order' by reference to the size, shape and arrangement of their horns and frills.

These large and very powerful animals may have been the

equivalent of the black rhinoceros of today as feeders on low browse – there was after all no grass at this time. Quite mobile and probably fast-running, when pushed, they would have been formidable opponents of the larger carnosaurs such as the tyrannosaurs that lived at the same time. Quite what they ate is uncertain, but their powerful jaws would have given them the ability to slice up the toughest of plants.

Another of the best-known of all dinosaurs, *Triceratops* (three horned face) needs little explanation. The body form was very similar to the previous example except that it was larger (30 feet [9m] or more in length); the principal difference lay in the head, where there was a small nasal horn and a pair of large brow horns. Behind these horns the frill was large and broad, but this time solid, with a gently undulating margin formed by a row of small, triangular epoccipitals.

The large, paired brow horns and solid frill, suggest a slightly different social life compared to forms such as *Styracosaurus*. Paired brow horns can be interlocked in head-to-head pushing and wrestling contests, in the manner of living deer. In this case the solid frill may indeed have acted as a deflector of horns in case of slippage which would otherwise cause severe injury to an opponent. It is clear that there is no way that *Styracosaurus* could be involved in head-to-head pushing or wrestling matches of this type because a single nasal horn could not work in this fashion.

These dinosaurs were probaby preyed upon by the larger tyrannosaurs, and would have been formidable opponents. It seems quite likely that they lived in herds as one means of protecting the one stage of their life-cycle which would have been vulnerable to these predators: the young.

The last group of dinosaurs to be considered here represent the ultimate in defensive strategies to be adopted by any dinosaurs. Several moderately well preserved examples of ankylosaurs are known and can be divided into two groups: the ones with tail clubs (ankylosaurids) and those without (nodosaurids). Representatives of these are discussed below.

Euoplocephalus (true plated head) was an ankylosaurid dinosaur first discovered at the turn of the century from Alberta in Canada. Over the years a variety of part skeletons have been discovered which have allowed us to build up a reasonable picture of this dinosaur.

The head of the dinosaur was massive and heavily armored. The original bones of the skull are practically hidden beneath large, hard, bony plates which are stuck to them to provide greater strength and protection. The rear corners of the skull are also decorated by large conical plates and the lower jaw has large warty bony plates cemented to its sides. In addition to all this defensive armor there was even an armor plate in the eyelid, which must have shut against the claws of a predator like a steel

door. Behind this formidable array of armor, the body was equally well defended. The armor was divided into bands of much larger bony plates. On the neck the armor consisted of large plates and behind these were larger and higher blunt spikes. The armor was so arranged to combine protection with flexibility.

Beneath the armor plating there was a heavily-built quadrupedal dinosaur. The legs were strong and pillar-like to hold up the weight of the dinosaur, and probably to move it quite quickly on occasion (there is no reason to suppose that this was a very slow, ponderous dinosaur). The chest was broad and rounded and the tail was quite long and – most importantly – ended in a massive

club, comprising a group of large plates that have welded themselves together.

This dinosaur was a low browse feeding, heavily armored herbivore; probably armored in response to the attentions of the large tyrannosaurs of the time. The importance of the tail club to this type of dinosaur can only be understood with knowledge of the predators that may have tried to prey on this animal. Although Tyrannosaurs seem to have been big and extremely powerful creatures capable of tackling almost any dinosaur, they may have had one crucial fault, or perhaps one aspect of their design which could be exploited by a resourceful prey. This was the fact that they were bipedal carnivores, with very small arms. A

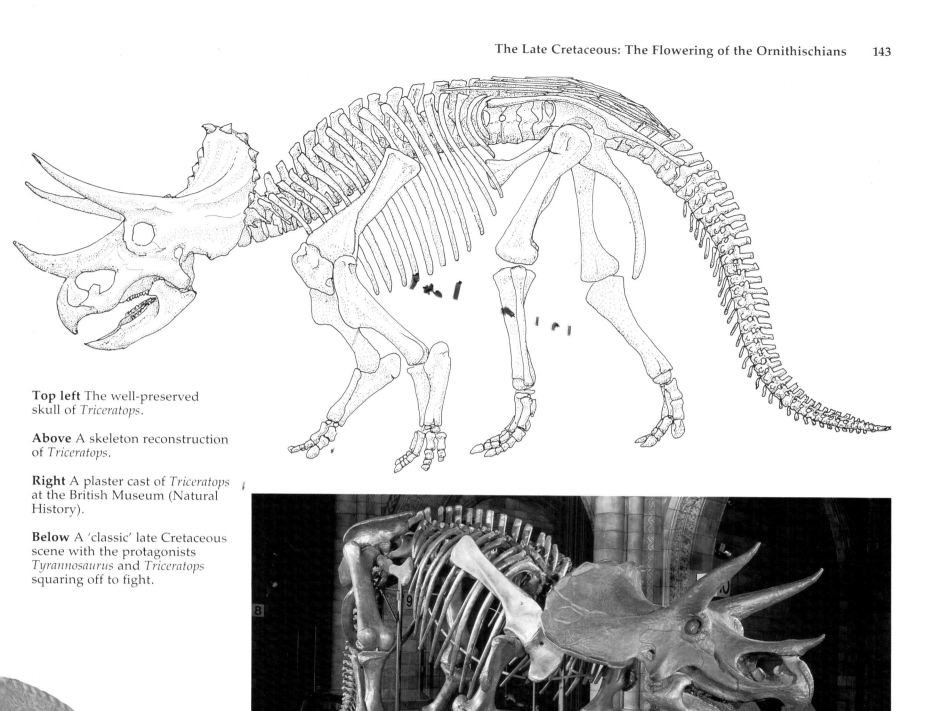

Top left The well-preserved skull of *Triceratops*.

Above A skeleton reconstruction of *Triceratops*.

Right A plaster cast of *Triceratops* at the British Museum (Natural History).

Below A 'classic' late Cretaceous scene with the protagonists *Tyrannosaurus* and *Triceratops* squaring off to fight.

fall to the ground by an animal the size of a tyrannosaur could have been fatal, they had no means of breaking their fall, through using outstretched arms for example, and could easily have broken a leg or hip bone. Once down the predator would rapidly attract the attention of other predators and soon become prey itself.

The importance of the tail club then is that this provided a fearsome weapon of defense for the ankylosaur. One well aimed swipe from the tail club could have easily toppled the mightiest tyrannosaur, and left it to its own doom.

Several ankylosaurs developed the tail club as a means of defense and their remains are found in North America and Asia in the late Cretaceous. They include *Ankylosaurus, Pinacosaurus, Saichania, Talarurus, Shamosaurus* and *Tarchia*.

Edmontonia (from Edmonton, Alberta) was a member of the other group of ankylosaurs, nodosaurids, which were not quite so common in the late Cretaceous. They were equally heavily armored, but tended to have narrower heads and frequently had a fringe of long spines around the flanks. Most importantly of all, these dinosaurs lacked a club on the tail, and therefore were without the all-important weapon which may have proved so useful for defending themselves.

It can only be guessed that the means of defense that these dinosaurs used was to crouch down against the ground, and rely

on the strength of the armor to withstand the attacks from the predators. The most important thing to avoid as far as these dinosaurs were concerned was being turned over by the predator, because once the belly was exposed they would have stood no chance, since it was practically unarmored.

A few dinosaurs of this type are found in late Cretaceous deposits, but their remains appear to be relatively rare compared to the ankylosaurs with tail clubs. These include *Nodosaurus, Silvisaurus, Panoplosaurus (Edmontonia)* and *Struthiosaurus*. To date no nodosaurids have been recovered from Asia, all have come from North America and Europe.

The type and variety of dinosaur found in the late Cretaceous appears to be the greatest of any of the ages looked at and give no real hint that the group was on the wane and heading for extinction. In fact, the groups seem to be becoming more vigorous, if the variety of new types is anything to go by. Yet for all the vigor of the dinosaurs, the end of this Period marks the extinction of them all. What happened and why it happened are still major unanswered questions. However, one grain of consolation can be gained from the knowledge that one group of animals alive today carries with it many dinosaur characters: birds. It has become evident over the past 15 years that the birds are indeed very close relatives of dinosaurs and may have been derived from a group of small active theropod dinosaurs at some time in the early Jurassic.

Above right Front view of the skull of the remarkable ceratopian *Styracosaurus*, showing the dramatic effect of the frill spikes.

Left *Tarbosaurus*, the large tyrannosaurid from Asia, makes an attempt to attack the ankylosaurid *Pinacosaurus*.

Right Flesh restoration of *Styracosaurus* based on a complete skeleton collected from the Red Deer River, Alberta.

CHAPTER 8

The Extinction of Dinosaurs

One of the eternal questions asked of any paleontologist is 'why did the dinosaurs become extinct?' It is a question that has haunted us all ever since it was first noted that dinosaurs did not appear to leave descendents in the Cenozoic Era, following the Cretaceous Period. The final disappearance of the dinosaurs is remarkable for its suddeness because, as was noted at the end of the last chapter, right up to the end, the groups which make up the dinosaurs showed no signs of waning and being on the point of disappearing anyway, but of actually starting new and previously untried ranges of body design.

Dinosaurs dominated the terrestrial environment for the best part of 150 million years, from the late Triassic onward. And looked at a little more broadly, reptiles of one sort or another dominated the seas as predators (as plesiosaurs and ichthyosaurs and toward the end of the Cretaceous as mosasaurs and, of course, the crocodiles), and the air (as pterosaurs although they had to share that environment with the birds in the latter half of the Mesozoic). The extinctions at the end of the Cretaceous are often quite unfairly thought of as a problem which concern the dinosaurs and dinosaurs alone – this is typified by the question so often heard above. As a result a number of theories have been put forward, in all seriousness, as means of explaining their demise.

A good example of this is one that was put forward many years ago. This is that the extinction of dinosaurs could be explained by the fact that the small mammals living at the same time may have taken to the habit of eating dinosaur eggs. The end result of this change in habit was the eventual annihilation of the dinosaurs! I do not think that it would take a genius to realize that this sort of theory is extremely unlikely to be true. We do not even known whether all dinosaurs laid eggs! In addition there are many species living today that eat eggs as a way of life, but they show no sign whatever of causing the extinction of the animals whose eggs

they take. In fact it would not make biological sense to hasten the end of the species upon which you depend for food. Nature tends always to maintain a balance between predator and prey and such would surely have been the case here as well.

The most obvious reason why this is a non-starter as a theory for the extinctions that occurred at the end of the Cretaceous, is simply that it was not just the dinosaurs that became extinct at the end of the Cretaceous, but a very wide range of other animals including pterosaurs, mosasaurs, plesiosaurs and ichthyosaurs; marine crocodiles, ammonites and chalky types of plankton. The end of the Cretaceous marked not just the end of one group, but the end of a wide range of organisms, and this sort of event is known as a mass extinction.

To put things into perspective, extinction is the eventual fate of all groups and species. As with an individual, species are born (originate), live for their duration and finally become extinct. So extinctions are to be expected throughout the fossil record. What is not necessarily expected is the simultaneous extinction of a whole range of organisms. Some species of organisms may indeed become extinct simultaneously purely coincidentally, but when whole groups of organisms appear to die off at the same time, then the question has to be asked whether there is a common cause that applies to them all, or is this a phenomenal piece of bad luck for the organisms concerned?

The other, and perhaps more difficult, series of facts which have to be considered at the same time as any theory is proposed to explain extinction, are the survivors. For example, why was it that birds were not obviously affected by the extinction event? And what about the bony fish? There are no major extinctions among these, nor are there among the fresh water crocodiles, or the lizards or snakes, sea turtles, salamanders, frogs and mammals. Why were certain groups apparently selectively destroyed

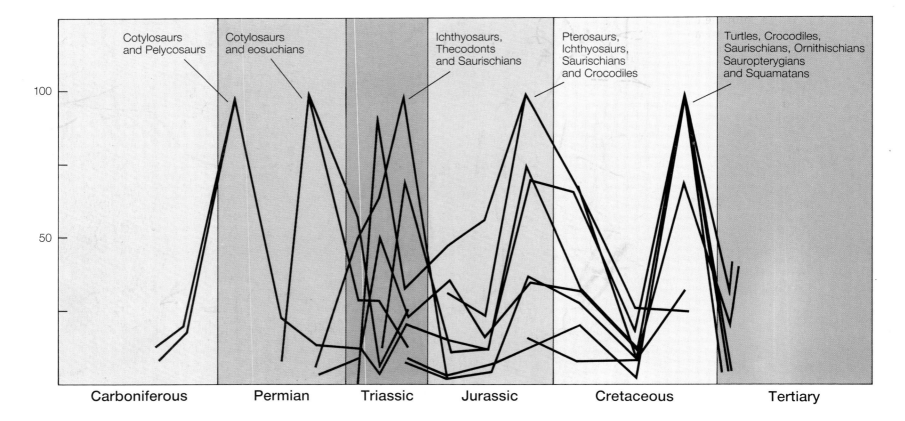

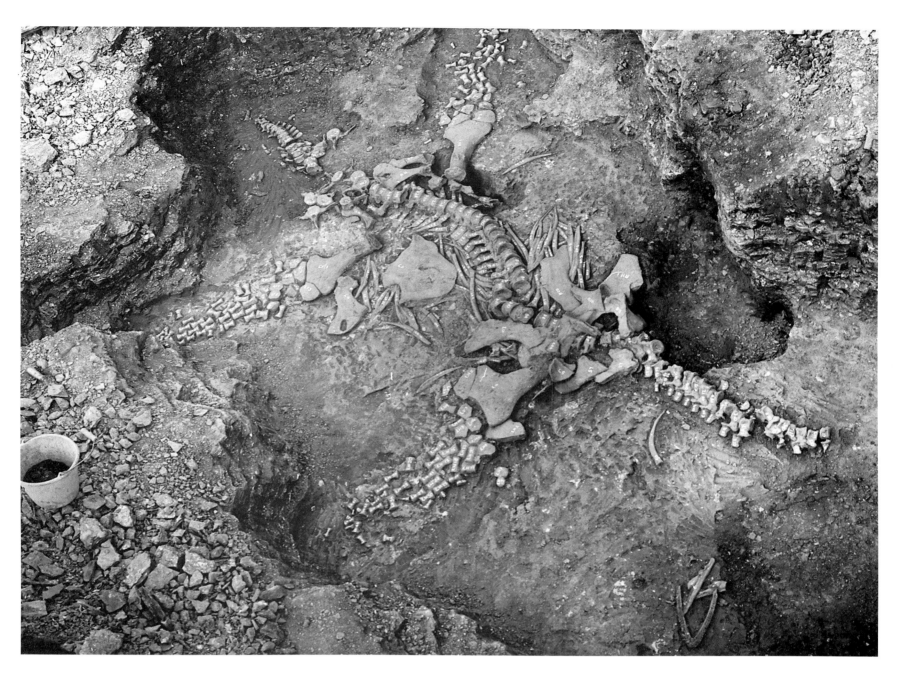

Above Plesiosaurs (large marine reptiles which are not dinosaurs) such as this one from Fletton clay pit near Peterborough, England, were not immune to the extinction that occurred at the end of the Cretaceous.

Left Chart of the changes in diversity of species through the ages of the Earth. It is clear that groups have come and gone at regular intervals. The end of the Cretaceous Period marked a particularly sharp dip in diversity.

Right An old engraving which was trying to create an impression of the world as it must have been during the reign of the dinosaurs on land. Lush vegetation and little scurrying mammals on land, giant sea monsters in the warm shallow seas.

Left A close-up of a finely preserved plesiosaur skull. Note the large eye socket; this was a visual hunter of most other sea creatures.

Below Tortoises seem to have plodded along right through the extinctions at the end of the Cretaceous as though nothing had happened.

Right Coelacanth fishes survived the Cretaceous extinctions as well. This fossil is very similar in most respects to the living coelacanth of the Indian Ocean.

Bottom right Crocodiles also survived the extinctions.

and others not? How could a factor that caused the extinction of so many groups on the one hand allow the survival of so many others?

Bearing in mind that we are dealing with an apparent mass-extinction rather than the localized extinction of a few species in the fossil record, then we can begin to eliminate many of the theories that have been put forward simply because they only explain why the dinosaurs may have become extinct and ignore the other groups concerned. Into this category must go the idea that, for example, dinosaurs were poorly designed and destined for extinction. As we have already seen this is clearly not true, and makes nonsense of the many advertising campaigns that use the dinosaur as a symbol of something that is slow, inefficient and ripe for extinction. This is also the case for theories that invoke diseases killing off dinosaurs.

Another rather quaint idea was that dinosaurs became extinct because of the evolution of *lepidoptera* (butterflies and moths) and their caterpillar larvae. The theory relies on the fact that the larvae

would cause the extensive defoliation of the plants forming the staple food of the herbivorous dinosaurs. As a consequence, these dinosaurs would starve and die, as would their predators, the carnivorous dinosaurs. Again we are faced with a credibility gap of enormous proportions if we are to believe that the appearance of caterpillar larvae is going to cause defoliation on a world-wide scale. And we still have to explain why this should have affected the marine creatures in the way that it did.

Other rather bizarre ideas concerning the extinction of dinosaurs include the idea that flowering plants evolved alkaloid poisons which dinosaurs could not detect, and this led to their constipation and eventual death. A gruesome tale to be sure, but unlikely to be true. However, it does give an insight into one area of origin of some theories for dinosaur extinction. The scientist who proposed this theory was a plant biochemist. He had done some experiments using tortoises as the test animals to determine whether they were able to detect the presence of plant defensive chemicals, such as alkaloids, when fed. His discovery was that

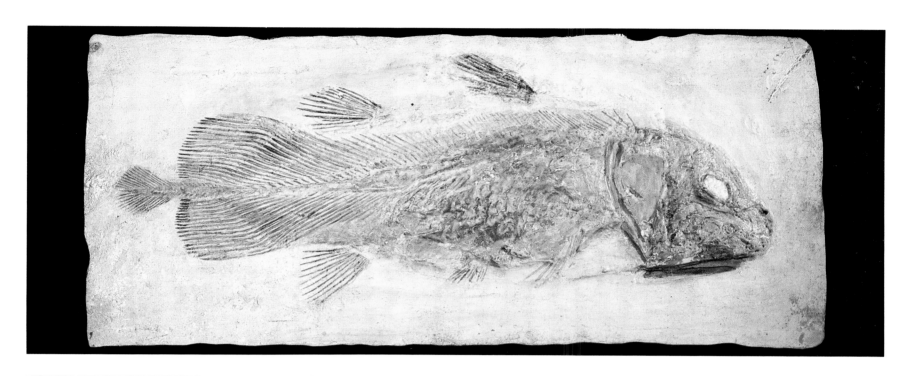

tortoises could not detect these chemicals and concluded that if they couldn't, then it was highly probable that herbivorous dinosaurs could not either, so a simple extrapolation from tortoise to dinosaur provided a theory to explain their extinction.

Unfortunately the tortoise is an extremely distant relative of any dinosaur group. Indeed it would probably not be stretching the point too far to suggest that we are more closely related to dinosaurs than are tortoises. And on top of that, the problems that dinosaurs may have faced from hostile plant chemicals is hardly going to be a major concern of many of the other groups that died at the end of the Cretaceous.

Another equally instructive example is the proposal made by a scientist who studied the properties of the eye. This proposal was that dinosaurs suffered from cataract opaqueness at the end of the Cretaceous and that this led to their extinction. I do not think that it will be necessary to pass further comment on this idea. But it does, as with the previous example, demonstrate that it can be naively easy to come up with a theory of dinosaur extinction. If you concentrate on one group, such as the dinosaurs alone, then there are any number of possibilities. If you can further restrict the theory so that it applies to just a select group of dinosaurs so much the better, but don't imagine that it will gain anything like acceptance among paleontologists. The theory will need to be broad and all encompassing, if it is to explain both the breadth and selectivity of the extinctions.

Current theories

If we exclude from any further consideration the theories that have been put forward to explain the extinctions at the end of the Cretaceous in terms of dinosaurs alone, we are left with precious few ideas let alone theories. At present there appear to be only two serious contenders which at least attempt to come to terms with the enormity of the difficulty of explaining an extinction event that is simultaneously taxonomically broad and selective in its effects. The first is what can be termed an 'extraterrestrial theory' in that it relies on the effect of an agent from outside the Earth. The other is what we might call a 'terrestrial theory' because it is based on changes which took place on Earth, without any obvious extraterrestrial agency.

There has been a longstanding theory of some form of cosmic agency causing large-scale extinctions on Earth. These have usually invoked cosmic rays flooding onto the Earth following a supernova elsewhere in our galaxy. This has always run into the problem of explaining the selectivity of the extinctions: why were some groups affected and not others? A second problem is that there do not seem to be any remnants of such a supernova in any of the nearby constellations which would be good candidates as the causative agents.

This theory has had an unexpected boost in recent years following the work of Luis Alvarez and Walter Alvarez in California (USA). While carrying out routine analysis of clay sediments which were deposited at or around the end of the Cretaceous

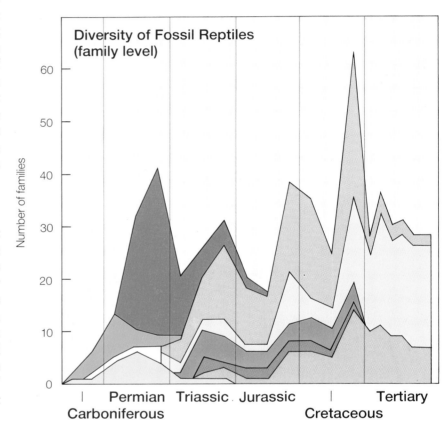

Anapsida	Pelycosauria
Archosauria	Sauropterygia
Ichthyosauria	Therapsida
Lepidosauria	Turtles

Above Chart showing the way in which diversities of various reptile groups changed with time.

Left Turtles – and tortoises such as this one – are clearly survivors.

Right The arid badland of South Dakota. Was it seasonal and more arid conditions like this which contributed to the extinctions of so many groups?

Left In recent years, extraterrestrial explanations have featured prominently in attempts to explain the extinctions of dinosaurs. Halley's comet proves that such bodies may collide with Earth.

Below Ammonites became extinct at the end of the Cretaceous. Could meteorite-induced changes in the atmosphere have caused their demise?

Right Vast explosions – much greater than this volcanic eruption – would have occurred following a large meteorite collision with earth. The explosion would have thrown millions of tonnes of dust and water vapor into the air and shrouded the Earth from the sun's rays. This could have sparked off a massive ecological disaster.

Period in various parts of the world, they discovered unexpectedly high levels of the element Iridium. This element is normally very rare in the Earth's crust for it is a heavy element which sank into the molten core of the Earth, while the crust was still molten, some 4000 million years ago. The most common source of higher levels of Iridium is from space, coming to Earth in the form of meteorites or asteroids.

The Iridium 'anomaly,' as it has been termed, needed explanation. The proposal that the team from California came up with was that the only way that high levels of Iridium could have formed in these late Cretaceous clay sediments was through the impact and vaporization of a large meteorite on collision with the Earth. It was proposed that a meteorite some 6-9 miles (10-15km) wide may have been involved and such a collision would have caused a massive explosion as it punched a hole into the crust of the Earth. The impact and explosion would have created a massive dust and water cloud which would have shrouded the Earth and remained in the atmosphere for a long time – perhaps months, others have suggested years. The biological effects of cutting off sunlight for extended periods of time may have been dramatic on life on Earth.

Cutting off the sun would have an immediate impact on the phytoplankton of the sea. These are the tiny organisms at the very base of the oceanic food chain. The death of these organisms, or their significant decline prior to the clearing of the atmosphere, would have had a dramatic effect on all the organisms in the food chain. The most immediate effect would be on the animals at the top of the food chain, the great carnivores of the sea, rather than the more adaptable animals at lower levels within the food chain. On land an equivalent effect would take place, with the arrest of all primary productivity. The knock-on effect would be on the consumers at all trophic levels, but most critically on the animals at the top of the food chain: the great herbivores and carnivores.

During times such as these the adaptable and resourceful organisms survive at the expense of the more highly specialized forms. Could this be the pattern that underlies the extinction event at the end of the Cretaceous? Were the ones that survived the more rugged and resourceful types? On land, mammals, lizards, frogs, salamanders and birds are all either very resource-

ful (the birds and mammals), or are very resistant and adaptable (the lizards, frogs and salamanders). By contrast, the larger dinosaurs and pterosaurs may have been much more vulnerable as specialized forms near to, or right at, the top of the food chain. Equally in the sea, the big marine reptiles are obvious potential victims at the top of the food chain. The chalky plankton may have been selectively killed by the lack of sunlight for a short period and may have been opportunistically replaced by the more robust species phytoplankton, which may have been able to survive during the period of darkness.

The ammonites are the main problem for this theory, however. Quite why they should have become extinct is not immediately obvious, since they would appear to have been resilient types, able to feed and scavenge with ease at a variety of depths in the oceans.

This theory therefore has the advantage of being broad in its effect, as well as theoretically at least selective in the way that the

environmental impact may have finally affected the organisms. At present a considerable number of scientists hold this theory with some faith.

The other idea – terrestrial theory – also has a considerable number of advocates. The contention is that the events of the late Cretaceous represent the end product of a long period of slow environmental change which built up to the effects seen so dramatically at the end of that Period.

Currently a considerable amount of careful work is being done in analyzing geological sections across the late Cretaceous and into the early Cenozoic, paying particular attention to the type and variety of animals and plants. The following observations have been made.

Between about 10 and 5 million years from the end of the Cretaceous the vegetation appears to have been very lush, with abundant tropical and subtropical species of plant. These conditions in turn supported a rich and varied fauna of dinosaurs. Within the

Left Lush tropical rainforests may have given way to increasingly mixed, open woodland in more temperate climatic conditions which may have occurred later in the Cretaceous Period. This type of change may have led to the differential survival of those animals best able to take advantage of the new conditions of life. Perhaps dinosaurs were simply the hapless victims of such a change; their world was changing and they were unable to adapt to it.

Above right This chart follows the demise of the ammonites as they approach the end of the Cretaceous Period. These really do pose a problem because any explanation for their extinction has to take into account what was happening not only on the land but also in the sea, where conditions were so different.

Right It is also possible that the great amount of volcanic activity at the end of the Cretaceous Period, which was linked to the large amount of continental movement taking place, may have also contributed to the climatic changes which have been proposed at this time. It was very notable how much dust the Mount St Helen volcano pushed into the atmosphere. What would the effect of many hundred such volcanic explosions be if they occurred at approximately the same time?

last 5 million years of the end of the Cretaceous the flora changed markedly, to one dominated by cool, temperate woodland plants. At the same time the dinosaurs became less abundant and varied, while the mammals become more conspicuous, larger and varied, elements of the fauna.

The implication of this work is very clear. The climate deteriorated rather markedly just near the end of the Cretaceous. The consequent change in vegetation type reflects the climatic shift and supported a less rich and varied fauna of dinosaurs. This climate may have favored insulated, endothermic mammals, rather than the larger uninsulated ectotherms (dinosaurs).

The cause of such a climatic change has been traced back to the recurrent theme of previous chapters in this book: continental movements. In the late Triassic/early Jurassic the continents were

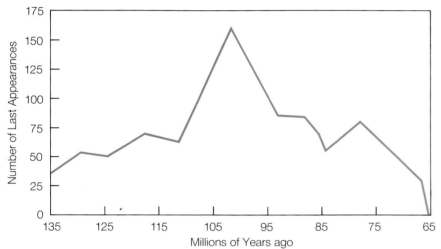

very much tied together as a supercontinent (Pangea) with a warm continental climate. Through the later Mesozoic we followed the gradual fragmentation of the supercontinent, until in late Cretaceous times the continents were not only separate, but also subdivided by inland seas in many instances. The implications of the introduction of seaways between continents and across them is to introduce more variable, seasonal, maritime conditions.

Could the climatically induced changes suggested here on the basis of an analysis of North American fossil communities account for the mass extinction at the end of the Period? As far as terrestrial communities are concerned, the answer is clearly yes! But what about the marine organisms? It is known that some species of plankton are very temperature sensitive. If this was the case with the chalky plankton, then the major extinction of these may be explained in terms of climatic deterioration. The extinction of a major component of the base of the food chain in the sea, may have had a profound effect upon the organisms higher up the food chain, causing the extinctions which are observed.

In neither theory is the evidence completely convincing, and there is much debate over the many issues raised by each line of thought. Is it possible to demonstrate that the extinctions at the end of the Cretaceous are entirely synchronous, as is required for a meteorite extinction model? Could the Iridium anomaly have been caused by volcanic activity, of which there was a great deal at the end of the Cretaceous Period?

This whole area is wracked by difficulty, which may only be solvable in the end by recourse to a time machine, but that does not stop the scientists striving for the answer among the rocks and fossils that are in existence at the moment.

CHAPTER 9

The Biology of Dinosaurs

As we have already seen in the discussion of the features of particular species of dinosaur, it has often been possible to gain some insight into the biology or way of life of these long dead creatures. Much of this is possible because of our knowledge of animals living today, and their own characteristics, and then applying this knowledge, where it seems appropriate, to dinosaurs. The information that we can use varies enormously: from actual bony remains, to fossil imprints of skin or feet, stomach contents, and eggs or on rare occasions nesting sites.

How dinosaurs moved

The bony skeleton provides a great deal of information about the biology of dinosaurs. The form of the skeleton indicates the way in which the dinosaur stood, and the shape and proportions of the legs indicate very clearly whether it was slow or fast moving. Short broad feet are mostly associated with thick, pillar-like legs (as seen in sauropodomorphs and stegosaurs). Such adaptations for bearing heavy weight are generally associated with a slower, ambling type of locomotion. But it must be remembered that living elephants which have these sort of limbs are still capable of charging quite fast at their enemies when they have the wish! Equally, long, narrow, slender-toed feet and long hind legs, such as those seen in many small theropods and ornithopods, are very similar in their proportions to fast-running animals such as gazelles or deer living today, and may well indicate equally fast running abilities.

The limbs also frequently indicate the food preference of the dinosaur, although this cannot always be totally relied upon. In most cases sharp, hooked claws indicate a flesh eater, whereas flattened and rounded or hoof-shaped claws suggest a plant eater. However, it is quite often the case that the plant eater (as in the case of early sauropodomorphs such as *Plateosaurus*) may have had large, curved claws on its hands which could have been used for defense against carnivores. Paradoxically, the largest and most fearsome of all carnivores, the tyrannosaurs, had small, flattened claws on their hands, which were little different in shape (though somewhat larger) than the claws on the hands of small ornithopods such as *Hypsilophodon*.

Additional clues concerning the mode of locomotion of dinosaurs may come from less obvious areas of the skeleton. The tail is one area in particular that has been mentioned. In a number of cases it has been seen that some dinosaurs, in this case small-to-medium sized theropods and ornithopods, have unusually stiff tails. The tails are held stiff by bony rods, and the reason for this appears to be that by doing so, the tail could act as a dynamic stabilizer. It could help the animal to either maintain its balance while running at speed on its hind legs, or allow it to change direction very rapidly. This would be done by swinging the tail

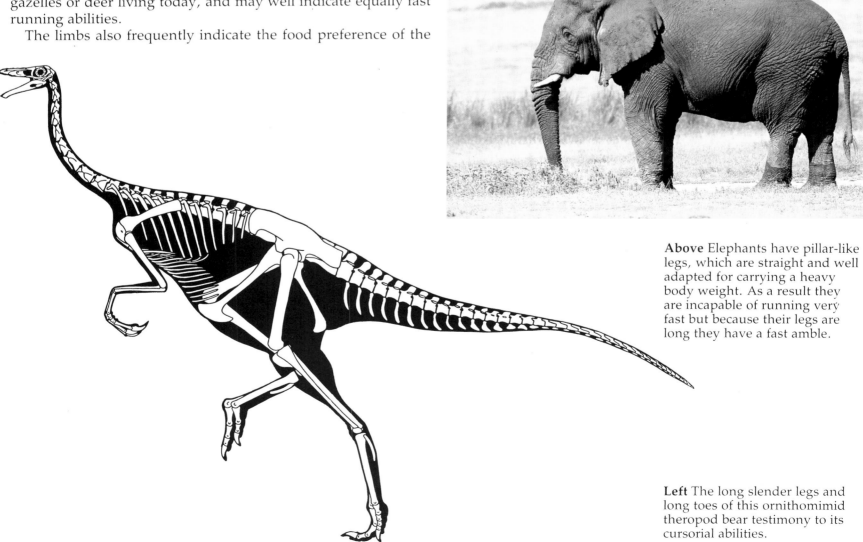

Above Elephants have pillar-like legs, which are straight and well adapted for carrying a heavy body weight. As a result they are incapable of running very fast but because their legs are long they have a fast amble.

Left The long slender legs and long toes of this ornithomimid theropod bear testimony to its cursorial abilities.

Left A prey's eye view of an attack by *Tyrannosaurus*. Although not sustained runners, these large dinosaurs could have caught their prey in swift rushes.

Bottom left The long grasping hand of *Deinonychus* end in sharp claws used for holding prey.

Below The short, stubby toes of *Diplodocus* are similar to those of an elephant and are clearly adapted to weight support.

Bottom The hind foot of *Deinonychus* has two slender running toes and an enlarged sickle-shaped claw on an inner toe, which was clearly an offensive weapon.

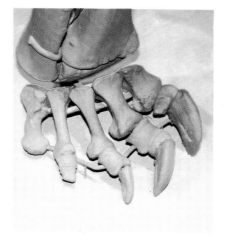

Left A very clear impression of the foot of a large theropod dinosaur. It is even possible to make out the shape of the sharp claw on the middle toe.

Below A set of theropod footprints from the early Cretaceous of southern England. These tracks were made alongside those which may have been left by *Iguanodon*. Was the predator stalking the prey?

Right The crest on the hadrosaurid ornithopod *Hypacrosaurus* is deep and shaped rather like that of a corinthian soldier's helmet. Compare it with that of the one below.

Bottom right The similarity between the crest of *Corythosaurus* and the one above is striking. The difference in height of the crests may just be due to differences of sex.

out to one side or the other, so that the animal would veer off, or perform the dinosaur equivalent of a side step. In high-speed animals such as these, the tail was clearly important as a means of either enabling the prey to be more elusive, or confering greater agility on the predator in pursuit of its prey.

Another area of investigation which can provide an insight into the mode of locomotion of dinosaurs is through the study of their footprints. This is rapidly becoming a very specialized branch of paleontology, known as paleoichnology. There are various places in the world where footprints are preserved, particularly in areas that were, at the time of dinosaurs, close to water, shore lines, river banks, the margins of shallow lakes, or dried out river beds. The details of the prints can vary enormously, but they are clearly the best possible evidence of the way that dinosaurs walked. They were usually formed when dinosaurs had walked across soft, drying mud. Once the tracks have been left, it is then required that the mud should have had a chance to harden a little, before either wind-blown sand from the surrounding area, or silt carried in on the next tide or by a river, buried the footprints. The progressive burial of the footprints eventually results in the impression being preserved as a permanent structure within the mud which is turned to rock.

Footprints of dinosaurs have been found in rocks spanning the entire age of the dinosaurs, from the late Triassic to the close of the Cretaceous, providing ample evidence of their walking or (more rarely) running abilities. The unfortunate fact with the trackway evidence of this type, is that it is singularly difficult to establish precisely which footprints go with which dinosaur. Obviously the shape of the foot bones of known dinosaurs provide a very good clue, but it is surprising how similar are the feet of many types of dinosaur. Dinosaurs are never so obliging as to die in their footprints, in order to provide us with the best possible evidence! But, depending on the quality of the footprints it may

be possible to deduce the speed at which the dinosaur was moving, the precise way in which it moved its feet during the stride, and the nature of the surface it was walking on (how sticky or dry it was).

Another unexpected insight which footprints may occasionally provide into the lives of dinosaurs concerns their social life. Sometimes footprints of several dinosaurs may be preserved in the same area. In some cases, the footprints may be of animals walking to and from a water hole, or along a strand line and tend to criss-cross one another, with no discernable pattern. On other occasions, the prints may all tend in the same direction, and even show some structure in their distribution across the surface. In the latter case this is very likely to provide evidence of dinosaurs moving as a herd. It has been claimed that in the case of some sauropods of the late Jurassic the dinosaurs were moving as a highly ordered herd. The largest footprints seem to have been made by

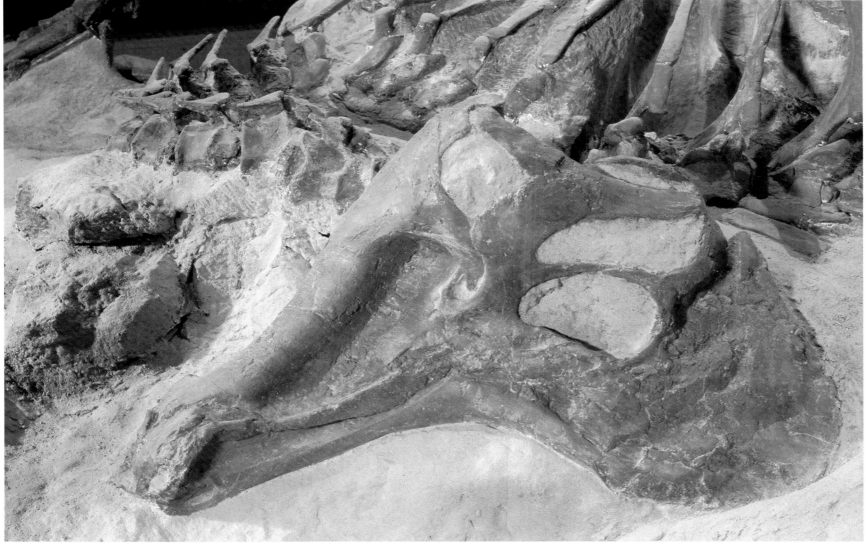

Left Compared to the two examples on the previous page, the crest of *Procheneosaurus* is very small. Despite its size, they are very similar. It was almost certainly a young corythosaur.

Below The formidable headgear of *Triceratops* was associated with defense (horns) and their social life (visual signals from the horns and crest).

Right Black rhinos look tolerably similar to larger ceratopians. The horns are again used for defense and as social signalling devices.

Bottom right *Chasmosaurus* with shorter horns and a more elaborate frill was clearly distinguishable from the contemporary *Triceratops*.

animals moving at the edges of the track – that is to say at the sides (and probably the front and back) of the herd. These may well have been the largest, bull animals, which were acting as the protectors of the herd against attack from predators. In the center of the trackway were found smaller prints, presumably of smaller and therefore juvenile individuals, and possibly the tracks of smaller females.

Thus footprints can offer surprising information about the way of life of dinosaurs, in addition to the obvious information about the shape of their feet and the way that they walked.

Crests, horns and frills

The heads of dinosaurs were frequently ornamented in one way or another, and this often indicates something about the way of life of the animal.

Many theropods have some sort of crest on the head. One of the earliest theropods, *Dilophosaurus*, had two thin, but high crests running almost the complete length of the head. Many of the late Jurassic theropods also had assorted crests or horns on the nose (see *Ceratosaurus*). The purpose of these horns and crests is unlikely to have been for prey capture, especially the thin and quite fragile fin-like crests on the skull of *Dilophosaurus*. Rather, their purpose was most probably social: either for recognition of one another, or as a warning or sexual display. This could be compared to the brightly colored plummage of birds, or the horns or antlers of cattle and deer.

Ornithischian dinosaurs seem to have had by far the most extravagant types of headgear. Hadrosaurs had a strange variety of crests or ridges on their heads, for which numerous functions have been proposed. It is now thought that the crests served two main purposes. First, they were very clearly used as visual signals for recognition (after all it is the shape of the crests that enables us to tell them apart). Second they appear to have acted as resonators, so that these animals could recognize each other by their distinctive calls (just as crocodiles may roar, and birds may sing). If this is correct, and all the evidence seems to point in this direction, then the world of the dinosaurs may have been quite a noisy one.

The other group of dinosaurs that immediately springs to mind, when the subject of horns and frills is discussed, are the ceratopians. The horns are quite varied in size and position be-

tween the various types currently known, although two main patterns seem to predominate. First, there are those, such as *Styracosaurus*, *Centrosaurus* and *Monoclonius*, which have a single large nose horn and very small, or no, brow horns. In these the similarity to the living rhinoceros is particularly striking. The nose horn was clearly a formidable weapon of defense against the large tyrannosaurs which lived at the same time. It is also very probable that the horn was a display structure that would have been used for simple recognition and served to establish a 'pecking order' without the need for direct combat between individuals, which would have been fraught with danger. It seems quite likely that in cases of dispute, opponents would have faced one another, or stood sideways on, and waved the horn to display it to maximum advantage. The one with the most effective display would be the winner.

The second pattern of horns is seen in ceratopians such as *Triceratops*, *Chasmosaurus*, *Anchiceratops* and *Torosaurus*. These dinosaurs have long brow horns and short or non-existent nose horns. In this case, in addition to the defensive function of the horns, the likelihood is that the horns were again used for recognition

purposes, but also could have been used for physical combat – in head-to-head wrestling matches. The horns of opponents could be interlocked for tests of strength between individuals to settle territorial disputes.

The frills of all these ceratopians are also large and, although they look as though they acted purely as defensive shields, they may also have been used for visual display as part of their social repertoire.

Eggs and nests

The discovery of dinosaur eggs in the 1920s was a very significant event, and proved at long last that dinosaurs were similar to other reptiles in that they laid eggs in nests. Since that time a number of eggs have been found in various parts of the world, and on rare occasions, what appear to have been nesting sites of dinosaurs have been discovered. These discoveries have produced a great deal of information about the reproductive habits of dinosaurs and the degree to which they cared for their young.

The *Protoceratops* nest sites discovered in Mongolia revealed that these dinosaurs may well have shared nests because up to 30 eggs arranged in neat concentric circles were found. It seems very unlikely that individual females of this dinosaur, which had skeletons of only about 6 feet (2m) long, could have laid this number of eggs in a short period of time. The nests themselves appear to have been relatively simple, being little more than a shallow, scooped out depression in the sand, and it is most likely that the eggs once laid were abandoned by the parent animals, as happens with the majority of reptiles today. The young emerged from the eggs and had to fend for themselves immediately.

By contrast, some hadrosaur nest sites discovered more recently in Montana by the American fossil collector Jack Horner indicate a much more sophisticated behavior among these sorts of dinosaur. The nest sites seem to be very close together, and show signs of nests having been used over and again, which suggests that this was a regular nesting site visited by a large number of dinosaurs in a nesting colony. The hadrosaur which laid the eggs has been named *Maiasaura* (good mother reptile), for what appears to be good reason.

Careful investigation of a series of nest sites by Horner has shown that the nests built by *Maiasaura* were large and complex structures, being large mounds with scooped out centers, which seem to have been lined with vegetation. The eggs were laid in the nests and (as with crocodiles today) would have been covered with sand and more vegetation to keep the eggs moist and warm – ideal conditions for incubation. Once the hatchlings emerged from the eggs, it appears the adult animals began to feed them until they were large and strong enough to leave the safety of the nest. Horner has found many skeletons of young *Maiasaura* inside nests (clearly they were large enough to have left the nest, but had not chosen to), with worn teeth. This confirms the idea that food may have been brought to the nest by the adult animals.

The work of Horner provides a striking insight into the social life of dinosaurs and parental behavior towards the young, which is far removed from the traditional views of dinosaurs. However, there were clearly other dinosaurs which behaved much more like modern reptiles, indulging in little or no parental care of the young.

Feeding and food

The way in which dinosaurs fed can be deduced from a number of areas of investigation. The most obvious of these is the teeth and jaws. Large, sharp, serrated teeth are designed for cutting flesh and are therefore associated with a carnivorous diet, and this is the sort of tooth found almost universally within the theropods.

Above A beautifully made model of an embryo hypsilphodontid dinosaur (*Orodromeus*) inside an egg. Several eggs with embryos inside have been found in Montana by Jack Horner.

Left This area of Mongolia has yielded large quantities of dinosaur eggs and nests.

Right Nest sites of the hadrosaurid *Maiasaura* have been found in Montana which have told us a great deal about the social life of these dinosaurs and the way in which their young were reared. They show that hadrosaurs such as this cared for the hatchling dinosaurs by bringing food to the nest. Curiously *Orodromeus* (above) seems to have abandoned its young at an early stage – more like a typical reptile.

A few theropods seem to have smaller, slightly more spiky teeth, and these may have been used for a more varied diet which included insects, whose bodies could have been cracked open more effectively with that sort of design.

Having no teeth at all presents some problems for the paleontologist, as in the case of the ornithomimosaur theropods. In this case, comparisons have been made with the rather similar looking, large land birds of the present (ostrich, emu, rhea) and the suggestion has been made that they may have had a very broad diet of small animals, fruit or insects – basically anything that was reasonably nutritious and did not need slicing up in the mouth before swallowing!

Herbivores are quite easy to identify because they tend to have smaller, blunt, chipping sort of teeth, used for cutting vegetation rather than slicing meat. In the case of the large sauropodomorph dinosaurs they can be divided very clearly into two types. Those with teeth like apatosaurs, which are long and thin and clustered like a rake at the front of the mouth, and seem to have been used for raking in food, which was then swallowed; and those with teeth similar to brachiosaurs, which are larger, broader and generally more spoon-shaped. These latter have worn edges and seem to have been used to nip off vegetation, rather than as rakes.

In both of these examples it is fairly evident that little actual food processing (chewing) went on in the mouth. The food was swallowed and passed on for digestion in the stomach. The stomach was extremely large, in order to store the large amounts of plant food drawn in by the mouth, and acted like a huge fermentation tank. The plants were submerged in a broth of microorganisms which were able to digest the tough chemical (cellulose) in plant tissues. This is very much the same process taking place in living cattle which have large stomachs acting in just the same way. Unlike cattle, the dinosaurs had one additional feature. Within the muscular wall of the stomach, or in a separate compartment close to the stomach, were pebbles which the dinosaur had deliberately swallowed. These pebbles (gastroliths, literally 'stomach stones') were used to grind the plant tissues to a fine slurry in order to help the microbes, and speed up digestion. Gastroliths, which are usually smooth, angular pebbles, are frequently found associated with the skeletons of these animals.

Ornithischians were all herbivores and developed a wide variety of ways of dealing with a diet of plants. One common feature to them all is the loss of teeth from the tip of the lower jaw and their replacement by a sharp, horn-covered beak. This was obviously a successful adaptation because the pattern is found in this group until the end of the Cretaceous Period, and provided them with a perfectly serviceable, continuously growing, cropping device.

Behind the beak, the teeth ranged in form from simple, leaf-shaped ones, used as simple shredders of vegetation (as in the case of small ornithopods, stegosaurs, ankylosaurs and pachycephalosaurs) to sophisticated batteries of teeth, such as the grinding batteries of hadrosaurs or the guillotine-like arrangement of ceratopians. Added to the variety of their teeth, the ornithischians had another general feature: the possession of cheek pouches. These served to retain the food in the mouth (preventing it from falling from the sides of the mouth) while these animals chewed their food.

The feeding strategies of ornithischians obviously differed from those of sauropodomorphs because they relied upon chewing to a much greater extent. Few ornithischians seem to have possessed gastroliths – or at least there is not much evidence of them in the skeletons described to date. However there is one notable exception to this, which is the early ceratopian *Psittacosaurus*. One skeleton of this animal was discovered in Mongolia with a large pile of small pebbles (more than 100) in the precise area of the stomach. This is proof positive that some ornithischians used

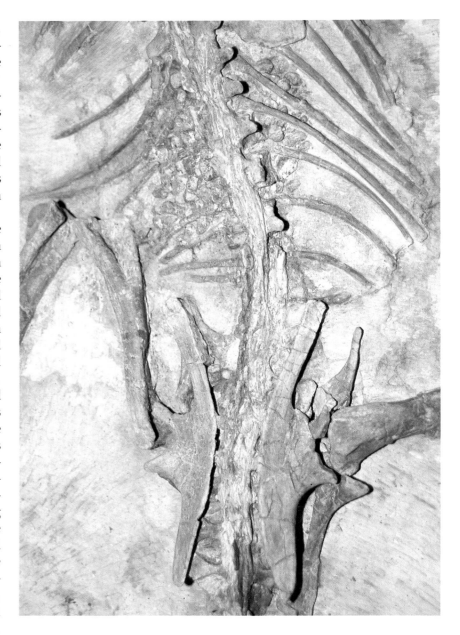

stomach stones, and it may be that ceratopians as a whole used them to assist the pulverizing of the plant food which they ate in such large quantities.

The precise diet of any dinosaur is almost impossible to know with certainty. The stomach contents are only very rarely preserved in any dinosaur. Even then there is always the suspicion that what is thought to be stomach contents actually could be debris, which has been washed up against the carcass of the dead animal while it was being buried in river sediments prior to it becoming a fossil.

The rake-like teeth look as though they may have been used to gather conifer needles from the trees on which they fed. It is also possible that the narrow beaks of small ornithopods were used for nipping off shoots and buds, while the broader beaks of larger ornithischians may well have been used to gather a wider range of plants. At the moment these are only guesses, however, and may be far from the truth.

Skin impressions

Rarely, and only in the right circumstances, have the impression of the skins of some dinosaurs been preserved. There are two famous examples of dinosaurs with skin preservation. These are both hadrosaurs (*Anatosaurus*), and they appear to have died and been preserved in sand dunes. The animals had died in a dry, semi-desert area and their carcasses had dried out in the air and therefore part-mummified before they were buried beneath drifting sand. The sand compacted against the parchment-like skin and retained the texture of the skin permanently. When the skeletons were discovered, the skin textures were seen as the skeletons

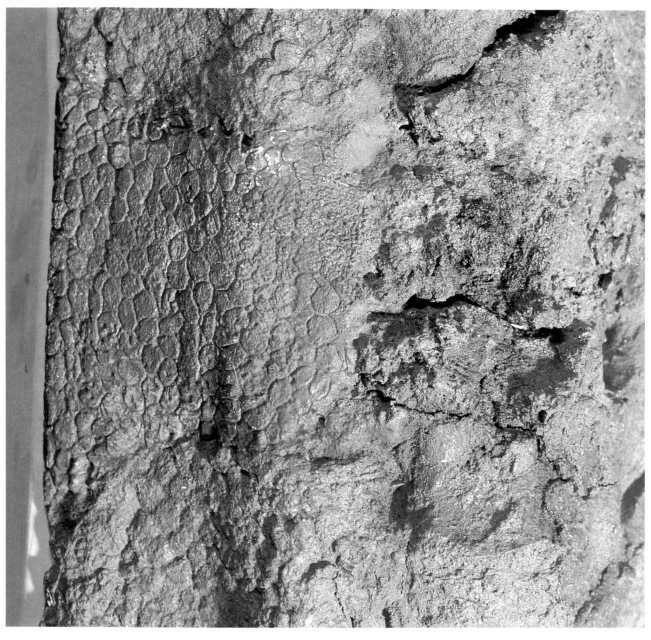

Left This remarkable skeleton of a *Psittacosaurus* from Mongolia has, preserved in the area of the stomach, a pile of pebbles (gastroliths). These are almost certainly the remains of a gizzard for grinding plants.

Above Hadrosaur teeth (battery) with literally hundreds of small teeth. They were cemented together to form a powerful grinding mill to pulverize the toughest of plant foods. The cutting edge is at the top, and becomes worn away as a sloping surface on the other side of the jaw from the photograph.

Right A skin impression from the tail of the hadrosaurid ornithopod *Edmontosaurus*. The skin surface has been preserved as an impression in the sand which originally buried the animal. Unfortunately, none of the original skin tissue is left so there is no possibility of discovering its original colour.

Left This is a skin impression from the tail of another hadrosaur. The body of the animal had clearly dried out so that the bones were very close to the surface and are here exposed in places.

Below The very heavily armored skin of the ankylosaurid *Euoplocephalus* showing not only the smaller bony plates in the flexible areas of the skin, but also the large protective bony spikes.

Right Modern reptiles have similar skin to that of dinosaurs, judging by what can be seen from the fossil impressions. The coloration of the skin is, however, a persistent problem. Many living reptiles have very brightly colored skin, but how far this applied to dinosaurs is impossible to tell.

were excavated and were preserved as an impression in the sandstone. These hadrosaurs are now on display in the American Museum of Natural History in New York, USA, and the Senckenburg Museum in Frankfurt, West Germany.

The skin impressions show a scaly skin, little different in most respects from that seen on living reptiles. Other skin impressions are known in other dinosaurs, but these are not as well preserved. All skin impressions so far discovered indicate the same general type of skin.

Physiological implications

Apart from the skin, which appears to be genuinely reptilian (dry and scaly), and the fact that many seem to have laid eggs, both of which point to the traditional view of them as reptiles, most of the attributes that can be deduced for dinosaurs point to surprisingly active, sophisticated animals living reasonably complex lives. If a comparison has to be drawn with animals today, then it is more often than not with the active and sophisticated mammals and birds, rather than with reptiles. Does this mean that dinosaurs were much like mammals and birds today, or are we misinterpreting what we see?

Unfortunately, it is impossible to know this information, because it was all locked up in the tissues of the living animal – the flesh and blood of the animal which rotted away millions of years ago. Not that this has prevented many paleontologists from trying to determine how it might have been. The central argument which has raged for the past 20 years is 'were dinosaurs warm-blooded (endothermic)?' Did dinosaurs generate body heat internally, as do mammals and birds today, or were they more like living reptiles, which are said to be 'cold-blooded' (ectothermic), relying on the sun to heat their bodies?

Before looking at the various theories that have been proposed arguing that dinosaurs either were or were not endotherms, it is necessary to briefly look at the dinosaur and mammal histories.

It is a documented fact from the fossil record that dinosaurs appeared almost at the same time as the first mammals. Dinosaurs then rose to dominate the Mesozoic world, until they became extinct at the end of the Cretaceous, after which time the mammals rose to dominate the world and have continued to do so to the present.

If we look around at the animals today then the large ones are predominantly mammals. Reptiles are generally rare, secretive animals largely confined to tropical regions. The only real exception to this are the oceanic islands, such as the Galapagos and Aldabra, where tortoises and lizards are particularly abundant, largely because of the absence of mammalian competitors.

The question that is posed is this. If mammals are so successful today, why should it have been that the dinosaurs, if they were conventional reptiles, dominated mammals for 150 million years of the Mesozoic? Surely to have been so successful, the dinosaurs must have been as physiologically competent as mammals today, otherwise mammals would have risen to dominate the world 150 million years earlier.

This can either be regarded as the ultimate observation proving that dinosaurs were endothermic, and all other evidence is simply further proof of this inevitable conclusion; or, as discussed earlier, it may be that being an endotherm is not always such an advantage to an animal. Endothermy is a very good way of surviving in a seasonal climate because an animal can keep itself active and warm all the time, but the cost is that it needs to consume vast amounts of food.

It does seem suspiciously as though the late Triassic was a time when the Earth was very warm and had little seasonality, both factors which would not necessarily have favored endothermic types. Another theory is based on the dinosaurs' posture. As was emphasized at the beginning of the book, dinosaurs walked and ran with their legs tucked beneath the body in a very mammal or bird-like way. Richard Owen noted this when he named the

Left Tortoises provide us with a 'classical' view of a reptile as a ponderous, slow-witted creature. The anatomical evidence suggests that dinosaurs are far from this state. Many were built for fast movement, implying a quick-wittedness as well.

Below A flock of ostriches. Unlikely though it may seem, it is probable that many dinosaurs were as active and fast moving as these large ground birds. This certainly applies with great force to the small, lightly built theropods (see page 156).

group back in 1841. Today only mammals and birds, both of which are endotherms, walk and run in this way. It is also true to say that some dinosaurs seem to have been built in such a way as to suggest that they were fast running and very active animals. This is particularly true of theropods and smaller ornithopods. Surely this is good evidence of the endothermic status of dinosaurs, for animals must be designed to perform within the limits of their metabolism. Put more simply, it would not be prudent to build a formula one racing car and then put the motor of a lawn mower in it! If dinosaurs are built as active creatures then their physiology must have reflected this, and points to an endothermic regime, because endothermy is associated with high activity levels among mammals today.

It has been observed, too, that *some* dinosaurs had large brains, chiefly some of the small theropods. Many other groups of dinosaurs seem to have singularly small brains when compared to their body size.

Large brains today are only found in animals that are endotherms and this is associated with the ability to maintain a regular supply of food and oxygen to the brain. However this argument does not seem to be particularly strong because analyses have shown that dinosaurs have brains which scale in size in a way that is typical for reptiles as whole. Yes, some theropods seem brainy, but this is only bright by reptile standards, and is not particularly meaningful when compared to mammals or birds.

When examined under a microscope, thin sections of dinosaur bone seem to be packed with masses of holes for blood vessels. At first sight this looks very similar to the structure of the bones of mammals and differs from the structure of the bone of reptiles, which seem to have far fewer holes for blood vessels. This implies that dinosaurs had bone like that of mammals rather than reptiles and is further proof of the similarity in their physiology.

However, from more recent evidence than that which was used in the original arguments, it would seem that dinosaur and mammal bones are not as similar as was first thought. What dinosaur bone seems to show in particular is that their bones grew very quickly. It may be simpler and more accurate to say that dinosaurs had 'dinosaurian physiology' from this sort of evidence.

It has also been argued that the fact that some dinosaurs had sophisticated batteries of teeth (hadrosaurs and ceratopians in particular) must have meant that they needed to eat vast quanti-

ties of food all of the time. This fits with the idea that dinosaurs were endothermic because, as explained above, one of the costs of being endothermic is a large appetite, as most of the food consumed is burned to produce chemical heat in the body.

Unfortunately the number of dinosaurs with sophisticated teeth is restricted to the two groups mentioned above. The others do not show such convincing evidence of this, and therefore must fail to add support to this idea.

Such large appetites contributed to another interesting idea put forward several years ago. A census was done using museum collections of specimens to see what number of dinosaurs were pre-

dators and prey, living at any particular time period. The figures seemed to suggest that for dinosaurs, there were very small numbers of predators to large numbers of prey animals.

The conclusion drawn from this evidence was that dinosaurs must be endothermic, as endothermic predators need large numbers of prey to feed upon because of their large appetites. By contrast ectothermic predators (such as crocodiles and snakes) feed very little and tend to live in communities where there are roughly equal numbers of predators and prey.

Again, unfortunately, since this original proposal was made several attempts have been made to analyze the data upon which the theory was based and all have come up with conflicting results. It is impossible to get an accurate estimate of the number of animals living at any particular time in the fossil record as most fossils are collected from time zones spanning one million years or more, which hardly constitute the members of a 'community.' This appears to be an example of a really interesting idea which cannot actually be applied to the problem in practice. In any case this sort of census would presumably only tell us about the physiology of the predator – it tells us nothing about the prey animals.

As has been discussed, some dinosaurs seem to have displayed remarkably complex types of behavior, the sort of behavior that is often associated with living mammals and birds rather than reptiles. The implication is once again that behavior patterns such as these are only possible for endothermic animals.

This is not true. Looking at the care of hadrosaurs, it has been known for some time that crocodiles show considerable parental care of their young. Crocodile parents help the young to get out of the nest, and carry them in their jaws to special nurseries, where they protect them from various predators until they are large enough to fend for themselves. This is surely sophisticated behavior being exhibited by a humble reptile.

Finally, in the mid-1970s some important work was done by Professor John Ostrom at Yale University demonstrating that birds may well have arisen from small theropod dinosaurs in the Jurassic Period. This work is discussed in the next chapter, but the crucial argument here is that if dinosaurs and birds are closely related and birds are known to be endotherms, then it seems at least possible that dinosaurs (or at least theropods) were endothermic as well.

While this is plausible, it is not essential to assume that dinosaurs were endothermic just because birds were. It is equally possible that endothermy evolved in birds, and that this is one of the features that may have distinguished the two groups in the beginning.

From the above abbreviated discussion, it should be apparent that the case for endothermy in dinosaurs is far from convincing, though there are many who favor this idea.

I, however, prefer to consider dinosaurs as ectotherms rather than endotherms for several reasons. First, they lived at a time of very warm, basically non-seasonal conditions, which would have made endothermy not such an essential adaptation. Second, dinosaurs were perfectly capable of being highly active creatures because they would have had a highly efficient blood circulation and heart, allowing an active life style without making it necessary to have an endothermic regime. Third, large animals, which is what many of the dinosaurs were, would have had very stable internal body temperatures because they were effectively thermally inert. Fourth, giant endotherms would have had enormous heat loss problems, especially if they were at all active (when muscles generate heat as well), which would have made endothermy a positive nuisance. Fifth, giant ectotherms would not have had the prodigious appetites of giant endotherms, calculations about which have suggested that giant endotherms the size of dinosaurs would have needed more than 24 hours in a day to consume the food that their bodies would have required!

All in all I consider dinosaurs to have been economical, highly active ectotherms, perfectly adapted to the mild climatic regimes which dominated the Earth at this time. Mammals and birds, the successful endotherms of today, are the perfect adaptation to a world dominated by seasonal climatic conditions – conditions ultimately inimical to dinosaurs.

CHAPTER 10
The Origin of Birds

For a long time it has been recognized that there is a close relationship between reptiles and birds. One look at the scaly legs and feet of any bird, and the fact that both groups lay similar sorts of eggs is enough to convince anyone of this fact. A more important question however is: which particular group of reptiles are birds most closely related to? I shall be looking at this question in this chapter and showing the way in which the answer has come to involve the dinosaurs in particular.

The issue of bird origins and relationships came to the forefront of biological and evolutionary thinking in 1861, with the discovery of the fossilized skeleton of a bird-like creature in a limestone quarry near Solenhofen in southern Germany. The quarry was in rocks of the late Jurassic age, and the limestone was being extracted commercially because it was extremely fine grained and could be used for lithographic printing purposes.

Because of the fine grain size of the sediment, which was laid down in the floor of a lagoon, the detailed structure of the skeleton of this creature was preserved in exquisite detail. More importantly from the point of view of indentifying the creature, the impressions of feathers were also preserved around the skeleton, proving that this must have been a bird. The fossil was named *Archaeopteryx lithographica* (ancient wing from the lithographic limestone) by Hermann von Meyer. Since that time a further five skeletons of this animal in various stages of completeness have been recovered from this area; the most recent being an announcement of the discovery of a skeleton in the summer of 1988.

The impression of feathers around several of the skeletons provide the most convincing evidence of this being a bird, because no other vertebrates alive are known to possess anything remotely like feathers. As a bird, however, this animal possesses a number of unusual features.

The head is quite long, and the snout pointed and slender, giving it a bird-like appearance. Despite this, the jaws are lined with small, sharply pointed teeth. All living birds lack such teeth, having horny beaks in their stead, although it is known that some bird remains from later in the Mesozoic (*Hesperornis* and *Ichthyornis*) also possessed teeth. The eye and the brain appear to be large in *Archaeopteryx* and this is bird-like, though it should be added that a number of small, theropod dinosaurs seem to have very similar heads.

The neck is long and curved, and the back short (though not as short and stiff as in modern birds). The hips are similar to those of dinosaurs, as is the tail, which is long and bony. In birds the tail is very short (the 'parsons nose') and broad, acting as a cushion into which the tail feathers are inserted – it is the feathers alone that give the appearance of a long tail.

The wings of *Archaeopteryx* are similar to those of modern birds, but not identical in all details. One crucial difference is the retention of three separate, clawed fingers on the hand. In birds the bones of the hand are largely welded together to form a strong support for some of the main flight feathers, and there are no separate claws. The one exception to this is a bird from South

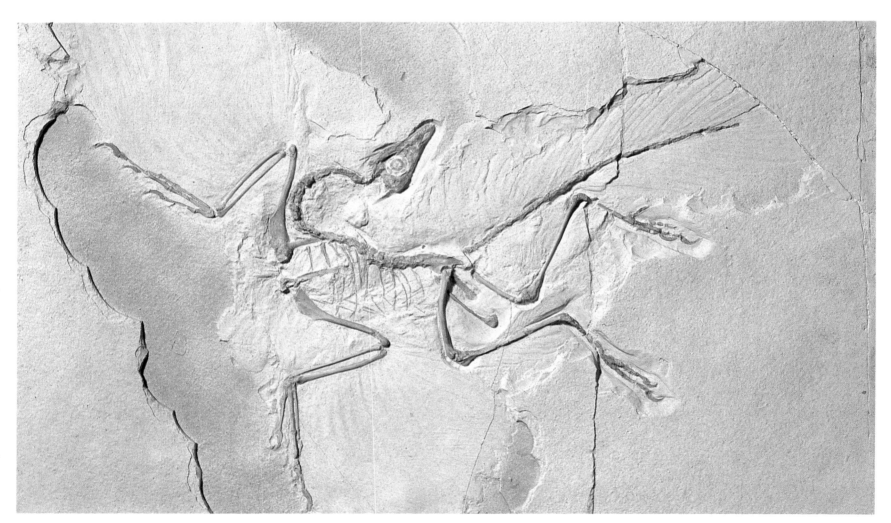

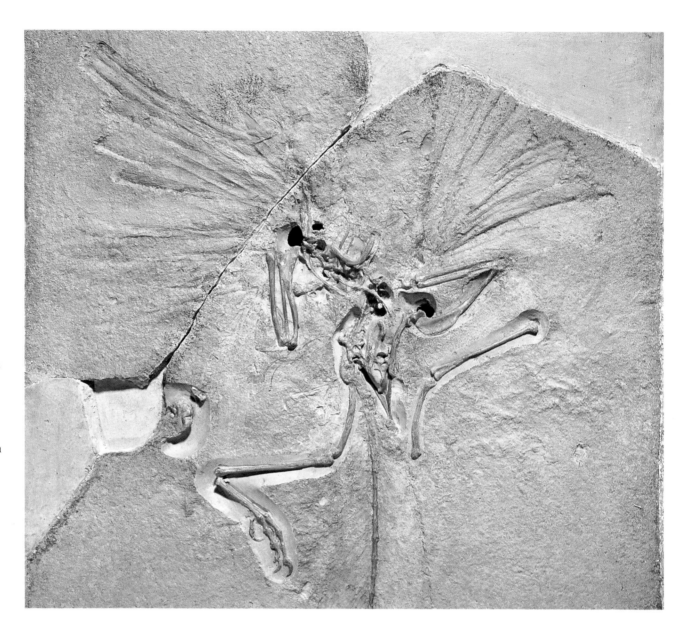

Below left This specimen of *Archaeopteryx* is known as the 'Berlin specimen' because it is now in the collections of the State Museum of Natural History, East Berlin. It is the best-preserved of the six skeletons known to date. The feather impressions can be seen very clearly around the arms (wings), legs and tail.

Right This was the first skeleton of *Archaeopteryx* to be discovered. It is known as the 'London specimen' because it was bought by the British Museum (Natural History) shortly after it was discovered in the 1860s. Again the feather impressions are very well preserved, but the head and neck are not nearly so well preserved as in the 'Berlin specimen'.

Below Skeletal drawings of *Archaeopteryx* showing its very theropod-like form. Note the length of the arms (wings).

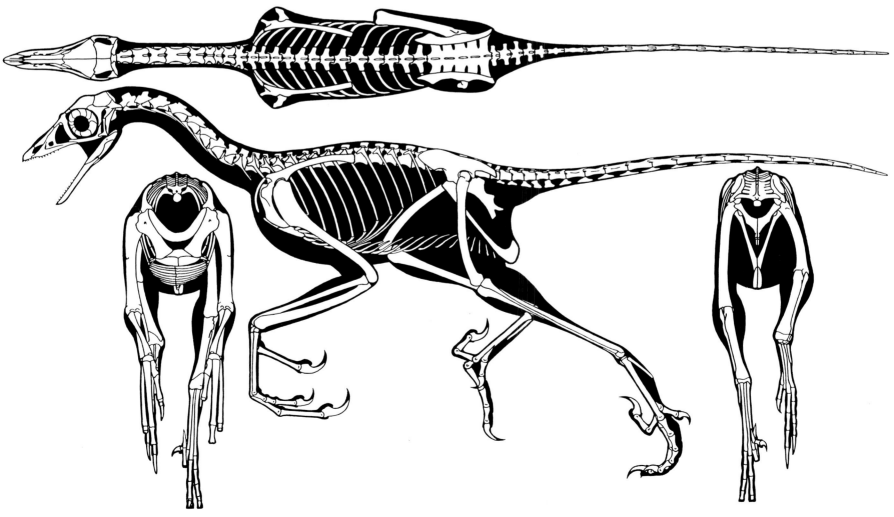

America named the Hoatzin (*Opisthocoma*) which, when it is a chick, clambers about the nest and climbs among branches in trees using a small, single claw on each hand. The claw is lost in the adults, which fly normally, if not particularly strongly, by bird standards. In most respects the hands and arms of *Archaeopteryx*, resemble those of small theropods, except that they are considerably longer than in these latter dinosaurs.

The shoulders are moderately bird-like in *Archaeopteryx*, particularly in that they possess a fused collar bone (the 'wishbone' or furcula) as found in birds. The legs also resemble those of birds (and small theropods) in that they are long and slender and have three well-developed and strongly clawed, forward-pointing toes. More like birds is the quite large reversed first toe, which may have been used for perching or climbing.

Archaeopteryx is clearly not a typical bird. It has many features which are to be seen in reptiles, and some more which particularly resemble those seen in some smaller theropod dinosaurs.

The relationship of birds and dinosaurs

In the late 1860s knowledge of dinosaurs was not particularly good. Of the few fragmentary remains that had been studied, a number were noted for the similarity of their hips and legs to those of birds. As a result it was suggested that birds and dinosaurs may be quite closely related. This view was largely overwhelmed and lost during the following decades because of the veritable avalanche of information on dinosaurs which emerged from North America through the Cope-Marsh rivalry. The sheer variety of dinosaurs became too great to retain the notion that all of them could have had a relationship with dinosaurs.

Then, in the 1920s the issue of the origin of birds was tackled by Gerhard Heilmann. The conclusion which he reached, after extensive comparisons of birds and *Archaeopteryx* with other groups of reptiles, was that although dinosaurs – and in particular theropod dinosaurs – seemed most similar to birds and *Archaeopteryx*, the most realistic ancestors had to be Triassic archosaurs of the type described in chapter 3. This was mainly because dinosaurs (or so he believed from the evidence of the time) did not possess a furcula ('wishbone'), yet archosaurs and birds did. He reasoned that birds could not have evolved from animals that did not have a furcula, and so their ancestors had to be traced further back into the Triassic. The similarities between birds and dinosaurs were therefore supposed to be coincidental or examples of a process known as convergent evolution.

So detailed and authoritative was this review that its findings remained unchallenged for 50 years until, in the mid-1970s the whole question of the origin of birds was re-examined by Professor Ostrom. Detailed comparisons were made between the fossil specimens of *Archaeopteryx* and other theropod skeletons. Among these was the small theropod *Compsognathus* which had also been found in similar quarries in southern Germany. As a result of this it became clear that *Archaeopteryx* resembled small theropod

Left The Hoatzin, *Opisthocoma*, is a rather poor flier from South America. It is of particular interest because its young retain claws on their wings which they use to scrabble about in the trees. The claws are lost when they leave the nest.

Top right The skeleton of a dead bird (blue footed booby). The lightness of their bones make it extremely unlikely that birds would survive the time required for burial and subsequent fossilization. This is why bird fossils are so rare.

Right *Compsognathus*. A detailed picture of the specimen from southern France. The bone is very well preserved and the animal as a whole was quite similar to *Archaeopteryx*. Indeed, several skeletons of *Archaeopteryx* have come to light in recent years because they were originally identified as *Compsognathus*!

Above The swift-moving theropod, *Compsognathus*, which has been found in rocks of the same age as those that have yielded *Archaeopteryx*. Though not a direct ancestor, it shows the clear similarities between small theropods and early birds.

Left A beautifully made model of how *Archaeopteryx* may have looked in life. Note the teeth, the clawed fingers and the reversed toe on the foot.

Right This is the 'Eichstätt specimen' of *Archaeopteryx* which was for many years recorded in the museum Eichstätt collection as *Compsognathus*. Note there are no feather impressions which added to the original confusion when classifying this fossil.

dinosaurs in more than 20 anatomical features. The problem which Heilmann faced – the lack of a furcula in theropods – was solved because this bone had since been described in a number of dinosaurs. Some of Ostrom's most telling pieces of evidence were: the strong similarity in the form of the hips of theropods to those of *Archaeopteryx*; the detailed similarity of all the bones of the forelimb in both types; and the detailed similarity in the structure of the hindlimb and foot.

The question which has to be asked is this: is it reasonable to suppose that all of the many similarities really arose as a result of convergent evolution? The answer would seem to be a definite no! If the similarities had been fewer then there would always have been an element of doubt, but the probability of so many similarities being produced coincidentally must be extremely small. This is not to say that there is no further discussion on this matter of bird origins.

A little earlier, in 1970, the proposal was made that ornithischian dinosaurs were possible ancestors of birds. The similarity in the structure of the hips was the main reason for this proposal, but it has not gained any serious consideration since 1970 on the basis that Heilmann had dismissed this idea very effectively in his work in the 1920s.

Instead, in 1972, the idea was proposed that birds may have originated from lightly built Triassic crocodiles. This was based on a very detailed analysis of the structure of the skulls of living birds, crocodiles and some fossil crocodiles. No account was taken of the structure of *Archaeopteryx* in this work, which must be

regarded as a weakness in the suggestion. In recent years the proposer of this theory has changed his mind, and now seems to favor the theropod-bird proposals of Ostrom.

Other recent proposals concerning the origins of birds are of two sorts, those based on new discoveries and those based on new interpretations.

New discoveries

Avimimus (bird mimic) is based on a rather fragmentary skeleton from the late Cretaceous of Asia. This material was described by Dr Sergei Kurzanov (Moscow) and he has claimed that this is a dinosaur which also possessed feathers on its forelimbs and may be related to the origin of birds or at the least a group of very bird-like, feathered theropods.

In recent years, following the work of Ostrom, it has been common to see reconstructions of some theropod dinosaurs with feathers covering at least part of their bodies. There is no good factual basis for this, merely the unstated belief that since birds evolved from some theropod group, perhaps feathers were also found in the more bird-like of theropods. In the absence of convincing evidence I do not approve of these reconstructions of feathered theropods, but whether I am correct to disapprove is a matter of personal taste, rather than based on my own scientific evidence.

Another discovery is *Protoavis* (first bird), based on a part skeleton which has been discovered in late Triassic rocks in Texas. To date there is no good description of this material, but it has been

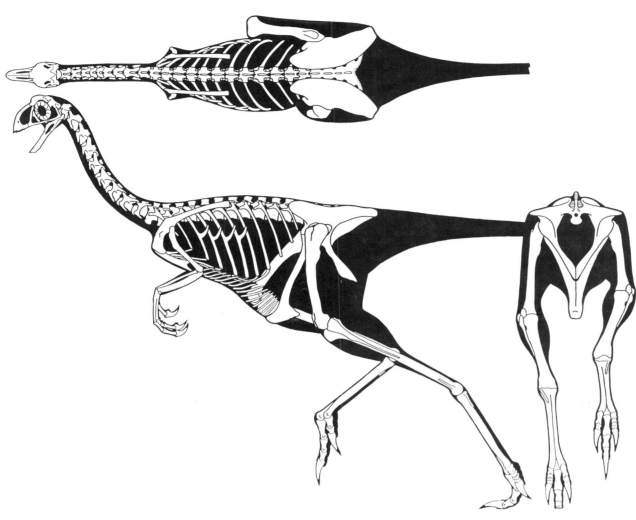

Left An artist's reconstruction of the skeleton of *Avimimus*, an apparently quite bird-like theropod from the late Cretaceous of Mongolia. This reconstruction was based on the material seen to the right.

Right *Avimimus*. The skeletal remains, as presently known, of this puzzling little theropod. These come from the Paleontological Institute, Moscow.

Far right A feather impression of an unknown bird from the Paleogene of Wyoming. Bird fossils are extremely rare and feathers even more so.

Below The tail of *Archaeopteryx* ('London specimen') has a thin row of tail bones surrounded by a fringe of feathers and is finely preserved. Hoyle and Wickramasinghe claim, I believe mistakenly, that this is a fake.

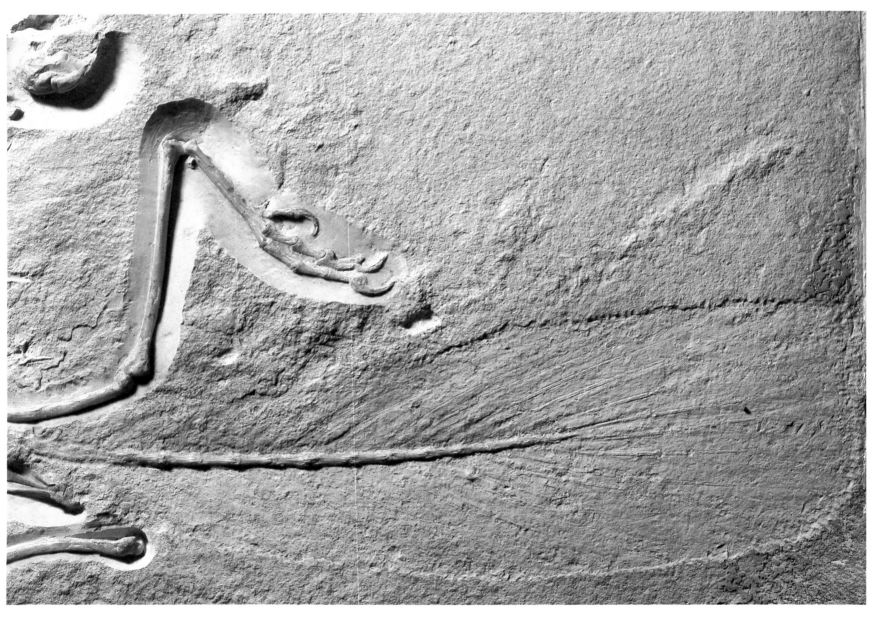

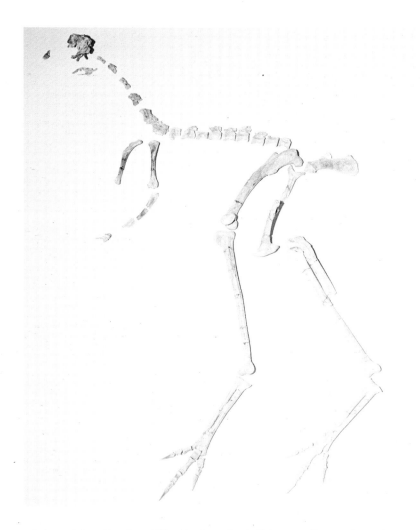

claimed by Sankar Chatterjee that this small creature has many bird-like features. These include long forelimbs, a furcula, flight muscle attachment areas on the arms and feather attachment scars on the arm bones. It also has the mix of reptile features seen in *Archaeopteryx*: a long tail, clawed fingers and teeth in the jaws.

At the moment this fossil is still being worked upon. If it is confirmed as an early bird then it may require a re-think of Ostrom's work, because this bird (if it is such) precedes almost all dinosaurs, and therefore suggests that Heilmann may well have been correct to postulate a Triassic archosaur as an ancestor of the birds after all. The alternative possibility, which at this stage cannot be dismissed, is that this fossil represents one of many lightly built, late Triassic archosaurs, and is not a bird at all. We shall await the results of the detailed study with considerable interest.

New interpretations

The most controversial proposal of recent years comes from two astronomers: Professor Sir Fred Hoyle and Professor Chandra Wickramasinghe. Both of these men have examined one of the *Archaeopteryx* fossils from southern Germany, and have come to the conclusion that it is a fake! It is really the skeleton of a genuine dinosaur (*Compsognathus*) which has had arranged around it a collection of impressions of chicken feathers. The impressions of the feathers were made using a limestone mixture into which the feathers were pressed until the mixture had set.

Both of these scientists are eminent in their own chosen area of science but it is unfortunate that they have not taken into account the weight of geological and paleontological evidence in existence. As has been demonstrated by a number of studies, *Archaeopteryx* is nothing like *Compsognathus* in detailed structure, and it is foolish to believe that paleontologists would be confused over this point. As for the faking of the feather impressions, it is perhaps naïve to suggest that scientists cannot recognize a fake when they see one, especially one where the features (*i.e.* the feathers) are of such crucial importance.

It would appear that Hoyle and Wickramasinghe have decided that *Archaeopteryx* is inconvenient for their own theory of the extinction and origin of groups. They believe that birds originated just after the extinction of dinosaurs – at the end of the Cretaceous Period – rather than at the end of the Jurassic. They believe, too, that dinosaurs became extinct in a viral epidemic which came from outer space. The genes from such viruses grafted themselves on to animals which survived the plague at the end of the Cretaceous, transforming them into birds.

The origins of flight

There are many flying animals today, ranging from those which are really passive gliders: flying fish, tree frogs, flying snakes, flying lizards, flying lemurs and flying squirrels; to those which are able to use powered flight: bats and birds. In the past there was one notable addition to this group, the pterosaurs.

Both pterosaurs and birds evolved from an archosaurian stock – be they Triassic archosaurs or Jurassic theropods. In the case of pterosaurs there seems to be little dispute about the origins of their type of flight. It is assumed that they evolved from a group of small Triassic archosaurs which had become arboreal; these tree-climbing forms took to the habit of gliding, either as a means of breaking their falls from trees, or as a means of getting from tree to tree, without having to return to the ground each time. From gliding, and the development of gliding surfaces (protowings), pterosaurs became gradually more adept flyers with membranous wings supported by the arm and fingers. Eventually they became active fliers, flapping the wings.

In the case of the birds, the origins of flight have always been more contentious, being split into opposing factions. One group advocates an origin very similar to that of pterosaurs ('trees down') and the other advocate a 'ground up' theory.

For the 'trees down' theory, the same arguments apply as stated previously. The earliest birds, or protobirds, are thought to have been agile tree-climbing creatures. The clawed hands and grasping feet of *Archaeopteryx* are suggestive of such a mode of life – or at least of its recent descent from an animal of this type.

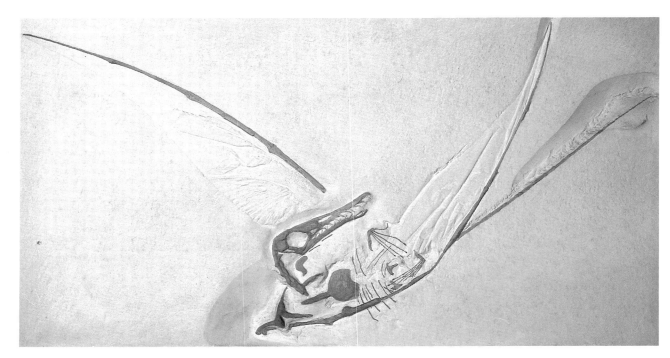

Left This beautifully-preserved pterosaur, *Rhamphorhynchus*, includes an impression of the skin of the wings and the tail fin. It is even possible to make out the fine strands of tissue in the wing membrane.

Below Other early fliers include the Triassic reptiles *Longisquama* (top) which may have spread the tall scales out to form a gliding wing; and *Podopteryx*, which had leg wing membranes.

Right A well-preserved specimen of *Pterodactylus* from the lithographic limestone of Bavaria (southern Germany).

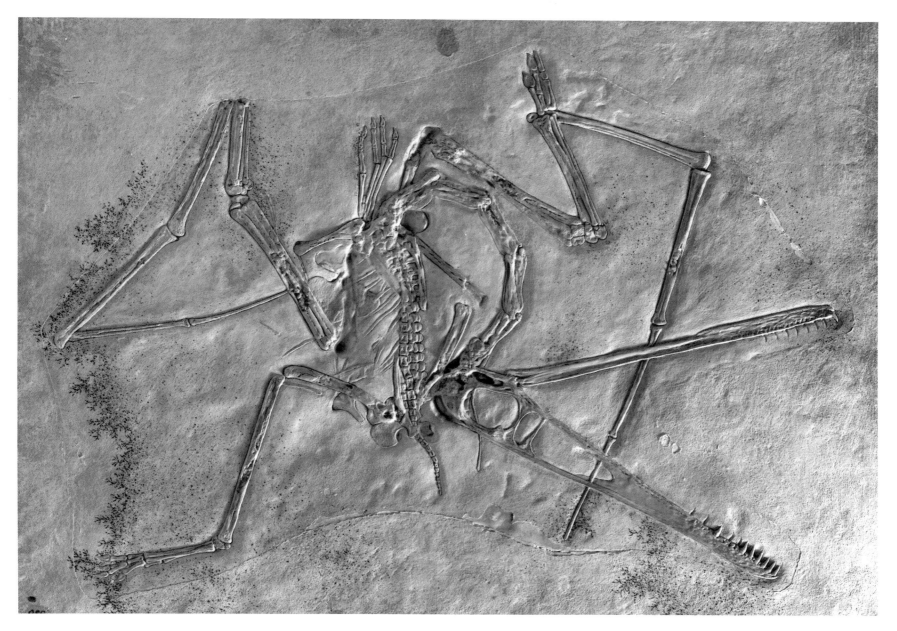

From an energy conservation point of view, the development of feathers as a means of breaking the fall of a protobird by slowing its descent to the ground and later utilizing the feathers for controlled gliding to the next tree seems eminently plausible. Anything which saves the necessity of travelling up and down trees by either climbing or gliding between them must be an energetic advantage. The shift from passive gliding using outstretched wings to powered flapping flight in order to at first extend the flight path and then fly totally independently would only need be a matter of time in order to evolve the necessary anatomical changes which might make it possible.

The alternative 'ground up' argument has been around in one form or another since the late 1870s, and the most recent advocate of this notion has been Professor Ostrom. The idea comes from the observation that some small dinosaurs were very fast runners. It is argued that protowings could be flapped as the animal ran, in order to gain even more propulsion. The idea would seem to be that the wings acted like the propellers or jet engines on the wing of a modern aircraft. From this role as propellers, the small protowings would become larger and could eventually generate lift which could be used for takeoff.

Most objectors to this theory suggest that having protowings would actually increase the frictional drag on the animal as it was running, or may actually create some lift. Either of these effects would slow the runner down and would therefore be counterproductive to a potential flier.

Ostrom provided a novel twist to this argument about the origin of flight from the ground. He noted that *Archaeopteryx* must have been a poor flier and concluded that it probably fed upon in-sects; its teeth were small and spiky and seemed well suited to cracking open the hard cuticles of such animals. The feathered arms were proposed as insect traps, within which flying insects may have become tangled. At first *Archaeopteryx* may have made small fluttering jumps to catch insects on the wing, and with the passage of time this action could have evolved into an ability to flap clear of the ground for progressively longer and longer periods.

Interesting though these latter suggestions are, the concensus at the moment favors the 'trees down' theory on energetic grounds.

Conclusions

The present views seem to favor the origin of birds from theropod dinosaurs at some time in the early Jurassic. The discovery of *Protoavis* is interesting, since it suggests a late Triassic origin for birds and one which may point to an origin of birds from advanced archosaurs rather than true dinosaurs. However, at present, the evidence from *Protoavis* has not been presented in detail and it is not proven beyond doubt that this is a genuine early bird fossil.

The tendency for several artists to reconstruct theropod dinosaur sprouting feathers is not supported by any factual evidence at the present and seems unwise to me. Close relatives of birds they may have been, but birds they clearly were not, no matter how bird-like an artist may wish to make them look.

The origin of flight was most probably one which arose in small, climbing protobirds, which first developed an ability to glide from tree to tree, and later refined this into a mechanism of powered flight.

CHAPTER 11

Fieldwork and Study

Paleontology, like any other science, is based on factual material, in this case fossils. Unlike the situation in the past, when the amount of work that was done was in direct proportion to the numbers of fossils that had been found at that particular time, there are now large collections in museums all around the world with much material waiting to be worked on. In addition techniques of study change with time, so that material that was studied many years ago can be re-examined using new techniques and reveal new facts that lay previously unrecognized.

However interesting it might be to study old collections, there is still a need to collect new material. Each new find adds another small piece to the jigsaw that makes up our knowledge of the history of the Earth. The source of new material can vary enormously, from odd bones being found by accident through every intermediate stage, to the activities of highly organized paleontological expeditions formed by collaboration of experts in Museums and Universities.

How to find your fossil

Fossils are not just found anywhere. They are formed in sediment and the act of burial protects the remains from being scavenged and completely destroyed by other organisms, or being des-troyed by the natural forces of decay and erosion. Rapid burial is most likely to occur in the sea, where a constant 'rain' of sediment falls on the sea floor. As a result there is a very strong bias in the fossil record toward sea creatures. Land dwellers such as the dinosaurs also get preserved by burial, but the carcasses have to be washed into a lake or into the sea, and this is a much more chancy process. A considerably more rare way of becoming buried by sediment is through being buried by wind-blown sand, but as we have already seen in chapter 9 this can occur.

Normally only the hard parts of skeletons are preserved as fossils because these are the most resistant to decay. Soft tissues decay quickly, but in some cases even soft parts are preserved as impressions on the surface of the rock on which the animal died. Such is the case with skin impressions.

Bearing these facts in mind, it is obvious that the remains of dinosaurs, all of which were land creatures, are going to be very rare. We are going to be relying on the fact that occasionally the carcasses of animals are going to get washed into a river, and from there into a lake or the sea and buried before it has been completely destroyed by processes of decay.

So to find dinosaurs it is necessary to look in rocks of the correct age. It is no good looking in rocks that are either too early or too

Left This dried-out water course provides a good exposure of sedimentary rock which will be worth investigating closely for fragments of fossil bone.

Above This is the field camp at Hughenden in Queensland, ready for an expedition to look for dinosaurs in the early Cretaceous of Australia.

Right Scouring exposed areas looking for tiny fragments of fossilized bone can be a very tedious and time consuming business. However, patience is sometimes rewarded by exciting discoveries.

Left Having found a few broken remains on an exposure, it is then a matter of careful exploration to find out the source of the fossils. Once identified, the digging can then begin in earnest. Here a team of Polish and Mongolian scientists are carefully excavating the remains of a large sauropod dinosaur (*Opisthocoelicaudia*) from the late Cretaceous of the Gobi Desert.

Bottom left Further on in the excavation and with more of the dinosaur exposed, the next task is to make plans for the removal of the skeleton in manageable pieces. Quite often the field site is in an inaccessible area and no heavy machinery can be brought in to lift large skeletons. In this case plans have to be drawn and the skeleton divided into smaller pieces.

Right The bones are protected by layers of paper and then covered in plaster of Paris or polyurethane foam to save them from damage in transit.

late for dinosaurs. This requires good geological maps. Detailed geological maps are now available for most parts of the world, and can be used to identify rocks of Mesozoic age (Triassic, Jurassic and Cretaceous). Having found rocks of the correct age, it is then necessary to identify the precise type of rocks that are exposed. It is important to find sedimentary rocks (rocks that were formed by the build up of layers of sediment) on the bottoms of swamps, the bends of rivers, lakes and the sea – though in the case of the sea we are only really interested in the sea floor which was quite near to land, which would be the area in which any carcasses from land animals may have floated and then sunk.

Finally, it is necessary to find areas of land of the right age and type which are also being actively eroded. River banks are one such area, as are sea cliffs which are constantly being attacked by wave action. Man is also a useful force of erosion. Quarrying, road construction, railway construction and many other civil engineering projects are liable to expose new deposits of rock which may be very valuable for research purposes.

Expeditions

To find dinosaurs, or any other fossils for that matter, it is necessary to be well prepared. The area must be decided upon after consultation of geological maps, and preferrably by a preliminary reconnaisance.

Most expeditions are meticulously planned, because they involve a great deal of manpower and usually involve a degree of international collaboration. Once in the field, the real work of the expedition tends to be rather tedious, involving a great deal of hard physical work. Teams have to spend days scouring likely rock exposures, getting used to the quality of the rocks, learning

to recognize the clues that might lead to the discovery of fossils (it is necessary to 'get your eye in') and this can take a surprisingly long time.

One standard way of searching for fossils is to walk along the bottom of gullies, escarpments or small cliffs, looking intently at the scree. Scraps of bone discovered here may mean there is a skeleton weathering out of the rock higher up the slope, and it is then a matter of scrambling up the slope and discovering the source of the fossils.

Excavation

Having located a skeleton, or part of a skeleton, it has to be excavated so that it can be removed safely and transferred to a laboratory where it can be prepared under ideal conditions.

The techniques used for excavating a skeleton tend to vary according to the size of the skeleton and the quality of the rock. Small fossils in soft rock are easily excavated using simple tools such as trowels and old knives. However it must be stressed just how important it is to record the precise position where the fossil was found, both on a map and in a sketch of the rock exposure (or if possible by photographing the specimen in position before removing it). It is also important to keep careful notes on this discovery which can be attached to the fossil as a label. All this information makes the fossil valuable scientifically because it can help an expert enormously over the task of identifying it and studying it at a later date.

Larger fossils may need more careful excavation. It is often the case that the fossil is broken or crumbly, so the surface may need to be hardened using proprietary glues or resins for hardening which can be painted or sprayed on to the fossil. It may then be carefully removed, wrapped in paper and stored in sample bags (along with all the notes!). In other cases it may be necessary to encase the specimen in a plaster of Paris or polyurethane foam jacket.

Skeletons may require a great deal of manpower to deal with them. A great deal of rock may have to be removed to expose the entire skeleton requiring picks and shovels, power hammers, even large earth-moving vehicles, and on rare occasions explosives. Skeletons cannot be lifted whole, so the upper surface is partially cleaned, divided into manageable blocks, all of which are carefully labelled and marked on a master-plan of the skeleton and then encased in protective layers of plaster. The lower surface is then excavated so that the blocks can be lifted over and plastered from beneath ensuring they are completely safe for transport back to the laboratory.

Laboratory work

Once the specimens collected in the field have arrived at the laboratory the most lengthy period of work begins. In the case of a dinosaur skeleton this may mean five or more years of painstaking work.

All the packaging has to be removed first, and the blocks reassembled into their positions as they were found in the field, to make sure that nothing has been lost and also to decide on the best way of tackling the huge task. Blocks are then slowly prepared using a variety of tools ranging from very fine needles and probes, for removing rock literally grain by grain from very delicate structures, to electrically powered vibrating needles, small pneumatic chisels or ultrasonic probes. In some cases it may be appropriate to use special chemical to attack and dissolve the rock

Above Plaster of Paris is being applied to the upper surface of this skeleton in preparation for removal. In the foreground is a block which has been turned over and plastered and reinforced with a wooden stake.

Left A large dinosaur footprint (*Iguanodon*) revealed in a fall of rocks from the cliffs at Hanover Point on the Isle of Wight.

Top right Frank Howie preparing a fossil skull using an air driven vibrating chisel in the laboratory of the British Museum (Natural History).

Top far right Bolting together the framework to hold heavy dinosaur bones.

Bottom right A latex mold is being made of this vertebra so that cast copies can be made.

Far right bottom Hauling away a very heavy dinosaur footprint.

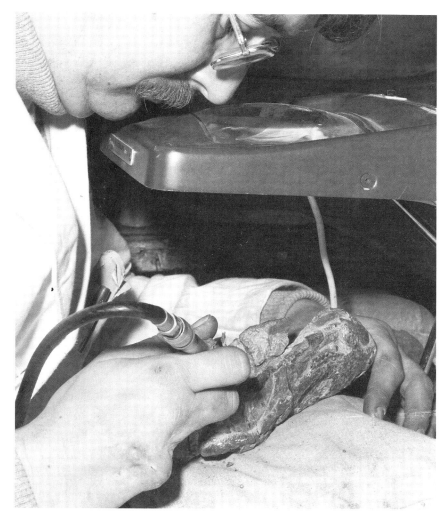

around the fossil. The care and patience required for this sort of work is immense and says a great deal for the dedication of the museum preparators who undertake much of the work.

The aim of all this work by preparators is two-fold. First, to prepare the material for scientific study, and second to produce museum display specimens.

Display

Museum displays are very important because they attract a wide range of interest from the general public; indeed there are few things more attractive to the general public than a new dinosaur exhibition.

In order to display dinosaurs, museums need on the whole to find a large space (not always easy in these days of crowded galleries and small museums). If they have the space then they can either arrange a display of the skeleton on the floor of the gallery, arranging the bones as they were originally found, but cleaned up

so that they look more interesting; or, if they have the resources, build a special metal frame to mount the skeleton upon. The latter makes a much more dramatic, and therefore more attractive display. However, as such a display tends to cost an enormous amount of money it tends to be a critical decision as to whether or not to exhibit skeletons in this way. On the whole, small museums cannot fund such displays and they remain the province of the larger state, or provincial, museums.

Study

Following all the detailed preparatory work the specimen is then ready for detailed scientific study. The bones must be carefully examined, photographed in many cases, and frequently drawn and described. This is the 'nuts and bolts' end of the science, which is long and rather painstaking work, but important if the scientific community is going to be able to understand more of the new animal. After the descriptive work has been finished the

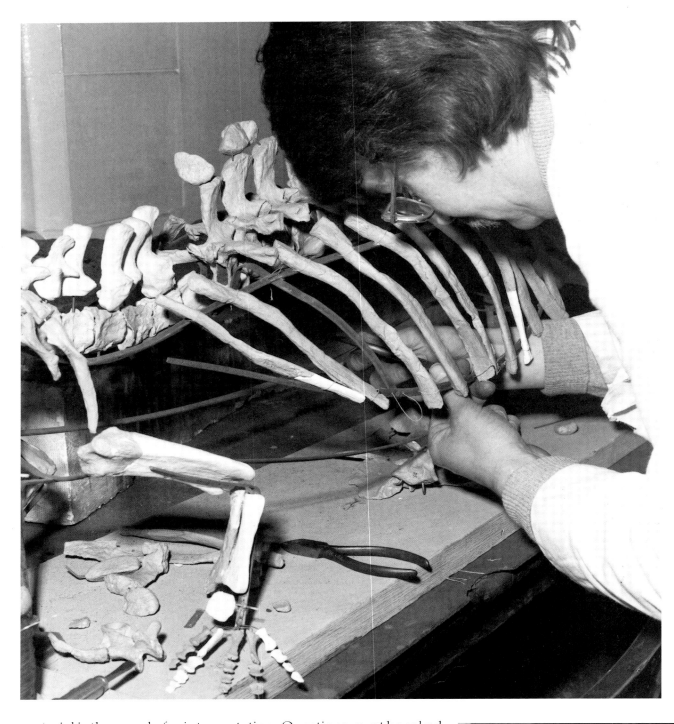

Left The extremely delicate work involved in making a skeleton secure on its frame, so that it can be displayed to the public.

Below An extremely attractive and imaginative display of a dinosaur restoration (*Stenonychosaurus*).

Top right A museum display of the nest of the hadrosaurid *Maiasaura* with some hatchlings shown just emerging from eggs. This sort of display does much to introduce the idea that dinosaurs were once alive, rather than being mere museum curiosities.

Bottom right A full skeletal restoration of the dinosaur *Iguanodon bernissartensis*, as it used to appear in the dinosaur gallery of the British Museum (Natural History). The gallery has now been dismantled and some dinosaurs moved to the main hall. This dinosaur has been sent to Manchester City Museum.

material is then ready for interpretation. Questions must be asked and answers suggested on the basis of what is known of the skeleton, and this can provoke more detailed study of the bones. For example at a very elementary level we need to know how all the bones fitted together in life. How did the creature walk or run? And to do this how were its legs constructed? And how did the muscles of the legs seem to work? This can tell us a lot about the way of life of the animal. The skull, as we have seen, is a very complex structure and can also tell a scientist a great deal about the way of life of the creature – what sort of food it ate and how, how well developed its senses were, and it can in many cases provide clues about its behavior.

The ultimate aim of all this work is to get as near as possible to a complete knowledge of the new animal. Much will be certain, based on the objective evidence of the bones, but much will be conjecture, based on how the scientist thinks the creature worked in life. This element of uncertainty is very challenging and raises interesting discussion and debate between scientists all over the world.

A few of the debates over dinosaurs, their lives and their times, have been alluded to in the earlier chapters and these have hopefully provided a taste of what it is like to be a paleontologist today as well as offering an insight into what it was like to be a paleontologist many years ago.

Glossary

Absolute dating Method of calculating the age of rock, and fossils found in it, by analyzing the rate of decay of the rock's radioactive elements.

Acetabulum Hip socket of thigh bone.

Allosaur Very large, powerful theropod dinosaur.

Ammonite Spiral-shelled mollusc of the Mesozoic Era, related to the octopus.

Angiosperm Flowering plant that bears its seeds in ovaries.

Ankylosaur Type of ornithischian dinosaur, characterized by its heavy armor.

Ankylosaurid As ankylosaur, but with the addition of a tail club.

Apatosaur Low-shouldered type of sauropod dinosaur.

Archosaur Major reptile of the Permian and Triassic Periods; ranging widely in form, it was an ancestor of the crocodile and probably related to the first dinosaurs.

Bennettitalean cycad Type of tree with short trunk and palm-like crown prevalent during the Jurassic Period.

Bipedal Two-footed.

Brachiosaur Gigantic, high-shouldered, giraffe-like type of sauropod dinosaur.

Camarasaur Gigantic type of sauropod dinosaur, often included with the brachiosaurs.

Carboniferous Period Geological period ranging from 345 million to 280 million years ago; the penultimate period of the Paleozoic Era.

Carnivore Meat-eating animal.

Carnosaur Large theropod dinosaur.

Cenozoic (or Cainozoic) Era Geological era dating from 64 million years ago, when the last dinosaurs disappeared, to the present.

Ceratopian Type of ornithischian dinosaur, characterized by a large frill of bone on the skull, horns on the nose or over the eyes and a hooked beak.

Coelurosaur Small theropod dinosaur.

Comparative dating Method of comparing ages of different rocks by examining differences or similarities between their fossils.

Coprolite Fossilized dropping.

Cretaceous Period Geological period extending from 130 million to 64 million years ago; the last period of the Mesozoic Era.

Cryptic A form of camouflage. Like a chameleon the coloring is used to merge into the background and on occasions will change completely to show emotions.

Cryptozoic (or Precambrian) Eon Geological eon from the formation of the Earth 4,600 million years ago until 600 million years ago.

Cycad Palm-like type of plant.

Cynodont Long-snouted, rather dog-like reptile of the Triassic Period.

Dicynodont Mammal-like reptile of the Permian and early Triassic Periods; typically, it had two long teeth and a sharp beak.

Digitigrade Walking on the toes.

Disruptive Coloration which breaks up the outline of an animal and serves to confuse the predator: blotches or stripes very effective.

Dromeosaurid Type of theropod dinosaur with a large sickle claw on each foot for killing prey.

Dryosaur Type of ornithopod dinosaur – Hypsilophodontid with no teeth at the tip of the upper jaw and only three toes.

Ecology Study of living organisms and their habits in relation to their environment.

Ectothermic Cold-blooded; depending on external sources for body heat.

Endothermic Warm-blooded; producing body heat by internal chemical reactions.

Epoccipital bones Bones which fringe the head shield in Ceratopians. Can be small and triangular or long spines as in *Styracosaurus*.

Fauna Animals of a particular region or period.

Femur Thigh bone.

Fenestra Window-like opening in a bone.

Flora Plants of a particular region or period.

Fossil Remains or impression of an animal or plant, preserved in rock.

Furcula Fused collar-bone (wishbone) in birds.

Gastralia Narrow, rib-like bones found in many theropod dinosaurs.

Gastroliths Stones swallowed by some dinosaurs to grind food in the stomach.

Gondwanaland Southern part of the supercontinent of Pangea, comprising present-day South America, Africa, India, Australasia and Antarctica. See also **Laurasia**.

Hadrosaur Duck-billed, sometimes crested type of ornithopod dinosaur.

Hadrosaurine Uncrested hadrosaur.

Herbivore Plant-eating animal.

Humerus Upper arm bone.

Ichthyosaur Large, fish-shaped marine reptile of the Mesozoic Era that swam using paddles.

Iguanodon Type of ornithopod dinosaur, characterized by specialized hands with a large, stiletto-like thumb.

Ilium Upper hip bone of a dinosaur, connecting with its backbone; see also **Ischium** and **Pubis**.

Insectivore Insect-eating animal.

Ischium One of the two lower bones of a dinosaur; it points downward and backward. See also **Ilium** and **Pubis**.

Jurassic Period Geological period extending from 205 million to 130 million years ago; the middle Period of the Mesozoic Era.

Laurasia Northern part of the supercontinent of Pangea, comprising present-day North America, Europe and Asia. See also **Gondwanaland**.

Lambeosaurine Crested hadrosaur.

Lepidoptera Order of four-winged insects that includes butterflies and moths.

Megalosaur Large theropod dinosaur of the late Jurassic Period.

Mesozoic Era Geological era extending from 245 million to 64 million years ago, during which dinosaurs evolved. It is divided into three Periods: the Triassic, Jurassic and Cretaceous.

Mosasaur Giant marine reptile of the Mesozoic Era, related to the present-day monitor lizard.

Multituberculate Nocturnal, mouse- or rat-like mammal of the Mesozoic Era.

Nodosaurid = nodosaur Ankylosaur dinosaur of the late Jurassic and Cretaceous Periods lacking a tail club.

Ornithischian One of the two main types of dinosaur, characterized by its bird-like hips and small beak. See also **Saurischian**.

Ornithomimosaur Ostrich-like type of saurischian dinosaur.

Ornithopod Small, two-footed, swift-moving type of ornithischian dinosaur.

Pachycephalosaur Type of ornithischian dinosaur with a thick-boned, domed skull.

Paleoanthropology Study of prehistoric man.

Paleoichnology Study of dinosaur footprints.

Paleontology Study of animal fossils.

Paleozoic Era Geological era ranging from 600 million to 245 million years ago; the earliest time to which unmistakeable fossils can be assigned. It is divided into the Cambrian, Ordovician, Silurian, Devonian, Carboniferous and Permian Periods.

Pangea Supercontinent, comprised of all the present continents joined together. It began to break up during the Jurassic Period.

Parasaggital Parallel to the midline of the body.

Pelage Fur.

Permian Period Geological period extending from 280 million to 245 million years ago; the last Period of the Paleozoic Era.

Petrification Process by which, through chemical changes, bone gradually turns into stone.

Phanerozoic Eon Geological eon covering the past 600 million years. It is divided into the Paleozoic, Mesozoic and Cenozoic (or Cainozoic) Eras.

Phytoplankton Plant plankton. See **Plankton**.

Plankton Minute animals and plants that drift in both salt and fresh water.

Plantigrade Walking on the soles of the feet.

Plate tectonics Study of the nature and movements of the plates that form the Earth's crust.

Plateosaur Long-necked early dinosaur that was the first known high-browsing animal.

Plenum Religious concept that God brought every living organism into being in a single act of creation.

Plesiosaur Large marine reptile of the Mesozoic Era that swam using paddle-like flippers.

Predentary bone Triangular bone covered by a horny beak on the end of the lower jaw of ornithischian dinosaurs.

Protodinosaur One of the very early dinosaurs concerning which paleontological evidence is sparse.

Psittacosaur Type of ceratopian dinosaur characterized by a parrot-like beak.

Pterosaur Flying reptile of the Triassic Period, probably related to the first dinosaurs.

Pubis One of the two lower hip bones of a dinosaur; in saurischians it points downward and forward, in ornithischians downward and backward, alongside the ischium. See also **Ilium** and **Ischium**.

Rhaetian Top-most stage at the end of the Triassic Period.

Rhynchosaur Reptile of the Triassic Period, characterized by its hooked beak, tusks and many sharp teeth.

Rostral Narrow, pointed bone forming the upper part of the beak in psittacosaurs and ceratopians.

Saurischian One of the two main types of dinosaur, characterized by its reptile-like hips. See also **Ornithischian**.

Sauropodomorph (or sauropod) Type of saurischian dinosaur, usually four-footed and plant-eating.

Seed fern Low, bushy, fern-like type of plant of the Triassic and Jurassic Periods.

Stegosaur Type of ornithischian dinosaur characterized by large plates or spines of bone along the back. The forelimbs are significantly shorter than the hindlimbs and the skull tends to be long and low.

Supra-acetabular crest Ridge above the hip socket for the thigh bone.

Taxonomy Scientific classification of organisms.

Theropod Type of saurischian dinosaur, usually two-footed and meat-eating.

Trace fossil Fossilized footprint, dropping, egg or other sign of an extinct animal.

Triassic Period Geological period ranging from 245 million to 205 million years ago; the first Period of the Mesozoic Era.

Trochanter One of the protuberances on the thigh bone to which leg muscles are attached.

Trophic Concerned with nutrition.

Tyrannosaur Theropod dinosaur with large jaws, massive, serrated teeth and very small forelimbs.

Vertebrate Animal with a backbone or spinal column.

Index

Page numbers in *italics* refer to illustrations

Acknowledgments

The publisher would like to thank
Jane Laslett the editor, David Eldred
the designer, Emma Callery for
editorial assistance and Moira Dykes
the picture researcher. Especial
thanks to Philip Hood of Young
Artists for his superb color
restorations and to David Nicholls of
University Museum, Oxford, for his
detailed line work on the pages
listed below. The publisher would
also like to thank the many
individuals, museums and agencies
who provided the illustrations:

**Academy of Natural Sciences,
Philadelphia** pages 186 below, 187
top.
Aldus Archive page 29.
**American Museum of Natural
History,** Courtesy Department of
Library Services pages 4-5, 52 below,
83 top & right, 90 below, 91 top, 108
top, 112 below, 132, 133, 137, 140,
144.
**Arizona State Museum, University
of Arizona** page 62 top.
**Bernard Price Institute for
Paleontological Research,
University of the Witwatersrand,
Johannesburg** pages 70, 71 right.
British Museum (Natural History),
Courtesy of the Trustees pages 8
below, 15 below, 18 below, 19 top,
20, 21, 28 below right, 30 left, 38
below, 39 top, 64 below, 102 below,
103, 105 below, 106 below, 119 below,
143, 174, 178 top, 179.
Bruce Coleman Ltd/ Jen & Des
Bartlett page 65 below/ Erwin &
Peggy Bauer page 150/ Jane Burton 60
below, 61 below, 178 below/ Robert P
Carr 151/ Gerald Cubitt 149 below/
Adrian Davies 152 top/ Peter
Davey 9 top left, 161/ MPL Fogden
12/ Michael Freeman 152 top, 172/
Udo Hirsch 57, 65 top, 168 top/
David C Houston 173 top/ Carol
Hughes 15 top/ Steve Kaufmann 154/
Frans Lanting 13/ Hans Reinhard 56/
David F Robinson 8 top/ Werner
Stoy 153.
**The Carnegie Museum of Natural
History** pages 88-89.
**Courtesy Field Museum of Natural
History, Chicago** pages 7 below, 40,
37 below, 41 both, 73 bottom left, 121
top, 142, 148 below.
Geological Museum, London page
59.
Geoscience Features Picture Library
pages 37 top two, 83 left, 99 left.
Hulton Picture Company page 34
top.
**Stephen Hutt, Museum of Isle of
Wight Geology** page 184 below, 185
bottom two.
Imitor pages 6 below, 7 top, 9
below, 28 top & left, 30 right &
below, 31 left, 36 below, 42, 60 top,
62 below, 63 both, 73 bottom right,
80, 106 top, 110, 111, 147, 148 top, 149
top, 158 both, 166 below, 170, 171,
176, 185 top two, 186 top, 187 below.
Indian Statistical Institute, Calcutta
pages 38 top, 86.
**Institute of Geology &
Paleontology, University of
Tübingen** pages 18 top, 38 below, 39
top, 52 top.
Institute of Paleobiology, Warsaw/
Photo Wojciech Skarzynski pages 11
below, 14 top, 34 below, 35 below,
102 top, 121 below, 126, 127, 128, 129,
139 top, 182 both.
**Institut Royal des Sciences
Naturelles de Belgique** pages 1, 32,
108 below, 109 below.
**Institute of Vertebrate Paleontology
& Paleoanthropology, Beijing** page
84.
The Mansell Collection page 147.

**Mongolian Academy of Sciences,
Geological Institute, Ulan Bator**
pages 110, 113.
Pat Morris Photographics page 31
right, 36 top, 78, 79, 166 top, 175.
**Museo Civico di Scinze Naturali,
Bergamo** page 53.
**Museum of Northern Arizona,
Flagstaff** page 50, 77 top.
**Museum of Paleontology,
University of California at Berkeley**
page 68 below.
**Photo Courtesy Museum of the
Rockies** page 162 top.
**National Museum of Natural
History, Institute of Paleontology,
Paris/** Denis Serrette pages 81, 173
below.
**Reproduced with permission of the
National Museum of Natural
Sciences, National Museums of
Canada** pages 134, 139 below, 160
top, 119 top, 124 top.
National Museums of Scotland
pages 33, 46.
**Natural History Museum,
Homboldy University, Berlin** pages
87, 93 top.
**Courtesy The Natural History
Museum of Los Angeles County**
page 82.
Dr DB Norman pages 14 below, 25
below, 43, 44, 48 below, 71 left, 73
top, 74, 75, 76, 77 below, 88, 91
below, 98, 99 right, 112 top, 141, 157
right & bottom two, 164, 165, 180, 181
both, 183, 184, top.
Oxford Scientific Films/ Rafi Ben-
Shahar page 58/ Deni Bown 115
right/ L Bucci-Panda Photo 167/ MPL
Fogden 10/ CW Helliwell 9 top right/
Breck D Kent 11 top/ Tom Leach 156/
Zig Leszczynski 155/ Richard
Packwood 6 top/ Charles Palek 177
right.
Oxford University Museum pages
69, 105 center.
**Paleontological Institute, Academy
of Sciences, Moscow** pages 162
below, 177 left.
**Peabody Museum of Natural
History, Yale University** pages 39
below, 64 top, 100, 109 top, 116 main
picture, 117.
**Port Elizabeth Museum, South
Africa** page 48 top & right, 49.
Royal Ontario Museum, Toronto
pages 97, 115 left, 116 left & right,
130.
Science Photo Library/ Sinclair
Stammers page 48 center left.
Senckenberg Museum, Frankfurt
page 90 top.
Smithsonian Institution pages 23
top, 25 top, 26-27, 89 top, 94 top, 95,
136 top.
South African Museum, Cape Town
page 68.
**Tyrell Museum of Paleontology,
Alberta** pages 66, 94 below, 123, 129,
157 top left, 159 both, 160 below.
Weidenfeld Archive page 19 top.
Zigong Dinosaur Museum page 35
top/ Xinhua News Agency page 93
below.

Artwork Credits

John Brennan pages 16, 17, 20-21, 26,
40, 55, 58, 59, 78, 98, 115 below, 131,
146, 150, 155.
Philip Hood © illustrations/ Young
Artists pages 2-3, 22, 24-25, 32,
50-51, 67, 70, 118, 122-123, 132-133,
134-135, 137, 138-139, 140, 141, 142-
143, 144-145, 161, 163.
Steve Kirk pages 12 bottom two, 13
bottom two.
David Nicholls pages 18, 20 below,
23, 37, 45, 46, 47, 51, 52, 54, 63, 69,
72, 76, 77, 79, 80, 82, 95, 97, 120, 121,
122, 125, 127, 128, 129, 136, 143.
Gregory S Paul pages 49, 66, 84, 86,
103, 110, 119, 126, 130, 156, 171, 175,
176.